Robert F. Davis

W9-CCI-852

Basic Switching Circuit Theory

Basic Switching Circuit Theory

MOSHE KRIEGER

Department of Electrical Engineering
Syracuse University

THE MACMILLAN COMPANY
New York

COLLIER-MACMILLAN LIMITED
London

First Printing

Library of Congress catalog card number: 67–11884

THE MACMILLAN COMPANY, NEW YORK
COLLIER-MACMILLAN CANADA, LTD., TORONTO, ONTARIO

Printed in the United States of America

Preface

Switching circuit theory consists of a study of the mathematical models needed to analyze and synthesize circuits made up of two-state or bistable devices. The name *switching circuits* was first applied because switches were the first practical bistable devices in use. The first extensive uses of switching circuits were in railway signaling and control devices, and in automatic telephone exchanges. Today, switching circuits are used widely, from vending machines to digital computers, with the latter being the largest single application.

The early work in the design of switching circuits was done by rule of thumb, using a set of handbook techniques. The first mathematical treatment of switching circuits was performed by C. E. Shannon, who used a two-valued Boolean algebra to describe the behavior of relay contact circuits in his paper "A Symbolic Analysis of Relay and Switching Circuits," *Trans. AIEE*, **57**, pages 713–723 (1938). Another early investigation, which at first does not appear related to switching circuit theory, but which presents one of the first models of automatic digital computers and data-processing devices, was performed by A. M. Turing and was reported by him in the paper "On Computable Numbers, with an Application to the Entscheidungsproblem," *Proc. of the London Math. Soc.*, **2–42**, pages 230–265 (1936). These early investigations stimulated interest in the theory of switching circuits, as they furnished the opportunity to replace empirical design procedures by exact ones. It should be noted that the basic mathematics required in this field was developed earlier. It is based on the algebra of logic developed by G. Boole and reported in his book (originally published in 1854), *An Investigation of the Laws of Thought* (New York: Dover, 1951).

These investigations into switching circuit theory were accelerated during the Second World War, when the development of automation and digital computers became a primary part of the war effort. Work on the first automatic digital computer was started in 1939, and it was placed in operation in 1944 at Harvard University. This joint effort of IBM and Harvard University

v

was under the supervision of Professor H. H. Aiken. Called "Automatic Sequence-Controlled Calculator (Mark 1)," it was constructed almost entirely from relays. Today, less than a quarter of a century later, the electronic digital computer has progressed from the status of a scientific curiosity used only by researchers into a tool widely used in such applications as taking inventories, calculating and executing payrolls, controlling airport traffic, and many others. It is truly a basic tool in most engineering investigations. Perhaps only slightly less spectacular have been the advances in other applications of switching circuits—automatic cross-country telephone exchanges and tele-metering devices. The results of these efforts can also be seen in the large number of publications in the form of reports on actual circuits, theoretical research papers, and books. This abundance of literature also represents a pitfall in the study of switching circuit theory, for the rapid development produced experts in specific fields of interest who investigated the same general problems from very specific points of view and produced a large body of conclusions that have not been integrated adequately into a general theory.

Another serious problem in the presentation of switching circuit theory is the rapid and continuous development of physical devices. The earliest switch-ing systems used electromagnetic relays and diodes as basic components. Today, the range of components is extremely large and is increasing all the time. Components include transistors, tunnel diodes, magnetic cores, mag-netic surfaces, microwave devices, cryogenic devices, and others. Presently, one of the major purposes of switching circuit theory is to provide procedures for the design of simpler and more reliable circuits. Since these procedures are to a large extent dependent on the physical characteristics of the devices, the theory must be oriented partially toward existing devices.

From this short historical review of switching circuits, it is apparent that in a relatively short time an extensive and varied literature has arisen. Thus, in presenting a course in switching circuit theory a major problem is the proper choice of the material to be covered. Another problem is the presen-tation of material that is general and not device-oriented, because such material becomes obsolete very quickly, owing to the rapid advancements in technology.

This book has evolved from a set of notes used in a one-term graduate course on switching theory at Syracuse University. It has been written to serve as a text for a beginning graduate or advanced undergraduate course in switching circuit theory. Its goal is to bring the student to a level at which he can read the current literature of the subject. The objectives that have guided me in the form of presentations and in the choice of material were as follows:

1. To present material for students who have a variety of backgrounds and interests.
2. To provide freedom for a particular lecturer to present his points of view.

3. To maintain a balance between mathematical and intuitive presentation of the material.

To approximate these ideal objectives, the number of topics included in this book was kept to a minimum, but whenever possible a given topic was presented from more than one point of view. The problems at the end of each chapter were chosen to provide further clarification of the topics rather than practical examples.

In Chapter 1, the basic concepts of Boolean algebra are developed. Boolean algebra is first defined as an abstract n-valued algebra; only afterward is the particular case of a two-valued Boolean algebra introduced. To provide a more intuitive understanding, the algebra of classes is next introduced. After presenting the different logical connectives, the canonical representation of logical functions is developed. This chapter provides the basic mathematical background for the remainder of the text. Actually, these concepts are developed in more detail than the remainder of the text would warrant, but this was done to enable the student to understand more advanced literature.

In Chapter 2, a symbolic representation of switching devices in terms of gates is introduced and the remainder of this chapter considers the design of combinational circuits, that is, the translation of logical functions into a set of interconnected gates. At first a trial-and-error translation is considered to illustrate some of the basic properties. Then, after introducing the n-cube and Karnaugh-map representations of Boolean functions, simplification procedures that use a specified measure of simplicity are developed.

Chapters 3 and 4 present sequential switching circuits. The theory of asynchronous sequential circuits is treated first in Chapter 3, as it is more intuitive in nature. The design is introduced by first presenting the existing difficulties while analyzing an asynchronous sequential circuit. The actual design is obtained by transforming the sequential problem into a combinational one with added memory devices.

Chapter 4 presents the design of synchronous sequential circuits. In the first part of the chapter the differences and similarities between synchronous and asynchronous systems are considered in detail. The remainder of the chapter deals with the actual design of synchronous sequential circuits, with main emphasis on the simplification of incompletely defined systems.

In this book, with the exception of Chapter 3, where it is felt that the use of relays as an example of switching devices provides further insight into the problem, all physical considerations and device theory are excluded. This was done deliberately, as devices seem to cause the greatest divisions among investigators who specialize in different aspects of switching circuit theory.

Because this is an introductory textbook, all the results obtained are well known; the only originality claimed is in the point of view, the mode of presentation, and the choice of material. In the footnotes of each chapter, only the most important sources have been presented, and even these could not all be included, because of space restrictions. I thus take this opportunity to apologize to all whose results may have been used without detailed citation.

Appendixes I and II provide suggested lists of topics in combinational and sequential switching circuit theory. The purpose of these lists is to serve as a guide for students in selecting, for further investigation, topics not included in this book. Each topic in these lists is given with a brief list of references to provide a starting point for investigation. Such investigation, it is hoped, will serve either as final papers or as materials presented by students in seminars, because it is important that the student read original papers and be able to organize and present the material in these papers.

I wish to express my thanks and appreciation to Professors M. Yoeli and S. Seshu, whose excellent teaching aroused my interest in this material. I also acknowledge my indebtedness to the members of the faculty of the Department of Electrical Engineering, Syracuse University, for the encouragement and help they offered me. I should like to single out D. P. Reynolds who patiently edited, and in many cases had to translate, both the original notes and the final manuscript, and G. Foster, who used an initial version of the notes and gave suggestions for their improvement. I also wish to thank Professor A. Edrei of the Department of Mathematics, Syracuse University, for his suggestions on the presentation of Chapter 1. I thank Mrs. L. Capra for her patient typing of the initial set of notes and final manuscript.

Finally, I wish to thank my family for their constant encouragement, and I wish to apologize for my neglect of them during this project.

Syracuse, New York   M.   K.

Contents

Basic Switching Circuit Theory

CHAPTER

1

Mathematical Background

1-1. INTRODUCTION

In this chapter we consider the basic mathematics required in the analysis and synthesis of switching networks. The distinguishing feature of present-day switching devices is the use of two-valued signals. The formal study of switching networks uses an algebra called *switching algebra*. Shannon[1] introduced switching algebra by reinterpreting a two-valued Boolean algebra in terms of switching devices. Shannon showed that the basic properties of series and parallel combinations of bistable electrical devices can be represented by this algebra.

In presenting the mathematical background, we start with Boolean algebra,[2] introduced from a mathematical point of view, that is, as an abstract algebra. This approach was chosen because abstract algebra has become an important tool for the modern engineer, and most of the modern literature on

[1] C. E. Shannon, "A Symbolic Analysis of Relay and Switching Circuits," *Trans. AIEE*, **57**, 713–723 (1938). This paper uses the hindrance concept rather than the transmission concept used in this book, hence opposite notation.

[2] G. Boole (1815–1864) introduced in *An Investigation of the Laws of Thought* (New York: Dover, 1951) the first systematic treatment of logic, and developed for this purpose an algebraic system now called *Boolean algebra*.

1

switching circuits is in this language. After the axiomatic presentation of the general Boolean algebra, the results and theorems are translated into the language of algebra of classes, to provide the reader with a more intuitive understanding of the subject.

Later in the chapter some of the results of symbolic logic are introduced, to extend the set of operators that can be synthesized simply using electronic and magnetic devices. At the end of the chapter Boolean functions are defined and their canonical representations derived.

1–2. BASIC DEFINITIONS

To study an algebraic structure we need to define it in terms of postulates. These postulates form the basic assumptions from which we can prove or deduce all the properties of the system. To do this, we first define a vocabulary.[3]

Definition 1. A *binary operator*, $*$, defined on a set S of elements $(a, b, c, \ldots)$, is a rule that assigns, to each ordered pair (a, b) of elements from S, a unique element $c = a * b$ in S.

Note that this definition requires that the value c be uniquely determined by a and b and that it be an element in the same set. These two properties are referred to as the *substitution law* and the *law of closure*, respectively.

Operations on pairs of elements arise in many instances. For example, if we consider all the real numbers as elements of a set R, the subtraction operation on this set is a binary operation. On the other hand, if we consider the set P that includes all the positive integers, then subtraction is not a binary operation on this set, because the difference of two positive integers is not always positive. Actually, it is not necessary that the binary operation or the elements have a similarity in another field or that the operation have intuitive meaning. As an example, consider the set of elements and the binary operators defined in Problem 1 at the end of the chapter.

Binary operators are classified according to simple identities that they do or do not satisfy. Some of the basic identities, sometimes referred to as *basic laws*, are defined as follows.

Definition 2. *Commutative law.* A binary operator $*$ defined on a set of elements S is said to be commutative if and only if for every a and b in S,

$$a * b = b * a.$$

---

[3] The definitions used in this section are taken from the book by G. Birkhoff and S. MacLane, *A Survey of Modern Algebra* (New York: Macmillan, 1965). It is advisable for the student unfamiliar with the nomenclature used in this section to read Chap. I of their book.

Definition 3.   *Associative law.* A binary operator $*$ defined on a set of elements S is said to be associative if and only if for every a, b, and c in S,

$$a * (b * c) = (a * b) * c.$$

Definition 4.   *Law of idempotency.* A binary operator $*$ defined on a set of elements S satisfies the law of idempotency if and only if for every a in S,

$$a * a = a.$$

Definition 5.   *Distributive law.* If $\circ$ and $*$ are two binary operators defined on the same set of elements S, $\circ$ is distributive over $*$ if and only if for every a, b, and c in S,

$$a \circ (b * c) = (a \circ b) * (a \circ c).$$

Definition 6.   *Identity element.* An element e_* in a set of elements S is an identity element for the binary operator $*$ if and only if for every a in S,

$$a * e_* = e_* * a = a.$$

Definition 7.   *$*$-ive inverse.* A binary operator $*$ on a set of elements S is said to have $*$-*ive* inverse if and only if for every a in S there exists an element b in S such that

$$a * b = e_*.$$

In the above definitions we used the equivalence relationship ($=$) without defining it, assuming intuitive understanding. That is, given $a = b$ we check by examination whether or not these elements of set S are equal. Because we are using the approach of modern algebra, we can define it as follows.

Definition 8.   An *equivalence relation* is a binary relation on a given set of elements S (that is, for any two elements a and b in S either $a = b$ or $a \neq b$) that satisfies the following laws:

(a)   Reflexive: $a = a$ for all a in S.
(b)   Symmetric: If $a = b$ then $b = a$ for all a and b in S.
(c)   Transitive: If $a = b$ and $b = c$ then $a = c$ for all a, b, and c in S.
(d)   Substitution: If $a = b$ then by substituting a for b in any relation an equivalent relation will be obtained.

If we now consider the rules of addition and multiplication in the algebra of real numbers, we find that these operations are binary operators. The reader should satisfy himself that he understands Definitions 2 to 7 by checking to see which of these laws are satisfied in elementary algebra.

1-3. LAWS OF BOOLEAN ALGEBRA

In defining Boolean algebra, as in defining any algebraic system, there are two basic approaches. One approach is to define a large number of basic laws this algebra satisfies. In this case not all the laws are independent; that is, some of them can be deduced from others. The advantage of this approach is that it becomes simpler to prove and deduce new identities. In the second approach, the algebraic system is defined by a small number of independent laws, called *postulates*, and all the other laws are deduced from these as theorems. The advantage of the second approach is that a given system can be checked easily to see whether or not it is a specific algebra.

In this section we define Boolean algebra using the second approach. We use Huntington's[4] definition, but this is not unique, as other sets of postulates could have been used.[5, 6]

Definition 9. *Boolean algebra.* A set B of elements $(a, b, c, \ldots)$, together with two binary operators ($\cdot$) and ($+$), form a Boolean algebra if and only if the following four postulates hold:

P-1: Both binary operators ($\cdot$) and ($+$) are commutative.

P-2: Both binary operators ($\cdot$) and ($+$) have identity elements; that is, both $e_.$ and e_+ exist.

P-3: Each binary operator is distributive over the other.

P-4: For every element a in set B, there exists an element a' in B, the complement of a, such that $a \cdot a' = e_+$ and $a + a' = e_.$.

Principle of Duality. Every statement or algebraic identity deducible from the postulates of a Boolean algebra remains valid if the binary operators ($\cdot$) and ($+$), and the identity elements $e_.$ and e_+, are interchanged throughout.

This principle is based on the symmetric definition of Boolean algebra with respect to the two binary operators and the respective identity elements. As a result of this principle, all Boolean identities that include one or both binary operators, or the identity elements, appear in pairs, referred to as *dual pairs*. Thus, after an identity is proved, its dual pair is obtained by interchanging the binary operators and the identity elements.

At this point we should check the exact meaning of Huntington's postulates. Postulate P-1 is self-evident. In checking postulate P-2, we see that it requires only the existence of identity elements, without stating the uniqueness of these elements. We shall prove their uniqueness.

Theorem 1. *The identity elements of a Boolean algebra are unique.*

Proof: Assume that there are two e_* elements, say, e_{*1} and e_{*2}. From the definition of the identity element, the following two equations must hold for all a in B:

$$a * e_{*1} = a,$$
$$a * e_{*2} = a.$$

[4] E. V. Huntington, "Postulates for the Algebra of Logic," *Trans. Am. Math. Soc.*, **5**, 288–309 (1904).

[5] M. H. Stone, "Postulates for Boolean Algebras and Generalized Boolean Algebras," *Am. J. Math.*, **53**, 703–732 (1935).

[6] M. H. Stone, "The Theory of Representation for Boolean Algebras," *Trans. Am. Math. Soc.*, **40**, 37–111 (1936).

Now if we substitute in the first equation $a = e_{*2}$ and in the second equation $a = e_{*1}$, we obtain

$$e_{*2} * e_{*1} = e_{*2},$$
$$e_{*1} * e_{*2} = e_{*1}.$$

From postulate P-1,

$$e_{*1} * e_{*2} = e_{*2} * e_{*1}.$$

And from the definition of a binary operator (Def. 1),

$$e_{*2} = e_{*1}. \qquad \text{Q.E.D.}$$

Here $*$ was used as a general binary operator; thus the result stands for both $e.$ and e_+.

We also find that postulate P-3 is self-evident (by considering Def. 5), but postulate P-4 should be explained further. This postulate defines an operator on a single element of the set B. Because of this, *complementation* is generally referred to as a *unary operation*.

Theorem 2.   *The complement, a', of any element a of a Boolean algebra is unique.*

Proof: Assume that there are two elements a' corresponding to a given a, say, a'_1 and a'_2. From postulate P-4 the following two sets of equations must hold:

$$a + a'_1 = e., \qquad\qquad a + a'_2 = e.,$$
$$\text{and}$$
$$a \cdot a'_1 = e_+, \qquad\qquad a \cdot a'_2 = e_+.$$

$$
\begin{array}{lll}
a'_1 & = e. \cdot a'_1 & \text{by P-2} \\
 & = (a + a'_2) \cdot a'_1 & \text{by P-4} \\
 & = a \cdot a'_1 + a'_2 \cdot a'_1 & \text{by P-3} \\
 & = e_+ + a'_2 \cdot a'_1 & \text{by P-4} \\
 & = a'_2 \cdot a + a'_2 \cdot a'_1 & \text{by P-4} \\
 & = a'_2 \cdot (a + a'_1) & \text{by P-3} \\
 & = a'_2 \cdot e. & \text{by P-4} \\
 & = a'_2 \quad \text{Q.E.D.} & \text{by P-2.}
\end{array}
$$

At this point we shall prove some more identities of a Boolean algebra.

Lemma 1.   *For all a in B, the following relationships hold:*

$$e. + a = e. \qquad \text{and} \qquad e_+ \cdot a = e_+.$$

Proof: We shall prove only one of the identities; the other then follows from the principle of duality.

$$
\begin{array}{lll}
e. & = a + a' & \text{by P-4} \\
 & = a + a' \cdot e. & \text{by P-2} \\
 & = (a + a') \cdot (a + e.) & \text{by P-3} \\
 & = e. \cdot (a + e.) & \text{by P-4} \\
 & = a + e. & \text{by P-2} \\
 & = e. + a \quad \text{Q.E.D.} & \text{by P-1.}
\end{array}
$$

Corollary 1. *There exists a unique relationship between the identity elements of a Boolean albegra:*

$$e'_. = e_+ \qquad and \qquad e'_+ = e_..$$

Proof: By equating $a = e_+$ in the first identity and $a = e_.$ in the second identity of Lemma 1, we obtain

$$e_. + e_+ = e_. \qquad and \qquad e_+ \cdot e_. = e_+ .$$

Thus, by postulate P-4 and Theorem 2,

$$e'_. = e_+ \qquad and \qquad e'_+ = e_.. \qquad \text{Q.E.D.}$$

Theorem 3. *The* law of absorption *holds in a Boolean algebra; that is, for all a and b in B,*

$$a + a \cdot b = a \qquad and \qquad a \cdot (a + b) = a.$$

Proof: Only one of the relationships needs to be proved, as they are dual pairs:

$$
\begin{aligned}
a &= e_. \cdot a & &\text{by P-2} \\
&= (e_. + b) \cdot a & &\text{by L-1} \\
&= e_. \cdot a + b \cdot a & &\text{by P-3} \\
&= a + b \cdot a & &\text{by P-2} \\
&= a + a \cdot b \quad \text{Q.E.D.} & &\text{by P-1.}
\end{aligned}
$$

Lemma 2. *For all a and b in B, the following relationships hold:*

$$a + a' \cdot b = a + b \qquad and \qquad a \cdot (a' + b) = a \cdot b.$$

Proof:

$$
\begin{aligned}
a + a' \cdot b &= (a + a') \cdot (a + b) & &\text{by P-3} \\
&= e_. \cdot (a + b) & &\text{by P-4} \\
&= a + b & &\text{by P-2,}
\end{aligned}
$$

and from the principle of duality it follows that

$$a \cdot (a' + b) = a \cdot b \qquad \text{Q.E.D.}$$

Corollary 2. *The law of cancellation does not hold in a Boolean algebra.*

Proof: The *law of cancellation* states that if $a \cdot b = a \cdot c$ then $b = c$, or if $a + b = a + c$ then $b = c$.

To prove Corollary 2 we shall show, by a counterexample, that the above statements do not necessarily hold. From Lemma 2,

$$a \cdot (a' + b) = a \cdot b.$$

If the law of cancellation holds, this implies that for all a and b in B,

$$a' + b = b.$$

Now let $a = b$; thus

$$b' + b = b.$$

But this implies that $b = e.$, which is not necessarily true.

To complete the proof, the same steps are applied to the dual statement; that is,

$$a + a' \cdot b = a + b \qquad \text{L-2}$$

This implies

$$a' \cdot b = b.$$

Let $a = b$,

$$b' \cdot b = b$$

or

$$e_+ \neq b \qquad \text{Q.E.D.}$$

Corollary 3.   *For all a, b, and c in B, if $a \cdot b = a \cdot c$ and $a + b = a + c$ then $b = c$.*

Proof:

$$
\begin{aligned}
b &= b \cdot (a + b) & \text{by T-3} \\
&= b \cdot (a + c) & \text{by substitution} \\
&= b \cdot a + b \cdot c & \text{by P-3} \\
&= c \cdot a + b \cdot c & \text{by substitution} \\
&= c \cdot a + c \cdot b & \text{by P-1} \\
&= c \cdot (a + b) & \text{by P-3} \\
&= c \cdot (a + c) & \text{by substitution} \\
&= c \qquad \text{Q.E.D.} & \text{by T-3.}
\end{aligned}
$$

Theorem 4.   *The* law of idempotency *holds in a Boolean algebra; that is, for all a in B,*

$$a \cdot a = a \text{ and } a + a = a.$$

Proof:

$$
\begin{aligned}
a &= a \cdot e. & \text{by P-2} \\
&= a \cdot (a + a') & \text{by P-4} \\
&= a \cdot a + a \cdot a' & \text{by P-3} \\
&= a \cdot a + e_+ & \text{by P-4} \\
&= a \cdot a & \text{by P-2,}
\end{aligned}
$$

and from the principle of duality,

$$a + a = a \qquad \text{Q.E.D.}$$

Theorem 5.   *Both binary operators of a Boolean algebra are associative; that is, for all a, b, and c in B,*

$$
\begin{aligned}
a + (b + c) &= (a + b) + c = a + b + c, \\
a \cdot (b \cdot c) &= (a \cdot b) \cdot c = a \cdot b \cdot c.
\end{aligned}
$$

The proof of this theorem is quite long and requires a few tricks. It will not be reproduced here, as it has no value in itself. A graphical verification of this theorem will be given in Section 1-4.

Theorem 6.   De Morgan's theorem, *or the* law of dualization. *For all a and b in B,*

$$(a \cdot b)' = a' + b' \quad \text{and} \quad (a + b)' = a' \cdot b'.$$

Proof: We shall prove only one of the identities, as the second is its dual pair. The proof is based on the property of uniqueness and the definition of complement.

$$
\begin{aligned}
(1) \quad (a \cdot b) \cdot (a' + b') &= (a \cdot b) \cdot a' + (a \cdot b) \cdot b' && \text{by P-3} \\
&= (a \cdot a') \cdot b + a \cdot (b \cdot b') && \text{by P-1 and T-5} \\
&= e_+ \cdot b + a \cdot e_+ && \text{by P-4} \\
&= e_+ + e_+ && \text{by L-1} \\
&= e_+ && \text{by T-4.}
\end{aligned}
$$

$$
\begin{aligned}
(2) \quad (a \cdot b) + (a' + b') &= [a + (a' + b')] \cdot [b + (a' + b')] && \text{by P-3} \\
&= [(a + a') + b'] \cdot [(b + b') + a'] && \text{by P-1 and T-5} \\
&= [e_. + b'] \cdot [e_. + a'] && \text{by P-4} \\
&= e_. \cdot e_. && \text{by L-1} \\
&= e_. && \text{by T-4.}
\end{aligned}
$$

Thus, by postulate P-4 and Theorem 2,

$$(a \cdot b)' = a' + b' \qquad \text{Q.E.D.}$$

Theorem 7.   *The complementation operator in a Boolean algebra satisfies the law of involution. That is, for all a in B,*

$$(a')' = a.$$

Proof: From postulate P-4 the complement of *a* satisfies the simultaneous equations

$$a + a' = e_. \quad \text{and} \quad a \cdot a' = e_+.$$

But these are the exact equations that define the complement of (a'). Thus, from Theorem 2,

$$(a')' = a \qquad \text{Q.E.D.}$$

These are some of the basic laws of a Boolean algebra. For ease of reference they are summarized in Table 1.

Up to this point we have defined a Boolean algebra as an abstract mathematical structure without attaching any intuitive meaning to the set of elements and the two binary operators. Actually, as they were not defined, they can have no meaning. To obtain better understanding of Boolean algebras we state a theorem and list a few examples of Boolean algebras.

TABLE 1

The Laws of Boolean Algebra

Laws of Binary Operator $(+)$		Laws of Binary Operator $(\cdot)$
$a + b \in B$	CLOSURE D-1	$a \cdot b \in B$
$a + b = b + a$	COMMUTATIVE P-1	$a \cdot b = b \cdot a$
$a + (b + c) = (a + b) + c$	ASSOCIATIVE T-5	$a \cdot (b \cdot c) = (a \cdot b) \cdot c$
$a + (b \cdot c) = (a + b) \cdot (a + c)$	DISTRIBUTIVE P-3	$a \cdot (b + c) = (a \cdot b) + (a \cdot c)$
$a + a \cdot b = a$	ABSORPTION T-3	$a \cdot (a + b) = a$
$a + a' \cdot b = a + b$	L-2	$a \cdot (a' + b) = a \cdot b$
$a + a = a$	IDEMPOTENCY T-4	$a \cdot a = a$
e_+ is unique	T-1	$e_{\cdot}$ is unique
$e_+ + a = a$	P-2	$e_{\cdot} \cdot a = a$
$e_{\cdot} + a = e_{\cdot}$	L-1	$e_+ \cdot a = e_+$
$a + a' = e_{\cdot}$	P-4	$a \cdot a' = e_+$
$e'_+ = e_{\cdot}$	C-1	$e'_{\cdot} = e_+$
$(a + b)' = a' \cdot b'$	DUALIZATION T-6	$(a \cdot b)' = a' + b'$

$a' \in B$ and is unique, P-4 and T-2
$(a')' = a$ INVOLUTION   T-7

Theorem 8.   *For every integer $n > 0$, there is a Boolean algebra having 2^n elements, and every finite Boolean algebra has exactly 2^n elements.*

The proof of this theorem is beyond the scope of this text. It should be noted that this theorem states that all finite Boolean algebras have 2^n elements, and that there exist infinite Boolean algebras, as the theorem does not place an upper limit on n.

Now we shall introduce three examples of finite Boolean algebras. In each of these examples we shall define the set of elements B, the two binary operators, and the complementation. The format of these examples was specially chosen to permit the interested reader to consider a Boolean algebra either as an idempotent ring or as a distributive and complemented lattice.

EXAMPLE 1.   The set of elements of B is $\{1, 2\}$.

$$a + b \equiv \text{the least common multiple of } a \text{ and } b,$$
$$a \cdot b \equiv \text{the greatest common divisor of } a \text{ and } b,$$
$$a' \equiv \frac{2}{a}.$$

The binary operators and the complementation can be represented in tabular form as shown in Fig. 1–1.

$+$	1	2		$\cdot$	1	2		a	a'
1	1	2		1	1	1		1	2
2	2	2		2	1	2		2	1

Figure 1–1.   Operators of Example 1. A two-valued Boolean algebra.

EXAMPLE 2.   Let the set of elements B be $\{1, 2, 3, 6\}$.

$$a + b \equiv \text{the least common multiple of } a \text{ and } b,$$
$$a \cdot b \equiv \text{the greatest common divisor of } a \text{ and } b,$$
$$a' \equiv \frac{6}{a}.$$

The tabular representation is given in Fig. 1–2.

+	1	2	3	6		·	1	2	3	6		a	a'
1	1	2	3	6		1	1	1	1	1		1	6
2	2	2	6	6		2	1	2	1	2		2	3
3	3	6	3	6		3	1	1	3	3		3	2
6	6	6	6	6		6	1	2	3	6		6	1

Figure 1–2. Operators of Example 2. A four-valued Boolean algebra.

EXAMPLE 3.   The set of elements B are $\{1, 2, 3, 5, 6, 10, 15, 30\}$.

$$a + b \equiv \text{the least common multiple of } a \text{ and } b,$$
$$a \cdot b \equiv \text{the greatest common divisor of } a \text{ and } b,$$
$$a' \equiv \frac{30}{a}.$$

We stated that these examples represent Boolean algebras, but this statement has to be proved. The statement concerning Example 1 will be proved in the text; the proof of Example 2 is left as a problem. To prove that a set of elements, together with the two binary operators, form a Boolean algebra, it is necessary to determine whether they satisfy the four postulates of Huntington (Def. 9). The actual proof will be given for a modified form of Example 1 —after renaming the elements such that $\{1, 2\} \equiv \{0, 1\}$. This was done to obtain the familiar form of a two-valued Boolean algebra. Under this transformation the tables of Fig. 1–1 defining the two binary operators become as shown in Fig. 1–3.

+	0	1		·	0	1
0	0	1		0	0	0
1	1	1		1	0	1

Figure 1–3. Binary operators of a two-valued Boolean algebra.

P-1: Both binary operators are commutative, as the tables are symmetric with respect to the diagonal. Thus postulate P-1 is satisfied.

P-2: From the tables $e_+ \equiv 0$ and $e. \equiv 1$. Thus postulate P-2 is satisfied.

P-3: To check the distributive property:

(1) $a + b \cdot c \stackrel{?}{=} (a + b) \cdot (a + c)$

Let $a = 0$: $0 + b \cdot c = (0 + b) \cdot (0 + c) = b \cdot c$

Let $a = 1$: $1 + b \cdot c = (1 + b) \cdot (1 + c) = 1$

Since these are true for all b and c, $+$ is distributive over $\cdot$.

(2) $a \cdot (b + c) \stackrel{?}{=} a \cdot b + a \cdot c$

Let $a = 0$: $0 \cdot (b + c) = 0 \cdot b + 0 \cdot c = 0$

Let $a = 1$: $1 \cdot (b + c) = 1 \cdot b + 1 \cdot c = b + c$

Since these are true for all b and c, $\cdot$ is distributive over $+$. Thus postulate P-3 is satisfied.

P-4: From the tables $0' = 1$ and $1' = 0$. Thus postulate P-4 is satisfied.

All four postulates are satisfied, so the set of elements $\{0, 1\}$, together with the two binary operators as defined in Fig. 1–3, form a Boolean algebra.

Note that in checking postulate P-3 we make use of the binary-operator characteristics contained in Fig. 1–3 and postulates P-1 and P-2 rather than conduct an exhaustive search. As there are three variables involved and each can take on two values, there are 8 (2^3) combinations to be checked. To avoid mistakes this is done in tabular form, referred to as a *truth table*. The rows of a truth table are the three-digit binary numbers corresponding to the three variables *abc*. To see this, consider part (1) of postulate P-3, as shown in Fig. 1–4.

Row Number	a	b	c	$b \cdot c$	$a + b \cdot c$	$a + b$	$a + c$	$(a + b) \cdot (a + c)$
0	0	0	0	0	0	0	0	0
1	0	0	1	0	0	0	1	0
2	0	1	0	0	0	1	0	0
3	0	1	1	1	1	1	1	1
4	1	0	0	0	1	1	1	1
5	1	0	1	0	1	1	1	1
6	1	1	0	0	1	1	1	1
7	1	1	1	1	1	1	1	1

Figure 1–4.   Truth table of the identity $a + b \cdot c = (a + b) \cdot (a + c)$.

1–4. ALGEBRA OF CLASSES (SETS)

This section provides a graphical interpretation of Boolean algebras. This is done by introducing some of the basic ideas of the algebra of classes. In contrast to previous sections, this section is largely intuitive in nature. By a *class*, or a *set*, we mean an arbitrary collection of things, and the notation $x \in A$ is used to abbreviate the statement "*x* is a member of class *A*." A specific class is defined by some property, or combination of properties, that its members have in common and that is used to test whether or not a given object belongs to the class.

To define the operations of the algebra of classes, we must first define some relations between two classes. When all the members of a class *A* are also members of a class *B*, then we say *A* is a *subclass* of *B*, $A \leq B$, and *B* is a *superclass* of *A*, $B \geq A$. And we say that two classes *A* and *B* are *equal*, $A = B$, if and only if $A \leq B$ and $B \leq A$. With the help of these statements we can now define two particular classes. The *null class*, $\varnothing$, is a class void of members and is a subclass of all the considered classes. The *universal class*, *I*, is a superclass of all the considered classes.

The algebra of classes deals with the different combinations of classes under the influence of the following operations:

Definition 10.   *Intersection*, $A \cap B$, defines the class whose members are both in class *A* and in class *B*.

Definition 11.   *Union*, $A \cup B$, defines the class whose members are either in class *A* or in class *B* or in both.

Definition 12.   *Complement*, $\overline{A}$, defines the class whose members are in the universal class *I* but not in class *A*.

Note that Definitions 10 and 11 define binary operations on the classes $A, B, C, \ldots$ subclasses of the universal class *I*. The next logical step would be to prove that the algebra of classes is a Boolean algebra. This is left as a problem. It is interesting to note that the binary operators and the identity elements of a Boolean algebra can be interpreted in two ways in the algebra of classes. That is, the set $\{ \cdot, +, e., e_+ \}$ can be translated into either one of two sets $\{ \cap, \cup, I, \varnothing \}$ or $\{ \cup, \cap, \varnothing, I \}$. Actually, the correspondence between a Boolean algebra and the algebra of classes is much stronger. Stone[7] proved that any Boolean algebra is isomorphic to the algebra of classes; that is, there is a one-to-one correspondence. Thus the results of this section will hold true for any Boolean algebra.

As already stated, the purpose of this section is to provide a graphical interpretation of the laws of Boolean algebra shown in Section 1–3. This is obtained by using the Venn-diagram interpretation of algebra of classes. The Venn diagram is also called a *circle diagram*, as the classes are represented by circles, the inside representing the members of the class and the outside representing the members not included in the class. As an example, consider

---

[7] M. H. Stone, *Trans. Am. Math. Soc.*, **40**, 37–111 (1936).

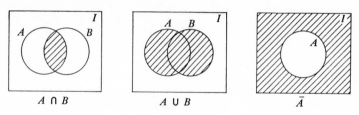

Figure 1–5. Venn-diagram interpretation of intersection, union, and complement.

the Venn-diagram representations of the three operations defined by Definitions 10, 11, and 12, shown in Fig. 1–5.

In Fig. 1–5 Venn diagrams of one and two classes are shown. These diagrams can be extended to include three and four classes (Fig. 1–6), but above this number the method becomes too complex for practical use.

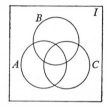 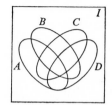

Figure 1–6.   Venn diagrams for three and four classes.

Venn diagrams, in a slightly modified form referred to as *Karnaugh maps*, form one of the most important tools in switching-circuit design. This will be discussed in detail in Chapter 2. At this point we shall use the Venn diagrams of Figs. 1–7, 1–8, and 1–9 to show graphically some of the laws of Boolean algebra stated in Table 1.

Note that Figs. 1–7, 1–8, and 1–9 provide complete proofs for the associative, distributive, and dualization laws (T-5, P-3, and T-6), respectively. This is due to the two possible interpretations of the binary operators and identity

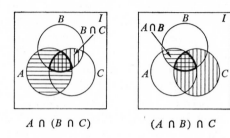

Figure 1–7. $A \cap (B \cap C) = (A \cap B) \cap C$.

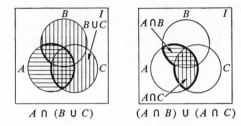

$$A \cap (B \cup C) \qquad (A \cap B) \cup (A \cap C)$$

Figure 1-8. $A \cap (B \cup C) = (A \cap B) \cup (A \cap C)$.

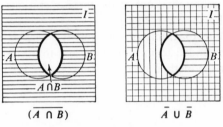

$$(\overline{A \cap B}) \qquad \overline{A} \cup \overline{B}$$

Figure 1-9. $(\overline{A \cap B}) = \overline{A} \cup \overline{B}$.

elements of a Boolean algebra. When the laws of the binary operators $(+)$ are to be proved, the translation $\{\cdot,\ +,\ e.,\ e_+\} \to \{\cap,\ \cup,\ I,\ \varnothing\}$ is used. On the other hand, when the laws of the binary operator $(\cdot)$ are to be proved, the translation $\{\cdot,\ +,\ e.,\ e_+\} \to \{\cup,\ \cap,\ \varnothing,\ I\}$ is used.

These were simple examples of the use of Venn diagrams to show Boolean identities. In Section 1-5 we shall give more complicated examples.

1-5. LOGICAL CONNECTIVES

Up to this point we have seen two isomorphic structures, the Boolean algebra and the algebra of classes. In this section we introduce, very briefly, some of the basic ideas of a third structure, *propositional logic*. Propositional logic is concerned with sentences and structures based on sentences. The sentences may be combined in various ways to form more complicated sentences whose truth or falsity is determined by the truth or falsity of their component sentences and the method of their combination.

In natural languages the sentences can be of many different types. As an example, consider the sentences "This is a book" and "We are on the moon." The first sentence is true and the other is obviously false. Another type of sentence is "There are living creatures on Mars." This statement can be true or false, but for lack of knowledge we are not able at this time to decide which. A third type of sentence is represented by paradoxes, as, for example, "The statement S states, 'The statement S is false'." If we assume that this sentence is true, the content indicates that it is false. Or if we assume that the statement is false, we infer from the content that it is true. Thus this sentence involves a contradiction, that is, undecidability. In propositional logic we restrict the sentences to a single type referred to as *propositions*. A proposition is a declarative sentence whose truth or falsity is a fact.

In propositional logic we say that two propositions p and q are combined under a rule defined by a logical connective c to form the combined proposition $p\,c\,q$. This is the only part of propositional logic that is discussed in this section.

One of the commonest connectives in a natural language is the conjunction "and." The corresponding logical connective is *conjunction* or "and" denoted "p & q," and the proposition p & q is true when and only when both proposition p and proposition q are true.

The other common conjunction of a natural language, "or," can have two distinct meanings, the inclusive and exclusive. Corresponding to the inclusive "or" we have the logical connective *disjunction* or "or" denoted "$p \vee q$," and the proposition $p \vee q$ is true when either p or q or both are true.

Corresponding to the adverb "not" of a natural language, in propositional logic we have the operation *negation*, denoted $\sim p$. That is, when p is true, $\sim p$ is false, and when p is false, $\sim p$ is true.

These operations can be represented in the tabular form of truth tables. In these tables the truth and falsity of the propositions are denoted by the letters T and F.

p	q	p & q		p	q	$p \vee q$		p	$\sim p$
F	F	F		F	F	F		F	T
F	T	F		F	T	T		T	F
T	F	F		T	F	T			
T	T	T		T	T	T			

Figure 1–10.   Truth tables of conjunction, disjunction, and negation.

At this point we shall digress and compare the tables of Fig. 1–10 with the tables of Fig. 1–3. That is, we are comparing the logical connectives with the binary operators of a two-valued Boolean algebra. If we now equate the pairs $\{T, F\} \equiv \{0, 1\}$, the logical connectives of conjunction and disjunction become the binary operators $(+)$ and $(\cdot)$. On the other hand, if we equate the pairs $\{T, F\} \equiv \{1, 0\}$, the logical connectives of conjunction and disjunction become the binary operators $(\cdot)$ and $(+)$. In both cases the operation of negation corresponds to complementation. In all further discussions we shall assume the translation $\{T, F\} \equiv \{1, 0\}$ and we shall refer to the binary operator $(\cdot)$ as "and" or *logical multiplication* and to the binary operator $(+)$ as "or" or *logical addition*.

To return to logical connectives, we can define the remainder by using a natural language as a model. This method becomes quite cumbersome, owing to the colloquial usage of these connectives in the language. As we are only interested in the truth-functional representation of these connectives, we shall use the truth table to define them. Using the notation $\{T, F\} \equiv \{1, 0\}$, a generalized truth table is as shown in Fig. 1-11.

p	q	$p \, c \, q$
0	0	?
0	1	?
1	0	?
1	1	?

Figure 1-11. General truth table for defining logical connectives.

Note that there are four rows in this table, as each of the propositions can take on two values. Using the notation of binary operators, these rows can be represented by $p' \cdot q'$, $p' \cdot q$, $p \cdot q'$, and $p \cdot q$. The combined proposition

TABLE 2
Definition of Logical Connectives

Row Number	p, q				Notation $p \, c \, q$	Name of Connective	Verbal Definition of Connective
	$p \cdot q$	$p \cdot q'$	$p' \cdot q$	$p' \cdot q'$			
0	0	0	0	0	F	FALSE	The joint statement is always false.
1	0	0	0	1	$p \cap q$	NEITHER-NOR	Neither p nor q.
2	0	0	1	0	q/p	BUT-NOT	q but not p.
3	0	0	1	1	$\sim p$	NOT p	The negation of statement p.
4	0	1	0	0	p/q	BUT-NOT	p but not q.
5	0	1	0	1	$\sim q$	NOT q	The negation of statement q.
6	0	1	1	0	$p \oplus q$	EXCLUSIVE-OR	Either p or q, but not both
7	0	1	1	1	$p \downarrow q$	JOINT-DENIAL	Negation of both p and q.
8	1	0	0	0	$p \, \& \, q$	CONJUNCTION	Both p and q.
9	1	0	0	1	$p \Leftrightarrow q$	EQUIVALENCE	p if and only if q.
10	1	0	1	0	q	STATEMENT q	Affirmation of statement q.
11	1	0	1	1	$p \rightarrow q$	IMPLIES	If p then q.
12	1	1	0	0	p	STATEMENT p	Affirmation of statement p.
13	1	1	0	1	$q \rightarrow p$	IMPLIES	If q then p.
14	1	1	1	0	$p \vee q$	DISJUNCTION	Either p or q or both.
15	1	1	1	1	T	TRUE	The joint statement is always true.

TABLE 3

The Logical Connectives

Logical Connective	Boolean Equivalent	Venn-Diagram Representation	Characteristic of Connective
$p \& q$ CONJUNCTION AND	$p \cdot q$		COMMUTATIVE ASSOCIATIVE
$p \lor q$ DISJUNCTION OR	$p + q$		COMMUTATIVE ASSOCIATIVE
$p \oplus q$ EXCLUSIVE-OR RING SUM SUM MODULO-2	$p' \cdot q + p \cdot q'$ $(p' + q') \cdot (p + q)$		COMMUTATIVE ASSOCIATIVE
$p \Leftrightarrow q$ EQUIVALENCE BICONDITIONAL DOT MODULO-2	$p' \cdot q' + p \cdot q$ $(p' + q) \cdot (p + q')$		COMMUTATIVE ASSOCIATIVE
$p \cap q$ NEITHER-NOR (N-OR)	$p' \cdot q'$		COMMUTATIVE NONASSOCIATIVE
$p \downarrow q$ JOINT-DENIAL SHEFFER-STROKE (N-AND)	$p' + q'$		COMMUTATIVE NONASSOCIATIVE
$p \rightarrow q$ IMPLIES CONDITIONAL	$p' + q$		NONCOMMUTATIVE NONASSOCIATIVE
p/q BUT-NOT INHIBIT AND	$p \cdot q'$		NONCOMMUTATIVE NONASSOCIATIVE

"$p\,c\,q$" can have either the value 0 or the value 1. Since there are four rows we can define $4^2 = 16$ different combinations, that is, sixteen ways of assigning values of 0 and 1 to the last column. These sixteen assignments are shown in Table 2, and they are listed according to the four-digit binary numbers 0000 to 1111. Table 2 gives the names, the notations, and a brief verbal definition of the logical connectives. The verbal definitions are the ones used in propositional logic. These are formal definitions and should not be confused with the colloquial usage in a natural language.

By checking Table 2 we see that the sixteen combinations define eight different connectives: CONJUNCTION (&), DISJUNCTION ($\vee$), EXCLUSIVE-OR ($\oplus$), EQUIVALENCE ($\Leftrightarrow$), NEITHER-NOR ($\cap$), JOINT-DENIAL ($\downarrow$), IMPLIES ($\rightarrow$), and BUT-NOT (/). There is also a unary operator, NEGATION ($\sim$). Just as in the case of binary operators, the Venn diagrams can provide a graphical translation for the logical connectives. Again there is the possibility of two different translations. In our presentation a circle represents each different proposition and any point inside the circle represents the value 1, a situation when the proposition is true. A point outside the circle represents the value 0, a situation when the proposition is false. Table 3 provides the Venn-diagram representations of these connectives together with their Boolean equivalents.

The last column of this table shows some of the characteristics of the logical connectives. These can be obtained either by translating the operations defined by the logical connectives into the binary operators of Boolean algebra, or by the use of Venn diagrams. As an example, we shall check the characteristics of the logical connective NEITHER-NOR by using both methods described above. It is left as a problem to check the characteristics of the other logical connectives of Table 3.

EXAMPLE 4.   Check whether or not the logical connective NEITHER-NOR is commutative and/or associative.

(a) By Venn diagram, as shown in Fig. 1–12.

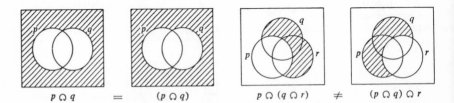

$$p \cap q \qquad = \qquad (p \cap q) \qquad\qquad p \cap (q \cap r) \qquad \neq \qquad (p \cap q) \cap r$$

Figure 1–12.   Venn diagrams of Example 4.

(b) By translation:

$$p \cap q = p' \cdot q' \qquad \text{by definition,}$$
$$q \cap p = q' \cdot p' \qquad \text{by definition.}$$

Thus $p \ominus q = q \ominus p$; that is, the logical connective NEITHER-NOR is commutative.

$$p \ominus (q \ominus r) = p' \cdot (q' \cdot r')' = p' \cdot (q + r) \qquad \text{by definition,}$$
$$(p \ominus q) \ominus r = (p' \cdot q')' \cdot r' = (p + q) \cdot r' \qquad \text{by definition.}$$

Thus $p \ominus (q \ominus r) \neq (p \ominus q) \ominus r$; that is, the logical connective NEITHER-NOR is not associative.

In this section we introduced the logical connectives. We saw that we could define them as eight binary operators and one unary operator. Two main points should be noted: that each of these logical connectives can be translated in terms of the binary operators of a two-valued Boolean albegra, and that the binary operators of a two-valued Boolean algebra are a subclass of these connectives. Thus, by introducing these logical connectives, the logical designer has greater latitude in his design. This becomes even more important when the logical design has to be translated into a specific piece of hardware, because certain connectives are simpler to realize in one hardware than in another.

1–6. LOGICAL FUNCTIONS

In this section we consider both propositional functions and two-valued Boolean functions under the common heading *logical functions*.

Propositional logic, like any other algebra, is composed of a set of symbols and a set of rules for manipulating these symbols. The symbols are the propositions that can take on two distinct values $\{0, 1\}$ or $\{F, T\}$, and the rules of manipulation are expressed by the definition of the particular logical connectives that are to be used. And, just as there are functions in conventional algebra, there are propositional functions in propositional logic.

Definition 13. A *propositional function* is the over-all proposition obtained by the combinations of basic propositions under the rules of logical connectives.

The task of investigating and classifying propositional functions becomes cumbersome if not hopeless, because of the large number of logical connectives. To simplify this task we define Boolean functions.

Definition 14. A *Boolean function* is an expression generated from $x_1, x_2, \ldots, x_n$, using only the operators $(\cdot)$, $(+)$, and $(')$, where the variables $x_1, x_2, \ldots, x_n$ assume values of a set B, which, together with the two binary operators $(\cdot)$ and $(+)$, form a Boolean algebra.

Note that Definition 14 defines a general Boolean function but as we are interested only in logical functions, we shall restrict the class B to two elements $\{0, 1\}$. It should be noted that in this case the set of Boolean functions of a two-valued Boolean algebra is a subclass of the propositional functions. But at the same time, since every logical connective can be expressed in terms of the operators $(\cdot)$, $(+)$, and $(')$, we can state the following theorem.

Theorem 9.   *Every propositional function can be expressed (represented) as an equivalent Boolean function*

No proof is necessary, as this theorem is a result of the above discussions. The result of this theorem is that every logical function can be expressed using only the operators AND $(\cdot)$, OR $(+)$, and NOT $(')$.

Definition 15.   *Functionally complete set of operators.* A set of operators is functionally complete if every logical function can be expressed entirely in terms of operators in the set.

Examples of a functionally complete set of operators are

(a)	SHEFFER-STROKE	$\downarrow$
(b)	NEITHER-NOR	$\cap$
(c)	IMPLIES, provided 0 is available	$\rightarrow$, 0
(d)	BUT-NOT, provided 1 is available	$/$, 1
(e)	AND with NOT	&, $'$
(f)	OR with NOT	$\vee$, $'$
(g)	IMPLIES with NOT	$\rightarrow$, $'$
(h)	BUT-NOT with NOT	$/$, $'$
(i)	EXCLUSIVE-OR with AND, provided 1 is available	$\oplus$, &, 1
(j)	EXCLUSIVE-OR with OR, provided 1 is available	$\oplus$, $\vee$, 1
(k)	EQUIVALENCE with AND, provided 0 is available	$\Leftrightarrow$, &, 0
(l)	EQUIVALENCE with OR, provided 0 is available	$\Leftrightarrow$, $\vee$, 0

Note that this list is far from being exhaustive, and considers only a minimally complete set of operators. An example of a nonminimal set is that composed of the operators AND, OR, and NOT, as shown by Theorem 9. The fact that this set of operators is a functionally complete set is also a by-product of the results of Section 1–7. The simplest way to check whether a set of operators forms a functionally complete set is to express the operators AND, OR, and NOT in terms of the operators of the chosen set. As an example of this, we shall check sets (c) and (g) of the above list.

EXAMPLE 5.   (a) Check if IMPLIES ($\to$) and NOT (') form a complete set:

(1) $p + q = (p')' + q = p' \to q.$
(2) $p \cdot q = (p' + q')' = (p \to q')'.$
(3) $p' = p'.$

Thus IMPLIES with NOT is a functionally complete set of operators.

   (b) Check if IMPLIES ($\to$) is a complete set provided 0 is available.

(1) $p + q = p' \to q = (p \to 0) \to q.$
(2) $p \cdot q = (p \to q')' = (p \to q') \to 0 = [p \to (q \to 0)] \to 0.$
(3) $p' = p' + 0 = p \to 0.$

Thus IMPLIES with 0 available is a functionally complete set of operators.

   We can see that any logical function can be expressed in terms of logical variables using only the operators belonging to a complete set. In practical design the choice of operators will depend on the actual hardware in which the design is to be accomplished. The use of minimal, or nonminimal, functionally complete sets is determined by the desirability criteria chosen, such as minimality, simplicity, and/or reliability. Also, in practical design some other operators can be defined, some suggested by physical characteristics of devices (for example, N-AND and N-OR), providing certain advantages for the hardware chosen. In Chapter 2 we shall introduce some of these operators and we consider in detail the idea of minimality.

1–7 CANONICAL REPRESENTATIONS OF BOOLEAN FUNCTIONS

   In Section 1–6 we defined logical functions and showed that they can be expressed as equivalent Boolean functions. In this section we consider some of the basic techniques for checking Boolean functions. Suppose it is desired to check the equivalence of two Boolean functions. The methods we have available up to this point are three: (1) we can show by algebraic manipulation, using the laws of Table 1, that one function is equal to the other; (2) we can derive the truth table of each of the functions and show that they are equivalent; and (3) we can obtain the Venn-diagram representations of both functions. These ideas will be illustrated by the following example.

EXAMPLE 6.   Show that the following two three-variable Boolean functions are equivalent:

$$f(x, y, z) = (x + y) \cdot (x' + z) \qquad \text{and} \qquad g(x, y, z) = x \cdot z + x' \cdot y.$$

(a) By algebraic manipulation: We shall start from $g(x, y, z)$ and show that it is equivalent to $f(x, y, z)$:

$$
\begin{aligned}
x \cdot z + x' \cdot y &= 0 + x \cdot z + x' \cdot y & \text{by P-2} \\
&= x \cdot x' + x \cdot z + x' \cdot y & \text{by P-4} \\
&= x \cdot (x' + z) + x' \cdot y & \text{by P-3} \\
&= (x' \cdot y) + (x) \cdot (x' + z) & \text{by P-1} \\
&= (x' \cdot y + x) \cdot (x' \cdot y + x' + z) & \text{by P-3} \\
&= (y + x) \cdot (x' \cdot y + x' + z) & \text{by L-2} \\
&= (y + x) \cdot (x' + z) & \text{by T-3} \\
&= (x + y) \cdot (x' + z) & \text{by P-1.}
\end{aligned}
$$

That is, $g(x, y, z) = f(x, y, z)$.

(b) By the truth-table method, as shown in Fig. 1–13.

Row Number	x	y	z	$x + y$	$x' + z$	$f(x, y, z)$	$x \cdot z$	$x' \cdot y$	$g(x, y, z)$
0	0	0	0	0	1	0	0	0	0
1	0	0	1	0	1	0	0	0	0
2	0	1	0	1	1	1	0	1	1
3	0	1	1	1	1	1	0	1	1
4	1	0	0	1	0	0	0	0	0
5	1	0	1	1	1	1	1	0	1
6	1	1	0	1	0	0	0	0	0
7	1	1	1	1	1	1	1	0	1

Figure 1–13. Truth table of Example 6.

(c) By Venn diagram, as shown in Fig. 1–14.

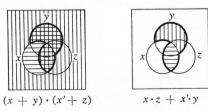

$(x + y) \cdot (x' + z)$ $x \cdot z + x' \cdot y$

Figure 1–14. Venn diagram of Example 6.

Even from this simple example we can see that the algebraic method requires a large amount of experience in selecting the best manipulations to use. For this reason the method becomes impractical when more complex functions are to be considered. When the truth-table method is used, this becomes quite cumbersome when the number of variables is large, as an n-variable function requires a truth table of 2^n rows. The same problems arise in the Venn-diagram method, as this method is impractical for more than four variables. Although we shall introduce other mapping techniques in Chapter 2, even with these maps it becomes impractical to handle more than six variables.

In this section we develop the canonical representation of Boolean functions. This enables us to represent a Boolean function in a unique functional form, thus simplifying the problem of comparing functions. In practice it is an algebraic representation of the truth table, generally obtainable with less labor than the above procedures, but its main advantage is that it is quite simple to program the procedure on a computer, because it is completely mechanical.

Before considering canonical expansions, we need to prove a theorem and introduce some nomenclature.

Theorem 10. Shannon's theorems. *Every Boolean function $f(x_1, x_2, \ldots, x_i, \ldots, x_n)$ of the Boolean variables $x_1, x_2, \ldots, x_i, \ldots, x_n$, in a two-valued Boolean algebra can be expressed in one of the following forms:*

(a) $\quad f(x_1, x_2, \ldots, x_i, \ldots, x_n) = x_i \cdot f(x_1, x_2, \ldots, 1, \ldots, x_n)$
$$+ x_i' \cdot f(x_1, x_2, \ldots, 0, \ldots, x_n),$$

(b) $\quad f(x_1, x_2, \ldots, x_i, \ldots, x_n) = [x_i' + f(x_1, x_2, \ldots, 1, \ldots, x_n)]$
$$\cdot [x_i + f(x_1, x_2, \ldots, 0, \ldots, x_n)],$$

$\qquad$ *for $\quad i = 1, 2, \ldots, n.$*

Proof: The method of exhaustion is used in this proof, that is, letting x_i take on the values 1 and 0.

(a) If $x_i = 1$, $\qquad f(x_1, x_2, \ldots, x_i, \ldots, x_n) =$
$$= 1 \cdot f(x_1, x_2, \ldots, 1, \ldots, x_n) + 0 \cdot f(x_1, x_2, \ldots, 0, \ldots, x_n)$$
$$= f(x_1, x_2, \ldots, 1, \ldots, x_n).$$

$\quad$ If $x_i = 0$, $\qquad f(x_1, x_2, \ldots, x_i, \ldots, x_n) =$
$$= 0 \cdot f(x_1, x_2, \ldots, 1, \ldots, x_n) + 1 \cdot f(x_1, x_2, \ldots, 0, \ldots, x_n)$$
$$= f(x_1, x_2, \ldots, 0, \ldots, x_n).$$

This proves part (a).

(b) If $x_i = 1$, $\qquad f(x_1, x_2, \ldots, x_i, \ldots, x_n) =$
$$= [0 + f(x_1, x_2, \ldots, 1, \ldots, x_n)] \cdot [1 + f(x_1, x_2, \ldots, 0, \ldots, x_n)]$$
$$= f(x_1, x_2, \ldots, 1, \ldots, x_n).$$

$\quad$ If $x_i = 0$, $\qquad f(x_1, x_2, \ldots, x_i, \ldots, x_n) =$
$$= [1 + f(x_1, x_2, \ldots, 1, \ldots, x_n)] \cdot [0 + f(x_1, x_2, \ldots, 0, \ldots, x_n)]$$
$$= f(x_1, x_2, \ldots, 0, \ldots, x_n).$$

This proves part (b), thus completing the proof of Theorem 10.

Either one of the forms of Theorem 10 can be used to obtain a complete expansion of a Boolean function. We shall use part (a), first expanding with respect to x_1; then each of the resulting functions is expanded with respect to x_2. This is repeated until each function becomes a constant. That is,

$$f(x_1, x_2, \ldots, x_n) = x_1 \cdot f(1, x_2, \ldots, x_n) + x_1' \cdot f(0, x_2, \ldots, x_n)$$
$$= x_1 \cdot [x_2 \cdot f(1, 1, \ldots, x_n) + x_2' \cdot f(1, 0, \ldots, x_n)]$$
$$+ x_1' \cdot [x_2 \cdot f(0, 1, \ldots, x_n) + x_2' \cdot f(0, 0, \ldots, x_n)]$$
$$= x_1 \cdot x_2 \cdot f(1, 1, \ldots, x_n) + x_1 \cdot x_2' \cdot f(1, 0, \ldots, x_n)$$
$$+ x_1' \cdot x_2 \cdot f(0, 1, \ldots, x_n) + x_1' \cdot x_2' \cdot f(0, 0, \ldots, x_n)$$
$$\vdots$$
$$= x_1 \cdot x_2 \cdots x_n \cdot f(1, 1, \ldots, 1)$$
$$+ x_1 \cdot x_2 \cdots x_n' \cdot f(1, 1, \ldots, 0) + \cdots$$
$$+ x_1' \cdot x_2' \cdots x_n \cdot f(0, 0, \ldots, 1)$$
$$+ x_1' \cdot x_2' \cdots x_n' \cdot f(0, 0, \ldots, 0). \tag{1}$$

The dual result is obtained by expanding the Boolean function, using the format of part (b). This result is shown in Equation (2).

$$f(x_1, x_2, \ldots, x_n) = [x_1' + x_2' + \cdots + x_n' + f(1, 1, \ldots, 1)]$$
$$\cdot [x_1' + x_2' + \cdots + x_n + f(1, 1, \ldots, 0)] \cdot \cdots$$
$$\cdot [x_1 + x_2 + \cdots + x_n' + f(0, 0, \ldots, 1)]$$
$$\cdot [x_1 + x_2 + \cdots + x_n + f(0, 0, \ldots, 0)]. \tag{2}$$

In both equations the Boolean functions $f(1, 1, \ldots, 1)$, $f(1, 1, \ldots, 0)$, $f(0, 0, \ldots, 1)$, and $f(0, 0, \ldots, 0)$ are functions of constants and are thus themselves constants having the value 0 or 1. These two expansions of Boolean functions are known as the *disjunctive canonical expansion* and the *conjunctive canonical expansion*, respectively. The disjunctive canonical expansion (D.C.E.) is also referred to as *expanded sum of products* or *minterm expansion*. The conjunctive canonical expansion (C.C.E.) is also referred to as *expanded product of sums* or *maxterm expansion*. These equations can be expressed in a more formal form, as shown by Theorems 11 and 12, using the following notations:

(1) $x_i^0 \equiv x_i'$ and $x_i^1 \equiv x_i$,

(2) $m_k = x_1^{\alpha_1} \cdot x_2^{\alpha_2} \cdot \cdots \cdot x_n^{\alpha_n}$,
$M_k = x_1^{\alpha_1} + x_2^{\alpha_2} + \cdots + x_n^{\alpha_n}$ and
$f(k) \equiv f(\alpha_1, \alpha_2, \ldots, \alpha_n)$,

where $\alpha_1, \alpha_2, \ldots, \alpha_n$ represents the decimal number k in binary notation. That is, $k = \sum_{i=1}^{n} \alpha_i \cdot 2^{n-i}$ and $0 \leq k \leq 2^n - 1$, and α_i is a constant having the value 0 or 1.

(3) $\xi_k \equiv f(k)$ and $\eta_k \equiv f(2^n - 1 - k)$.

Note the following relationship in binary numbers. Given the binary number $(\alpha_1 \alpha_2 \cdots \alpha_n)_2 = (k)_{10}$, then the binary number $(\alpha_1' \alpha_2' \cdots \alpha_n')_2 = (2^n - 1 - k)_{10}$. This can be proved quite easily by induction.

Theorem 11.   *Every Boolean function of n variables $x_1, x_2, \ldots, x_n$ over the Boolean algebra of two elements $\{0, 1\}$ can be expressed in a disjunctive canonical expansion (D.C.E.) as*

$$f(x_1, x_2, \ldots, x_n) = \sum_{i=0}^{2^n - 1} \xi_i \cdot m_i,$$

where $\xi_i = 1$ whenever $f(i) = 1$ and $\xi_i = 0$ otherwise.

Theorem 12.   *Every Boolean function of n variables $x_1, x_2, \ldots, x_n$ over the Boolean algebra of two elements $\{0, 1\}$ can be expressed in a conjunctive canonical expansion (C.C.E.) as*

$$f(x_1, x_2, \ldots, x_n) = \prod_{i=0}^{2^n - 1} (\eta_i + M_i),$$

where $\eta_i = 1$ whenever $f(2^n - 1 - i) = 1$ and $\eta_i = 0$ otherwise.

Before considering some examples and showing the procedures used in the expansion of a Boolean function, we shall check the meaning of these expansions in some known representations. As these expansions are algebraic representations of the truth table, we shall consider this representation first. To show this we shall use as an example the truth table for three variables, Fig. 1–15, arranging the rows of the truth table starting from 0 to 7 ($2^3 - 1$) to correspond to the binary numbers represented by the three variables $x_1, x_2,$ and x_3.

Row Number	x_1	x_2	x_3	$f(x_1, x_2, x_3)$	ξ_i	m_i	η_i	M_i
0	0	0	0	$f(0, 0, 0)$	ξ_0	$x_1' \cdot x_2' \cdot x_3'$	η_7	$x_1 + x_2 + x_3$
1	0	0	1	$f(0, 0, 1)$	ξ_1	$x_1' \cdot x_2' \cdot x_3$	η_6	$x_1 + x_2 + x_3'$
2	0	1	0	$f(0, 1, 0)$	ξ_2	$x_1' \cdot x_2 \cdot x_3'$	η_5	$x_1 + x_2' + x_3$
3	0	1	1	$f(0, 1, 1)$	ξ_3	$x_1' \cdot x_2 \cdot x_3$	η_4	$x_1 + x_2' + x_3'$
4	1	0	0	$f(1, 0, 0)$	ξ_4	$x_1 \cdot x_2' \cdot x_3'$	η_3	$x_1' + x_2 + x_3$
5	1	0	1	$f(1, 0, 1)$	ξ_5	$x_1 \cdot x_2' \cdot x_3$	η_2	$x_1' + x_2 + x_3'$
6	1	1	0	$f(1, 1, 0)$	ξ_6	$x_1 \cdot x_2 \cdot x_3'$	η_1	$x_1' + x_2' + x_3$
7	1	1	1	$f(1, 1, 1)$	ξ_7	$x_1 \cdot x_2 \cdot x_3$	η_0	$x_1' + x_2' + x_3'$

Figure 1–15.   Truth-table representation of canonical expansions.

In the disjunctive canonical expansion, $\xi_i = 1$ denotes the ith row of the truth table, where the function has the value 1, and these m_i's have to be included in the expansion. In the conjunctive canonical expansion $\eta_i = 0$ denotes the $(2^n - 1 - i)$th row of the truth table, where the function has the value 0, and these M_i's have to be included in the expansion. Figure 1–16 represents the Venn diagrams showing ξ_i's and η_i's.

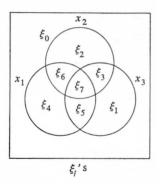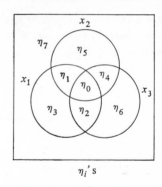

$\xi_i{}'$ s $\eta_i{}'$ s

Figure 1–16. Venn diagrams representing constants of canonical expansions.

From these representations we can reach several conclusions. First, that the canonical expansions are unique, because both the truth-table and Venn-diagram representations of a Boolean function are unique. Second, as there are 2^n rows in a truth table and the function can have, at each row, either the value 0 or the value 1, there are 2^{2^n} different n-variable functions. At this point we introduce the algebraic method of obtaining the expansions, as otherwise no reduction of work was achieved. The simplest way to show this procedure is by an example.

EXAMPLE 7.   Obtain the canonical expansions of the three-variable Boolean function $f(x, y, z) = x \cdot y' + x \cdot z' = x \cdot (y' + z')$.

(a) The disjunctive canonical expansion. In this example each of the terms includes only two variables, but in D.C.E. each of the terms includes all the variables. To obtain this we multiply each term by 1 in place of the missing variables, keeping in mind that $1 = a + a'$; that is,

$$
\begin{aligned}
x \cdot y' + x \cdot z' &= x \cdot y' \cdot 1 + x \cdot 1 \cdot z' \\
&= x \cdot y' \cdot (z + z') + x \cdot (y + y') \cdot z' \\
&= x \cdot y' \cdot z + x \cdot y' \cdot z' + x \cdot y \cdot z' + x \cdot y' \cdot z' \\
&= x \cdot y' \cdot z' + x \cdot y' \cdot z + x \cdot y \cdot z'.
\end{aligned}
$$

Therefore, $f(x, y, z) = m_4 + m_5 + m_6$.

Sometimes this is represented only by the numbers corresponding to the values of $\xi_i = 1$. This is generally referred to as the algebraic representation and denoted

$$
f(x, y, z) = \sum (4, 5, 6).
$$

(b) The conjunctive canonical expansion. In this case we start from the second form and add 0 whenever a variable is missing, keeping in mind that $0 = a \cdot a'$; that is,

$$x \cdot (y' + z') = (x + 0 + 0) \cdot (0 + y' + z')$$
$$= (x + y \cdot y' + z \cdot z') \cdot (x \cdot x' + y' + z')$$
$$= (x + y + z \cdot z') \cdot (x + y' + z \cdot z')$$
$$\cdot (x + y' + z') \cdot (x' + y' + z')$$
$$= (x + y + z) \cdot (x + y + z') \cdot (x + y' + z)$$
$$\cdot (x + y' + z') \cdot (x + y' + z') \cdot (x' + y' + z')$$
$$= (x + y + z) \cdot (x + y + z') \cdot (x + y' + z)$$
$$\cdot (x + y' + z') \cdot (x' + y' + z').$$

Therefore, $f(x, y, z) = M_7 \cdot M_6 \cdot M_5 \cdot M_4 \cdot M_0$.

Or, again using the algebraic representation, that is, listing the i's, where $\eta_i = 0$,

$$f(x, y, z) = \prod (7, 6, 5, 4, 0).$$

Actually, it is not necessary to calculate both canonical expansions, as one can be derived from the other. Suppose we are given the D.C.E.; that is, suppose we are given all the ξ_i's which are equal to 1. From this we can obtain all the ξ_i's equal to 0, and by the translation of $j = 2^n - 1 - i$ we obtain all the η_j's equal to 0, that is, the C.C.E. And, by executing a set of parallel operations we can derive the D.C.E., given the C.C.E. To illustrate this, we shall start from the D.C.E. of our previous example and derive the C.C.E.

EXAMPLE 8.   Obtain the C.C.E. of a three-variable Boolean function, given the D.C.E. as follows:

$$f(x, y, z) = \sum (4, 5, 6).$$

That is, $\xi_4 = \xi_5 = \xi_6 = 1$

or $\xi_0 = \xi_1 = \xi_2 = \xi_3 = \xi_7 = 0.$

As this is a three-variable Boolean function, $2^n - 1 = 2^3 - 1 = 7$; that is,

$$\eta_{7-0} = \eta_{7-1} = \eta_{7-2} = \eta_{7-3} = \eta_{7-7} = 0$$

or $\eta_7 = \eta_6 = \eta_5 = \eta_4 = \eta_0 = 0.$

From these we obtain the C.C.E.:

$$f(x, y, z) = \prod (7, 6, 5, 4, 0)$$

or $f(x, y, z) = M_7 \cdot M_6 \cdot M_5 \cdot M_4 \cdot M_0$

or $f(x, y, z) = (x + y + z) \cdot (x + y + z') \cdot (x + y' + z)$
$$\cdot (x + y' + z') \cdot (x' + y' + z').$$

1–8. CONCLUDING REMARKS

This chapter provides the necessary tools for study of the coming chapters. From the point of view of the remainder of the book, the main purpose of this chapter was to define a two-valued Boolean algebra, to develop its rules, and to show the canonical expansions. The algebra of classes was introduced to provide better understanding of the basic principles, and the logical connectives were introduced to provide greater versatility for the designer.

The presentation of this chapter was more detailed than subsequent requirements would indicate. This form of presentation was used for the following two reasons. In the author's opinion, such a detailed presentation is required for understanding and efficient use of Boolean algebra. The other reason was to introduce the generalized Boolean algebra. The logical designer today is restricted to the use of two-valued functions, because of the lower reliability of many-valued devices. There are today a number of research papers considering three-valued functions. These are generally based on a system of logic proposed by Post,[8] referred to as *Post algebras*. An example of an n-valued Post algebra is presented in Fig. 1–17.

$\cup$	1	2	3	$\cdots$	n		$\cap$	1	2	3	$\cdots$	n		p	$\bar{p}$
1	1	1	1	·	1		1	1	2	3	·	n		1	2
2	1	2	2	·	2		2	2	2	3	·	n		2	3
3	1	2	3	·	3		3	3	3	3	·	n		3	4
⋮	·	·	·	·	·		⋮	·	·	·	·	·		⋮	·
n	1	2	3	·	n		n	n	n	n	·	n		n	1

$$p \cup q = \min(p,q) \qquad p \cap q = \max(p,q) \qquad \bar{p} = p + 1 \quad (p \neq n)$$

Figure 1–17. Operators of an n-valued Post algebra.

The literature on Boolean algebra is large and varied. Most of the papers are quite abstract in nature and are quite hard to read without a good background in abstract algebra. Good examples are the papers by Huntington, Post, and Stone listed in the footnotes of this chapter. The interested reader is advised to consider as a reference a book that uses the mathematical approach but also treats the practical applications. Two such books are:

J. E. Whitesitt. *Boolean Algebra and Its Applications*. Reading, Mass.: Addison–Wesley, 1961. This book first introduces the algebra of sets and uses this as motivation for the precise development of Boolean algebra. The remainder of the book considers the different applications of Boolean algebra.

F. E. Hohn. *Applied Boolean Algebra: An Elementary Introduction*. Second Edition. New York: Macmillan, 1966. This book introduces Boolean algebra quite briefly, and most of the book considers applications—in particular, to switching circuits.

Other good reference books that use different approaches are:

B. H. Arnold. *Logic and Boolean Algebra*. Englewood Cliffs, N.J.: Prentice–Hall, 1962. This book is mainly mathematical in nature. It introduces Boolean

[8] E. L. Post, "Introduction to a General Theory of Elementary Propositions," *Am. J. Math*, **43**, 163–185 (1921).

algebra by first defining lattices and later introduces Boolean rings. Very little emphasis is placed on applications.

P. Rosenbloom. *The Elements of Mathematical Logic*. New York: Dover, 1950. This book is concerned mainly with logic and the theory of Boolean algebra is considered only as a by-product.

S. H. Caldwell. *Switching Circuits and Logical Design*. New York: Wiley, 1958. The approach of this book is completely applied and introduces two-valued Boolean algebra to provide the tools of study for switching circuits.

M. Phister. *Logical Design of Digital Computers*. New York: Wiley, 1958. This book covers in detail the theory of two-valued Boolean algebra. The approach is applied, as the main objective of the book is the design of digital computers.

Note that these books only represent a sampling of the existing literature. They were chosen to give maximum benefit to readers having different interests and backgrounds.

PROBLEMS

1. Which of the six basic laws expressed by Definitions 2 to 7 are satisfied for each of the pairs of binary operators of Fig. 1–18? Note that each of the binary operators is defined on a set of three elements $\{0, 1, 2\}$. The operators of pair (a) have no intuitive meaning. The operators of pair (b) represent the addition and multiplication tables modulo-3. The operators of pair (c) represent the binary operators of a three-valued Post algebra.

$\circ$	0	1	2		$*$	0	1	2
0	0	2	1		0	0	1	2
1	2	1	0		1	0	1	2
2	1	0	2		2	0	1	2

(a)

$+$	0	1	2		$\cdot$	0	1	2
0	0	1	2		0	0	0	0
1	1	2	0		1	0	1	2
2	2	0	1		2	0	2	1

(b)

$\cup$	0	1	2		$\cap$	0	1	2
0	0	0	0		0	0	1	2
1	0	1	1		1	1	1	2
2	0	1	2		2	2	2	2

(c)

Figure 1–18.

2. Given the set of three elements {0, 1, 2} and the two binary operators {+, ·} as defined by the tables of Fig. 1–19, find whether each of the four postulates of Huntington (Def. 9) is satisfied.

+	0	1	2		·	0	1	2
0	0	1	2		0	0	0	0
1	1	1	1		1	0	1	2
2	2	1	2		2	0	2	2

Figure 1–19.

3. Show that Example 2 is a Boolean algebra. In other words, show that the set of elements {1, 2, 3, 6} with the two binary operators {+, ·} defined by the tables of Fig. 1–20 is a Boolean algebra.

+	1	2	3	6		·	1	2	3	6
1	1	2	3	6		1	1	1	1	1
2	2	2	6	6		2	1	2	1	2
3	3	6	3	6		3	1	1	3	3
6	6	6	6	6		6	1	2	3	6

Figure 1–20.

4. Using the laws of a Boolean algebra, as stated in Table 1, prove the following identities:

(a) $(x + y) \cdot (x' + z) \cdot (y + z) = (x + y) \cdot (x' + z)$;

(b) $x' \cdot y \cdot z + x \cdot y' \cdot z + x' \cdot y' \cdot z = z \cdot (x' + y')$;

(c) $(x + y') \cdot (x' + y) \cdot (x + z) = (x + y') \cdot (x' + y) \cdot (y + z)$;

(d) $z + x \cdot y + x' \cdot z = (x + z) \cdot (y + z)$.

5. Assume that the identities of Problem 4 are expressed in a two-valued Boolean algebra. Prove these identities using both Venn-diagram and truth-table representations.

6. Check whether the following logical connectives are commutative, associative, or both: AND, OR, EXCLUSIVE-OR, EQUIVALENCE, NEITHER-NOR, SHEFFER-STROKE, IMPLIES, BUT-NOT.

7. Check whether the logical connectives AND and OR are distributive over the other logical connectives.

8. Express the logical connectives AND, OR, and NOT in terms of the logical connectives of each of the following sets:

(a) SHEFFER-STROKE ($\downarrow$);

(b) NEITHER-NOR ($\cap$);

(c) BUT-NOT (/) and NOT (');

(d) EXCLUSIVE-OR ($\oplus$) and AND (·) provided 1 is available;

(e) EQUIVALENCE ($\Leftrightarrow$) and OR (+) provided 0 is available.

9. Derive the equivalent Boolean functions and obtain the Venn-diagram representations of the following propositional functions:

(a) $f(x, y, z, \omega) = [x \oplus (y \cdot z)]/\omega$;
(b) $f(x, y, z, \omega) = [(x \rightarrow y) \Leftrightarrow (z \cdot \omega)] \cap x$;
(c) $f(x, y, z, \omega) = [(x + y) \rightarrow (x \cdot z)] \downarrow [\omega \cap (z + y)]$.

10. Derive the conjunctive canonical expansion starting from the disjunctive canonical expansion. (*Hint:* First obtain the D.C.E. of f' and negate the result.)

11. Obtain both the disjunctive and the conjunctive canonical expansions of the following three-variable Boolean functions:

(a) $f(x, y, z) = x + y'$;
(b) $f(x, y, z) = x' \cdot z + x \cdot z'$;
(c) $f(x, y, z) = (x + y) \cdot (x' + y')$;
(d) $f(x, y, z) = x' \cdot y \cdot z + x \cdot y$;
(e) $f(x, y, z) = x$.

CHAPTER

2

Design and Simplification of Combinational Circuits

2–1. INTRODUCTION

In this chapter we consider the problems that arise in the design of combinational circuits. The design is considered from a general point of view without introducing technical problems. The actual hardware realization is omitted, because the design and the simplification criteria change from one hardware realization to another. Also, recent technical advances in the design of logical elements have come at such a rate that many of the elements that could now be described will, or may, become obsolete tomorrow.

In this first part of this chapter we discuss very briefly the translation from the verbal specification to the logical-function description of a problem. In the remainder of the chapter it is assumed that the design specifications are given as logical functions. Then the translation of the logical function into a gate, or block-diagrammatic, realization is shown. Later in the chapter multiple-input and nonpropositional gates are introduced.

In the remainder of the chapter we consider the different systematic procedures for obtaining a specific minimization of the two-level gate realizations of Boolean functions.

2–2. PROBLEM SPECIFICATION IN TERMS OF LOGICAL FUNCTIONS

Ordinarily, problem statements are given verbally. These statements are then to be translated into functional form. This translation is generally done with the help of a truth table, that is, by checking all possible combinations of the input variables and listing the corresponding values of the output variables. The best way to see the actual procedures is to do a few examples.

EXAMPLE 1.   *Staircase lighting*. Obtain the logical function that describes the operation of a lamp controlled by three switches.

To solve this problem we need first to define its variables as binary variables. We shall denote by x_1, x_2, and x_3 the three control switches that are the inputs. Their respective ON and OFF positions we shall denote x_i and x_i'. The lighted and unlighted states of the lamp, the output, will be denoted z and z'.

The next step in the solution is to redefine the problem more exactly. First, we assume that the lamp is unlighted when all three switches are OFF. The lamp is to be turned on by changing the position of any one of the switches. Then the lamp is turned off by again changing the position of any one of the switches. Finally, the lamp is lighted when all three switches are ON. The results can be combined in a truth table, as shown in Fig. 2–1.

Row Number	INPUTS			OUTPUT
	x_1	x_2	x_3	z
0	0	0	0	0
1	0	0	1	1
2	0	1	0	1
3	0	1	1	0
4	1	0	0	1
5	1	0	1	0
6	1	1	0	0
7	1	1	1	1

Figure 2–1.   Truth-table representation of Example 1.

We can express the conditions under which the lamp is lighted as a Boolean function of the variables x_1, x_2, and x_3. That is, either one of the following functions is the solution of our problem:

$$z(x_1, x_2, x_3) = x_1' \cdot x_2' \cdot x_3 + x_1' \cdot x_2 \cdot x_3' + x_1 \cdot x_2' \cdot x_3' + x_1 \cdot x_2 \cdot x_3$$

$$\text{or} \quad z(x_1, x_2, x_3) = (x_1 + x_2 + x_3) \cdot (x_1 + x_2' + x_3')$$
$$\cdot (x_1' + x_2 + x_3') \cdot (x_1' + x_2' + x_3).$$

EXAMPLE 2.   *Full subtractor.* Obtain the logical functions describing the operation of a binary subtractor.

The circuit must have three binary inputs; the minuend (x), the subtrahend (y), and the borrow (b) from the lower-order digits. The binary outputs are the difference (D) and the borrow (B) to the next-higher-order digits.

In this example it is straightforward to construct a truth table from a knowledge of the rules of subtraction. The truth table is shown in Fig. 2–2.

Row Number	INPUTS			OUTPUTS	
	x	y	b	D	B
0	0	0	0	0	0
1	0	0	1	1	1
2	0	1	0	1	1
3	0	1	1	0	1
4	1	0	0	1	0
5	1	0	1	0	0
6	1	1	0	0	0
7	1	1	1	1	1

Figure 2–2.   Truth-table representation of a full subtractor.

The corresponding logical functions in algebraic form are

$$D(x, y, b) = \sum (1, 2, 4, 7) = \prod (7, 4, 2, 1)$$

and

$$B(x, y, b) = \sum (1, 2, 3, 7) = \prod (7, 3, 2, 1).$$

EXAMPLE 3.   *Prime detector.* The circuit whose logical function is to be obtained has four binary inputs (x, y, z, ω) and a single binary output (P). The four inputs represent a decimal digit (0–9) encoded as a four-digit binary number. The output is to be 1 whenever the decimal input is a prime number and the output is to be 0 whenever the decimal input is not a prime number.

In solving this problem we could have constructed a truth table, as in the previous example. But this is not necessary, because the rows of the truth table are numbered the same as the input. The prime numbers between 0 and 9 are 2, 3, 5, and 7. The corresponding logical function in algebraic form is

$$P(x, y, z, \omega) = \sum (2, 3, 5, 7) = \prod (15, 14, 11, 9, 7, 6).$$

But in this example there are six other possible input combinations that will never occur, because the input is a decimal digit. These are the input combinations corresponding to the rows 10, 11, 12, 13, 14, and 15 of the truth table. The outputs (P) corresponding to these rows are listed as don't-care conditions and can be assigned the value 1 or 0, depending on which produces a simpler realization. Thus the logical functions corresponding to this problem should be listed as

$$P(x, y, z, \omega) = \sum (2, 3, 5, 7) \qquad \text{and} \qquad d = \sum (10, 11, 12, 13, 14, 15)$$

or $P(x, y, z, \omega) = \prod (15, 14, 11, 9, 7, 6) \qquad \text{and} \qquad d = \prod (5, 4, 3, 2, 1, 0).$

From these examples we can see that the translation of a problem from its verbal statement to a functional specification is straightforward. The only problem arises when the verbal specification is ambiguous, but once an exact definition can be obtained the construction of the truth table becomes quite obvious. In many instances, the design specifications of a combinational circuit are initially presented in tabular form. As an example, this occurs in the solution of sequential circuits when the combinational design becomes a subsidiary problem. This will be considered in detail both in Chapters 3 and 4, where we shall also consider the translation problems of sequential circuits.

2–3. GATE REALIZATION OF COMBINATIONAL CIRCUITS

In this section we consider in detail the procedure for representing a logical function in block-diagrammatic form. That is, we obtain a schematic representation of switching circuits. To do this, we first define some terms.

Definition 1. A *switching circuit* is defined as a circuit having n inputs, $x_1, x_2, \ldots, x_n$, and m outputs, $z_1, z_2, \ldots, z_m$, and whose variables x_i and z_j each take on two distinct values.

Definition 2. A *combinational circuit* is defined as a switching circuit whose outputs $z_1, z_2, \ldots, z_m$ are determined entirely by its present inputs $x_1, x_2, \ldots, x_n$; that is,

$$z_j = f_j(x_1, x_2, \ldots, x_n) \qquad \text{for } j = 1, 2, \ldots, m$$

and f_j is a Boolean function.

Definition 3. A *sequential circuit* is defined as a switching circuit whose outputs $z_1, z_2, \ldots, z_m$ are determined both by its present inputs $x_1, x_2, \ldots, x_n$ and by its past history, that is, the past sequence of inputs. In this case the outputs are *not* Boolean functions of the present inputs.

Definition 4. A *gate* is a block-diagrammatic representation of a physical device that produces an output signal whenever the input signals combine according to the rules of the operation that this device realizes.

At first we consider only gates corresponding to the logical connectives defined in Chapter 1; that is, these gates can have at most two inputs. Such a gate is represented diagrammatically as shown in Fig. 2–3.

$$x_1 \circ\!\!-\!\!\longrightarrow \boxed{*} \longrightarrow y = x_1 * x_2$$

Inputs   Output

Figure 2–3.   Gate representation of a logical connective.

To obtain a gate realization of a combinational circuit now becomes straightforward. Since every logical function is obtained by combining variables with the help of logical connectives, the corresponding combinational circuit is realized by combining its signals in exactly the same manner, using gates instead of connectives. The simplest way to see this is by an example.

EXAMPLE 4. Obtain a gate realization of the following Boolean function:

$$f(x_1, x_2, x_3) = x_1 \cdot x_2 \cdot x_3 + x_1' \cdot x_2' + x_1' \cdot x_3'.$$

This function has three terms, and each term can be implemented separately. Then they can be combined in turn to give the over-all function. Figure 2–4 shows such an implementation. This implementation is self-explanatory when we rewrite the above functions with braces to show the order of combinations:

$$f(x_1, x_2, x_3) = \{(x_1 \cdot x_2) \cdot x_3\} + \{(x_1' \cdot x_2') + (x_1' \cdot x_3')\}.$$

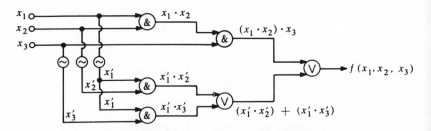

Figure 2–4.   Gate realization of $x_1 \cdot x_2 \cdot x_3 + x_1' \cdot x_2' + x_1' \cdot x_3'$.

From this example we can see that in combinational circuit design the question of realizability does not appear, because the gate realization is the graphical translation of a given logical function. Just as the logical-function representation is not unique, the gate realization of a combinational circuit is not unique. This raises the question of simplicity, whether we could have obtained a simpler realization. For the present we consider the number of gates used in a realization to be a rough measure of simplicity. To see this, consider rearranging the Boolean function of our previous example as shown.

EXAMPLE 5.

$$f(x_1, x_2, x_3) = x_1 \cdot x_2 \cdot x_3 + x_1' \cdot x_2' + x_1' \cdot x_3'$$
$$= x_1 \cdot (x_2 \cdot x_3) + x_1' \cdot (x_2' + x_3')$$
$$= x_1 \cdot (x_2 \cdot x_3) + x_1' \cdot (x_2 \cdot x_3)'.$$

The corresponding gate realization is shown in Fig. 2–5.

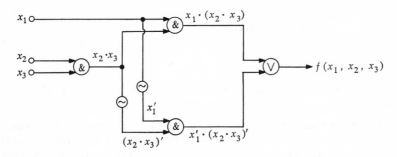

Figure 2–5. Gate realization of $x_1 \cdot x_2 \cdot x_3 + x_1' \cdot x_2' + x_1' \cdot x_3'$.

We can see that the second realization is simpler; it uses six gates, compared to the nine gates used in the first realization. In both these examples we tacitly assumed that only AND, OR, and NOT gates were to be used. Actually, we could use any functionally complete set of operators. As an example, we shall realize the above Boolean function using only SHEFFER-STROKE gates, and then using both AND and EQUIVALENCE gates.

EXAMPLE 6.   Obtain a SHEFFER-STROKE gate realization of the Boolean   *NAND*
function

$$f(x_1, x_2, x_3) = x_1 \cdot x_2 \cdot x_3 + x_1' \cdot x_2' + x_1' \cdot x_3'.$$

We start with $f(x_1, x_2, x_3) = x_1 \cdot (x_2 \cdot x_3) + x_1' \cdot (x_2 \cdot x_3)'$ and as $a \downarrow b = a' + b'$ we let $a = x_1' + (x_2 \cdot x_3)'$ and $b = x_1 + (x_2 \cdot x_3)$. Each of these functions can now be generated as follows:

$$a = x_1' + (x_2 \cdot x_3)' = x_1 \downarrow (x_2 \cdot x_3) = x_1 \downarrow \{(x_2 \downarrow x_3) \downarrow (x_2 \downarrow x_3)\},$$
$$b = x_1 + (x_2 \cdot x_3) = x_1' \downarrow (x_2 \cdot x_3)' = (x_1 \downarrow x_1) \downarrow (x_2 \downarrow x_3).$$

The corresponding gate realization is shown in Fig. 2–6.

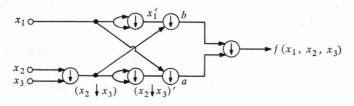

Figure 2–6. Gate realization of $x_1 \cdot x_2 \cdot x_3 + x_1' \cdot x_2' + x_1' \cdot x_3'$.

$$(AB)' \Rightarrow A \downarrow B \qquad (A+B) \Rightarrow A \uparrow B$$

EXAMPLE 7.   Using only AND and EQUIVALENCE gates, realize the Boolean function

$$f(x_1, x_2, x_3) = x_1 \cdot x_2 \cdot x_3 + x_1' \cdot x_2' + x_1' \cdot x_3'.$$

We start with $f(x_1, x_2, x_3) = x_1 \cdot (x_2 \cdot x_3) + x_1' \cdot (x_2 \cdot x_3)'$ and as $a \Leftrightarrow b = a \cdot b + a' \cdot b'$ we have $f(x_1, x_2, x_3) = x_1 \Leftrightarrow (x_2 \cdot x_3)$. The corresponding gate realization is shown in Fig. 2–7.

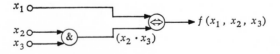

Figure 2–7.   Gate realization of $x_1 \cdot x_2 \cdot x_3 + x_1' \cdot x_2' + x_1' \cdot x_3'$.

From these examples we can see that, given the logical function in terms of a given set of connectives, the translation into a gate realization using the same set of connectives is straightforward. The major problem, however, is in translation of a Boolean function into a different set of connectives that uses fewer gates, because no procedure is defined and the translation must be done by trial and error.

When we check the number of gates required to realize a specific Boolean function we can make the following observations:

(1)   The number of gates required to realize a given Boolean function depends upon the set of connectives used. However, there is no way to tell without trial and error which set of connectives will give the simplest realization of a given Boolean function.

(2)   Even when using a specific set of connectives, the number of gates required depends on the way the Boolean function is expressed. Later in this chapter we shall develop a systematic procedure to simplify a Boolean function and obtain the corresponding minimal gate realizations using multiple-input AND and OR gates.

Thus far we have considered only the problem of synthesis. We have seen that every Boolean function can be represented by an interconnection of gates. Now the question arises whether every interconnection of gates can be represented by a Boolean function. The answer to this question is no, but the following statement can be made.

Given a set of interconnected gates that does not contain feedback loops and whose signals are connected only through gates, the output or outputs can always be expressed as a logical function of the inputs.

To understand this statement, consider the following example.

EXAMPLE 8.   Analyze the input-output behavior of the switching circuit shown in Fig. 2–8. Note the presence of a feedback loop.

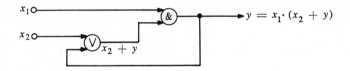

Figure 2–8.   Gate realization of $y = x_1 \cdot (x_2 + y)$.

To check the black-box behavior of this circuit we check the value of the output y for the possible input combinations: If $x_1 = 0$ then $y = 0$ independent of the value of x_2; if $x_1 = x_2 = 1$ then $y = 1$; if $x_1 = 1$ and $x_2 = 0$, the value of the output depends on its past value. If the output was 0, it will remain 0, but if it was 1, it will remain 1. Thus the output depends on the past history, that is, on the sequence by which a specific input combination was reached. Thus the circuit of Fig. 2–8 represents a sequential circuit. This can also be seen from the functional representation, because we cannot express the output y in terms of the inputs $x_1 x_2$, as there is no multiplicative inverse in a Boolean algebra.

This example was introduced to explain the first restriction of our statement, that is, that no feedback loops are allowed in combinational circuits. The second restriction states that no two signal lines can be connected together. This restriction was introduced to avoid undetermined values at any point. Assume that one signal has the value 0 and the other 1; the value of the signal at the connection of these two lines is undetermined.

2–4. NONPROPOSITIONAL GATES

In Section 2–3 we defined gates representing logical connectives. In this section we extend the number of switching gates to include nonpropositional gates. As a first extension we define gates with more than two inputs that retain the main characteristics of the logical connectives. To obtain such a gate it is required that the logical connective be associative. Thus we can have four such gates: multiple-input AND, OR, EXCLUSIVE-OR, and EQUIVALENCE gates. The block-diagrammatic representation of such a gate is shown in Fig. 2–9.

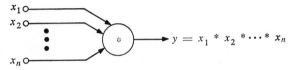

Figure 2–9.   Multiple-input logical gate.

Some other multiple-input gates are those that are artificially defined, as they are very easily implemented in hardware. Two very important examples are the *N*-OR (*D*) and *N*-AND (*T*) gates. The operations of these gates are defined as follows:

$$D(x_1, x_2, \ldots, x_n) \equiv (x_1 + x_2 + \cdots + x_n)' = x_1' \cdot x_2' \cdot \cdots \cdot x_n',$$
$$T(x_1, x_2, \ldots, x_n) \equiv (x_1 \cdot x_2 \cdot \cdots \cdot x_n)' = x_1' + x_2' + \cdots + x_n'.$$

These two gates may, at first, seem to be multiple-input NEITHER-NOR and SHEFFER-STROKE gates. But this is false, as the latter connectives are not associative. At most, *N*-OR and *N*-AND gates can be considered as generalizations of NEITHER-NOR and SHEFFER-STROKE gates, respectively. The best way to consider these gates is as an OR or AND gate whose output is complemented. The block-diagrammatic representation of these gates is as shown in Fig. 2–9, with the asterisk in the circle replaced by the letter *D* or *T*.

The third type of artificially defined gates consists of those that mimic a natural process. The most important and most studied is the *threshold gate*. The properties of this gate were studied under different names, such as threshold logic, linear input logic, majority logic, voting logic, etc. The interest in the threshold gate arose primarily because of its similarity to the accepted neuron model, and to the fact that it leads to simplified model representation for some of the theories of learning. From the point of view of the logical designer, the most important reason is that it is the most general gate yet defined.

Definition 5.   A *threshold gate* is a device that can be in either one of two distinct states, depending upon the magnitude of its binary inputs combined in a weighted form.

This is a very general definition of a threshold gate, and must be clarified before it can be of any use. Before the introduction of a more detailed definition of this gate, a simpler form, the *majority gate*, should be considered.

Definition 6.   A *majority gate* is a device with a finite odd number of binary inputs (x_i). The output F_N is also a binary variable, having that value which is applied to the majority of inputs.

Assuming the binary constant $\{0, 1\}$, the equation governing the behavior of a majority gate is

$$F_N = \begin{cases} 1 & \text{if } \sum_{i=1}^{N} x_i > \dfrac{N}{2} \ (\geq k), \\[2ex] 0 & \text{if } \sum_{i=1}^{N} x_i < \dfrac{N}{2} \ (< k), \end{cases}$$

where $\sum$ represents numerical summation and the number of binary inputs $N = 2k - 1$. There is a large body of literature describing procedures of synthesizing a Boolean function using majority gates. Some of the literature is listed in Appendix I, but the actual procedures will not be described, as they are beyond the scope of this text. Here we shall introduce very briefly the three-input majority gate that is of particular interest. The output of a three-input majority gate is 1 ($F_3 = 1$) whenever any two or more of its three inputs (x_1, x_2, x_3) are 1. In other words, the Boolean function describing the operation of this gate is

$$F_3(x_1, x_2, x_3) = x_1 \cdot x_2 + x_1 \cdot x_3 + x_2 \cdot x_3.$$

Note that if one of the variables is made a constant, this gate becomes either the AND or the OR gate. To see this, let the variable x_3 become first 0 and then 1. We see that $F_3(x_1, x_2, 0) = x_1 \cdot x_2$ and $F_3(x_1, x_2, 1) = x_1 + x_2$. Thus every gate realization using AND and OR gates can be translated into majority gates. Actually, the greater versatility of the majority gate will generally produce a simpler realization than the above translation. To see this, consider the following example.

EXAMPLE 9.   Obtain a three-input majority gate realization, by straight translation, of the Boolean function

$$f(x_1, x_2, x_3, x_4) = x_1 \cdot x_2 + x_3 \cdot (x_2 \cdot x_4 + x_1 \cdot x_4').$$

By translating the operations in the order defined by the parentheses we obtain Fig. 2–10. This gate realization requires six three-input majority gates,

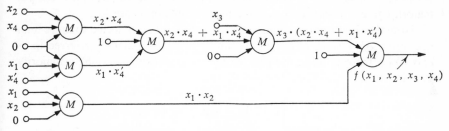

Figure 2–10. Three-input majority gate realization of $x_1 \cdot x_2 + x_3 \cdot (x_2 \cdot x_4 + x_1 \cdot x_4')$.

but using Akers[1] technique the same function can be realized using three three-input majority gates, as shown in Fig. 2–11.

Actually, if we are allowed to use N-input majority gates, we can generally obtain even simpler realizations. If we consider the Boolean function of Example 9, it can be shown that it cannot be realized with one majority gate.

---

[1] S. B. Akers, Jr., "Synthesis of Combinational Logic Using Three-Input Majority Gates," *Proc. Third Ann. Symp. Switching Circuit Theory and Logical Design* (1962), pp. 150–157. A very basic and clear presentation of synthesis using three-input majority gates. An extended version of this paper was published by the General Electric Co. as *TISR61ELS*-141.

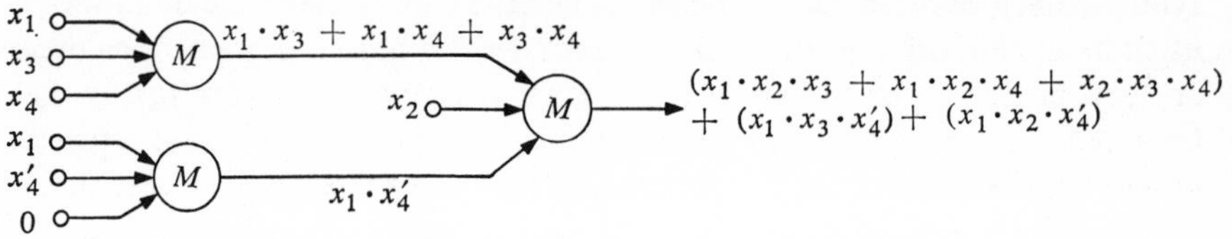

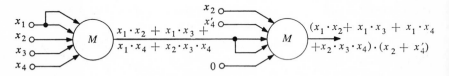

Figure 2–11. Three-input majority gate realization of $x_1 \cdot x_2 + x_3 \cdot (x_2 \cdot x_4 + x_1 \cdot x_4')$.

This realization requires at least two five-input majority gates, as shown in Fig. 2–12.

Figure 2–12. Five-input majority gate realization of $x_1 \cdot x_2 + x_3 \cdot (x_2 \cdot x_4 + x_1 \cdot x_4')$.

The reader should verify the final and intermediate results shown in Figs. 2–11 and 2–12. Use the facts that the output of a three-input majority gate is 1 whenever two or more of its inputs are 1, and that the output of a five-input majority gate is 1 whenever three or more of its inputs are 1.

Note that in the above examples a variable can be connected to more than one input. Also, some of the inputs can be constant, generally referred to as *bias*. With these in mind, we can rewrite the equation governing a majority gate as

$$
F_N = \begin{cases} 1 & \text{if } \sum_{i=0}^{n} m_i x_i > \dfrac{N}{2} \ (\geq k), \\[2ex] 0 & \text{if } \sum_{i=0}^{n} m_i x_i < \dfrac{N}{2} \ (<k), \end{cases}
$$

where n represents the number of variables,

x_i, $i = 1, 2, \ldots, n$ each represents one binary variable,

x_0 represents a constant called the *bias*, which is generally 1,

m_i represents the multiplicity of variable x_i and $0 \leq m_i \leq N$,

N represents the number of input lines of the majority device, and

$$
\sum_{i=0}^{n} m_i = N = 2k - 1.
$$

This last equation forms the bridge between the majority gate and the threshold gate. This can better be seen when the normalized form of a threshold gate as proposed by Minnick[2] is used.

Definition 7.   A *normalized threshold gate* is an n-input switching device whose output behavior $F(\overline{X})$ is defined as

$$F(\overline{X}) = \begin{cases} 1 & \text{if } \overline{M} \cdot \overline{X} + m_0 \geq 1, \\ 0 & \text{if } \overline{M} \cdot \overline{X} + m_0 \leq 0, \end{cases}$$

where $\overline{M} \cdot \overline{X}$ is the scalar multiplication of two n vectors

   $\overline{X}$ is an n tuple representing a specific input combination of the n binary inputs $x_1, x_2, \ldots, x_n$,

   $\overline{M}$ is an n vector representing the n weights $m_1, m_2, \ldots, m_n$ of a given threshold gate,

   m_i is an integer that is positive, zero, or negative for $i = 0, 1, \ldots, n$.

The quantity $\overline{M} \cdot \overline{X} + m_0$ is sometimes denoted T and written $T = \sum_{i=0}^{n} m_i x_i$, with $x_0 = 1$ referred to as bias and the other quantities having the same meaning as in Definition 7. The schematic representation of an n-input normalized threshold device is shown in Fig. 2–13.

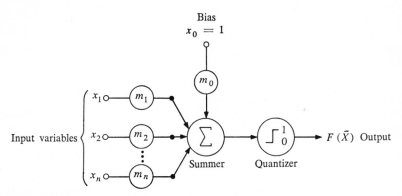

Figure 2–13.   Schematic representation of an n-input normalized threshold gate.

At this point we may ask the question as to what subset of the 2^{2^n}, n-variable Boolean functions can be realized using one threshold gate. The answer to this question follows from the definition of the threshold gate, in that the 2^n inequalities of Definition 7 have to be satisfied. That is, a Boolean function $f(x_1, x_2, \ldots, x_n)$ is realizable by a single threshold gate if and only if

[2] R. C. Minnick, "Linear-Input Logic," *IRE Trans. Electron. Computers*, **10**, 6–16 (1961). A very clear introductory presentation of threshold functions, discussing their basic properties.

there exist $(n + 1)$ integers $m_0, m_1, \ldots, m_n$, the weights, such that for each input n tuple $x_1, x_2, \ldots, x_n$ the following are satisfied:

$$\sum_{i=1}^{n} m_i x_i + m_0 \geq 1 \qquad \text{iff } f(x_1, x_2, \ldots, x_n) = 1$$

and $\qquad \displaystyle\sum_{i=1}^{n} m_i x_i + m_0 \leq 0 \qquad \text{iff } f(x_1, x_2, \ldots, x_n) = 0.$

The best way to see some of the problems that arise is by doing a few examples.

EXAMPLE 10.   Determine whether the three-variable Boolean function f can be realized with a single threshold gate

$$f(x_1, x_2, x_3) = x_1 + x_2 \cdot x_3.$$

To set up the necessary inequalities we need first to obtain the disjunctive canonical expansion of the given function. It is

$$f(x_1, x_2, x_3) = x_1' \cdot x_2 \cdot x_3 + x_1 \cdot x_2' \cdot x_3' + x_1 \cdot x_2' \cdot x_3$$
$$+ x_1 \cdot x_2 \cdot x_3' + x_1 \cdot x_2 \cdot x_3.$$

This provides the input combinations for which the function has the value 1 and has the value 0 for the remainder of the input combinations. Thus the inequalities that are to be satisfied are as follows:

(0)	$(x_1' \cdot x_2' \cdot x_3')$	$m_0 \leq 0$
(1)	$(x_1' \cdot x_2' \cdot x_3)$	$m_0 + m_3 \leq 0$
(2)	$(x_1' \cdot x_2 \cdot x_3')$	$m_0 + m_2 \leq 0$
(3)	$(x_1' \cdot x_2 \cdot x_3)$	$m_0 + m_2 + m_3 \geq 1$
(4)	$(x_1 \cdot x_2' \cdot x_3')$	$m_0 + m_1 \geq 1$
(5)	$(x_1 \cdot x_2' \cdot x_3)$	$m_0 + m_1 + m_3 \geq 1$
(6)	$(x_1 \cdot x_2 \cdot x_3')$	$m_0 + m_1 + m_2 \geq 1$
(7)	$(x_1 \cdot x_2 \cdot x_3)$	$m_0 + m_1 + m_2 + m_3 \geq 1.$

In this particular case it is quite simple to obtain a solution by trial and error; $(m_0, m_1, m_2, m_3) = (-1, 2, 1, 1)$. Note that this solution is not unique, as $(-1 - k, 2 + k + l, 1 + k, 1 + k)$ for all $k \geq 0$ and $l \geq 0$ is also a solution.

EXAMPLE 11.   Determine whether the given three-variable Boolean function f can be realized by a single threshold gate

$$f(x_1, x_2, x_3) = x_1 \cdot x_2 \cdot x_3 + x_1' \cdot (x_2' + x_3').$$

The corresponding set of inequalities is as follows:

(0)	$(x_1' \cdot x_2' \cdot x_3')$	$m_0 \geq 1$
(1)	$(x_1' \cdot x_2' \cdot x_3)$	$m_0 + m_3 \geq 1$
(2)	$(x_1' \cdot x_2 \cdot x_3')$	$m_0 + m_2 \geq 1$
(3)	$(x_1' \cdot x_2 \cdot x_3)$	$m_0 + m_2 + m_3 \leq 0$
(4)	$(x_1 \cdot x_2' \cdot x_3')$	$m_0 + m_1 \leq 0$
(5)	$(x_1 \cdot x_2' \cdot x_3)$	$m_0 + m_1 + m_3 \leq 0$
(6)	$(x_1 \cdot x_2 \cdot x_3')$	$m_0 + m_1 + m_2 \leq 0$
(7)	$(x_1 \cdot x_2 \cdot x_3)$	$m_0 + m_1 + m_2 + m_3 \geq 1.$

In this example it is very simple to detect that the inequalities are inconsistent. To see this we can add the rows numbered (3), (5), and (6), obtaining $(m_0) + 2(m_0 + m_1 + m_2 + m_3) \leq 0$, which contradicts the conditions of rows (0) and (7). Thus this function cannot be realized by a single threshold gate.

From these two examples we can see that a Boolean function is realizable by a single threshold gate if the 2^n resulting inequalities are consistent, and to check this the set of inequalities must be solved. For a large number of variables the hand computation becomes impractical, and computational programs based on linear-programming techniques have been developed. Even using large present-day computers the solutions of the 2^n inequalities become impractical as n increases, and so the number of inequalities must be reduced. To do this, the characteristics of Boolean functions realizable by a single threshold gate are used. These characteristics form a series of necessary conditions that these functions must satisfy. However, none of these is a sufficient condition for $n > 8$.

Up to this point we have introduced very briefly the notion of a function realizable by a single threshold gate. For the interested reader a list of references is included in Appendix I. The problem of representing a general Boolean function by a net of threshold gates is not covered as well in the literature. Most of the papers consider only special subsets of Boolean functions or networks with specific topological structures.

2–5. THE *n*-CUBE REPRESENTATION OF BOOLEAN FUNCTIONS

In this section we introduce a geometric representation of a Boolean function. This representation is introduced to provide a visual aid to the understanding of and the simplification of Boolean functions. Since we are considering a two-valued Boolean algebra, the values of an *n*-variable function are to be considered at 2^n discrete points, corresponding to the 2^n possible input combinations. The different inputs are unique combinations of 1's and 0's that define the 2^n vertices of a unit *n* cube in an *n*-dimensional space. Thus the values of an *n*-variable Boolean function can be represented as 1's and 0's on the vertices of a unit *n* cube. Examples of 1-, 2-, and 3-cubes, with the vertices labeled to correspond to the different input combinations, are shown in Fig. 2–14.

Note that the vertices of these *n* cubes correspond to the rows of an *n*-variable truth table and also to the minimal surfaces of an *n*-variable Venn diagram. Thus, in the following illustrations, for every existing term m_i in the disjunctive canonical expansion (D.C.E.) of a given *n*-variable Boolean function, the corresponding vertex, vertex i of the *n* cube, is marked by a dot (●) to show that the Boolean function has the value 1 for this input combination.

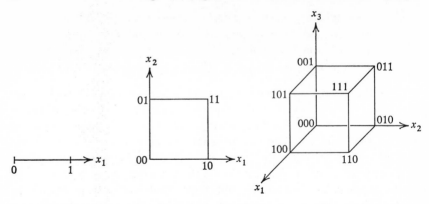

Figure 2–14. The n cubes corresponding to the one-, two-, and three-variable Boolean functions.

Or, if we start from the conjunctive canonical expansion (C.C.E.), for every term M_j, the vertex $2^n - 1 - j$ of the n cube will be marked by a circle ($\circ$) to indicate the input combination for which the Boolean function has the value 0. Thus the n-cube representation of a Boolean function is a geometric translation of the truth table.

    EXAMPLE 12.   Obtain the n-cube representation of the three-variable Boolean function

$$f(x_1, x_2, x_3) = x_3 + x_1 \cdot x_2.$$

    Since we are considering a translation of a truth table, the first suggestion is to obtain the disjunctive canonical expansion and mark the corresponding vertices. The D.C.E. of this function in algebraic form is

$$f(x_1, x_2, x_3) = \sum (1, 3, 5, 6, 7).$$

The constants in this form, translated into binary numbers, define the vertices of the 3-cube that have to be marked. The corresponding 3-cube is shown in Fig. 2–15.

    Actually, this is a long way to do the problem, as we could have considered each of the terms of the function and marked the n cube accordingly. That is, the first term is x_3, which means that the function has the value 1 whenever x_3 is 1, independent of the values of x_1 and x_2; thus the four vertices of the surface $x_3 = 1$ must be marked. The second term of this function is $x_1 \cdot x_2$, so the function has the value 1 whenever both x_1 and x_2 are 1, independent of the value of x_3. Thus the two vertices of the line representing the intersection of the two surfaces $x_1 = 1$ and $x_2 = 1$ must be marked. This is shown by the shaded surface and the heavy line in Fig. 2–15. At the unmarked vertices of the n cube the function has the value 0.

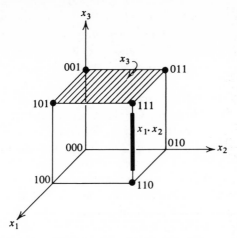

Figure 2–15.   The *n*-cube representation of $x_3 + x_1 \cdot x_2$.

EXAMPLE 13.   Obtain the *n*-cube representation of the three-variable Boolean function

$$f(x_1, x_2, x_3) = (x_1' + x_2) \cdot (x_2 + x_3') \cdot (x_1 + x_2' + x_3).$$

The conjunctive canonical expansion (C.C.E.) of this function is

$$f(x_1, x_2, x_3) = \prod (2, 3, 5, 6).$$

Thus the Boolean function has the value 0 at the vertices 5, 4, 2, and 1, as shown in Fig. 2–16.

Again we can consider each of the terms separately. For the function to be

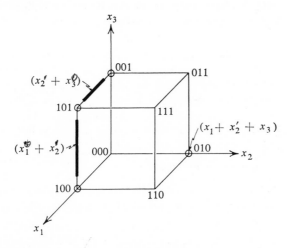

Figure 2–16.   The *n*-cube representation of $(x_1' + x_2) \cdot (x_2 + x_3') \cdot$ $(x_1 + x_2' + x_3)$.

0, it is required that at least one term be 0. For $x_1' + x_2$ as a term to be 0, both x_1' and x_2 must be 0; thus the line representing these two vertices is the intersection of the two surfaces $x_1 = 1$ and $x_2 = 0$. Similarly, the two vertices 1 and 5, $x_2 + x_3' = 0$, are represented by the line that is the intersection of the two surfaces $x_2 = 0$ and $x_3 = 1$. Finally, the vertex 2, $x_1 + x_2' + x_3 = 0$, is the intersection of the three surfaces $x_1 = 0$, $x_2 = 1$, and $x_3 = 0$. Because in this example we started from the C.C.E. or a nonexpanded product-of-sums form, we obtained the 0's of the function. The unmarked vertices of the n cube represent the input combinations for which the value of this function is 1.

From these examples we have seen that the n-cube representation of a Boolean function is derived in a straightforward manner by representing separately each term of a Boolean function. By a term we mean either a logical product or a logical sum involving i variables, depending upon whether the 1's or the 0's of a Boolean function are to be represented. At this point we consider in more detail the representation of such a term by introducing the geometric characteristics of a unit n cube. In this presentation we only consider terms of logical products, but all the results can be translated by using the principle of duality when terms of logical sums are to be used. We shall use the notion of a proper subcube of dimension $i < n$ of the unit n cube. By a proper subcube we mean an i cube whose faces and vertices are subsets of the faces and vertices of the n cube.

From the geometry of a unit n cube we note that all its proper subcubes can be described in one of two ways: either as intersections of maximal subcubes, that is, $(n - 1)$ cubes, or as defined by an appropriate set of vertices of the n cube. Where an $(n - 1)$ cube is defined by one variable only, because it is a maximal subcube of an n cube, the $x_i^{\alpha_i}$ define one of the $2n$, $(n - 1)$ cubes of an n cube. And a vertex, referred to as a 0-cube, is defined by all the n variables, as it is a minimal subcube of an n cube; thus $x_1^{\alpha_1} \cdot x_2^{\alpha_2} \cdot \cdots \cdot x_n^{\alpha_n}$ defines one of the 2^n vertices of an n cube.

Now consider an i cube. It is defined by the intersection of $n - i$, $(n - 1)$ cubes; thus it is represented by a term that includes $(n - i)$ variables, one for each of the maximal subcubes. If, on the other hand, we consider an i cube as defined by its vertices, it has 2^i vertices, each defined by a specific combination of n variables. But, as every vertex of an i cube is connected to i other vertices by the edges of the i cube, the set of 2^i vertices is represented by a term including $(n - i)$ variables. At this point we shall introduce two definitions and with their help clarify the above statements.

Definition 8.   *Adjacent vertices.* Two vertices are said to be adjacent whenever they are the end points of an edge of the n cube. That is, these vertices differ in one variable only.

Definition 9.   *Mutually adjacent vertices.* A set of 2^i vertices are said to be a mutually adjacent set if every vertex in the set is adjacent to i other vertices in the set. That is, these 2^i vertices define an i cube.

Thus we can make the following statements about the different subcubes of an *n* cube and the corresponding terms of an *n*-variable Boolean function:

(1)   A vertex of the *n* cube is represented by the presence of a term with *n* variables in the Boolean function. This is a 0-cube.

(2)   An edge of the *n* cube is represented by the presence of a term with $(n - 1)$ variables in the Boolean function. This is a 1-cube, consisting of the adjacent vertices.

(3)   A face of the *n* cube is represented by the presence of a term with $(n - 2)$ variables in the Boolean function. This is a 2-cube, consisting of four mutually adjacent vertices.

(4)   A cube of the *n* cube is represented by the presence of a term with $(n - 3)$ variables in the Boolean function. This is a 3-cube, consisting of eight mutually adjacent vertices.

(5)   In general, an *i* cube of the *n* cube, 2^i mutually adjacent vertices, is represented by the presence of a term with $(n - i)$ variables in the Boolean function.

It should be noted that in the above discussions we considered each of the terms of a Boolean function separately. But this does not mean that in obtaining the *n*-cube representation of a Boolean function the sets of vertices corresponding to the different terms form exclusive sets. Also in this presentation we used only one of the geometric characteristics of the *n* cube, the definition of its subcubes, but many other characteristics can be used. One, especially important, is used in the studies of the symmetry properties of Boolean functions.

Although we treated the *n*-cube representation from a general point of view, and although it was introduced as a general aid in the study of Boolean

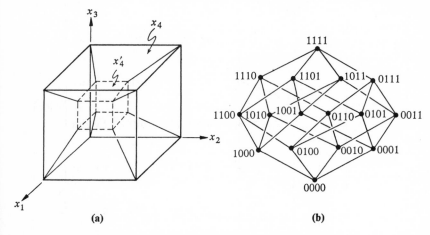

(a)   (b)

Figure 2–17.   Two possible organizations of 4-cubes.

functions, we shall restrict the examples to 3-cubes, that is, three-variable functions. This is deliberate, as even a 4-cube is hard to visualize, to say nothing of those of higher dimensions.

In Fig. 2–17 two possible organizations of 4-cubes are shown. Part (a) shows the geometric organization, where the adjacencies are easy to recognize, but it is quite cumbersome to draw. Part (b) shows a planar organization in the form of a lattice which is quite easy to draw, but the adjacencies are hard to recognize, thus losing the main advantage of the n-cube representation. Actually, the n-cube representation is very seldom used for more than three variables and becomes impractical as a graphical aid for more than four variables. This does not mean that the n-cube representation is ineffective for large numbers of variables, as all characteristics of an n cube can be used in the classification and characterization of Boolean functions, even though the actual graphical translation becomes impractical.

To see better some of the advantages of the n-cube representation, a three-variable tree, which is a translation of the truth table into connecting links, is shown in Fig. 2–18. In this representation the right column of points is used to indicate the value of the function for the different input combinations, corresponding to the vertices of the n cube. A point in another column is marked only if all the points connected to its right have the same value, so they

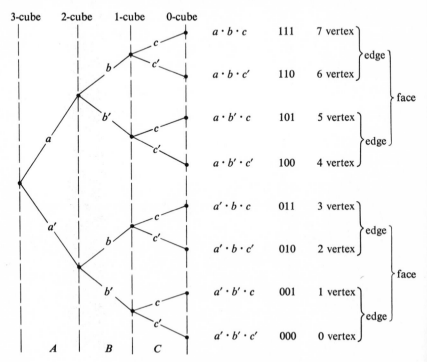

Figure 2–18.   Three-variable tree.

represent different subcubes of the *n* cube, as shown. However, not all the sub-cubes can be detected in this representation; for example, vertices 3 and 7 define an edge, but this is not shown in this representation. Also, points that are physically adjacent do not necessarily define an edge. For example, vertices 3 and 4 do not define an edge but are adjacent in this representation. Actually, an *n* cube includes all the *n*! possible trees of *n* variables that can be obtained by the different ordering of the *n* variables. By denoting the tree of Fig. 2–18 as T_{ABC} according to the ordering of the variables, the corresponding 3-cube includes all the following trees: T_{ABC}, T_{ACB}, T_{BCA}, T_{BAC}, T_{CAB}, and T_{CBA}. Note that this representation was introduced to show the advantages of the *n*-cube representation and in itself is of very little value. It is sometimes used in specialized cases of contact network synthesis. The most used graphical aid in the design of switching circuits is the Karnaugh map, which will be introduced later in this chapter.

2–6. SIMPLIFICATION OF BOOLEAN FUNCTIONS WITH THE *n* CUBE

In this section we introduce a systematic procedure to simplify Boolean functions using the *n*-cube representation as a graphical aid. The procedure starts from the canonical expansions. Using the *n*-cube, minimal sum of products (M.S.P.) and minimal product of sums (M.P.S.) are obtained. To define minimal, we start from the two canonical expansions as defined in Chapter 1. These expansions are

$$f(x_1, x_2, \ldots, x_n) = \sum_{i=0}^{2^n-1} \xi_i \cdot m_i = \prod_{i=0}^{2^n-1} [\eta_i + M_i].$$

Using multiple-input AND and OR gates, assuming the presence of both the variables and their complements, the corresponding gate realizations are as shown in Fig. 2–19. In Fig. 2–19, $\bar{X}^j$ is an arbitrary *n* tuple representing a particular combination of the *n* binary inputs, depending on the rows of the truth table that must be included in the specific expansion. The letter *l*

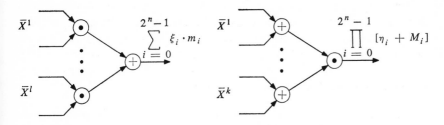

Figure 2–19.   Two-level realizations of the canonical expansions.

represents the number of rows of the truth table where the function has the value 1, and k is the number of rows of the truth table where the function has the value 0. This form of realization is referred to as *two-level realization*, since each signal passes through two gates. The relative "cost" of a two-level realization is now defined as follows.

Definition 10. *The cost of a two-level realization* is defined as the total number of lines connected to the gates of the realization.

If we consider the realizations shown in Fig. 2–19, we have the following cost factors. In the case of the D.C.E. there are l first-level n-input AND gates and one l-input OR gate; thus $nl + l = l(n + 1)$ is the relative cost. In the case of the C.C.E., there are k first-level n-input OR gates and one k-input AND gate; thus $nk + k = k(n + 1)$ is the relative cost. To reduce this cost we need to reduce the number of first-level gates and also to reduce the number of inputs to these gates. Before introducing the procedure that leads to the minimization described above, we shall briefly discuss the validity of the cost factor just defined. The reduction in the number of first-level gates corresponds to the reduction of the number of terms in the Boolean function, and the reduction in the number of inputs to the first-level gates corresponds to reducing the number of variables included in each term. Thus a minimal-cost realization corresponds to the simplest Boolean function expressed as sum of products or product of sums. The other question that must now be asked is how this cost function is reflected in the hardware realizations. If we consider diode switching circuits,[3] the cost factor defined above corresponds to the number of diodes required in the realization, but in other hardware realizations there is no such correspondence. On the other hand, in present-day technology, the wiring, that is, the interconnection of logical elements, is the most expensive part of manufacture, and the cost factor defined above corresponds closely to the number of connections that have to be made. The other question that can be asked is "Why the restriction to two-level realizations?" This is important today, mainly because of the delay that occurs in a gate, as this delay introduces timing difficulties when signals go through different numbers of gates. Also the problems of signal distortions and attenuations become excessive when the signals have to pass through a large number of gates.

The minimization procedure is based on the selection of the minimal number of subcubes of the n cube, so that all the marked vertices are included, thus reducing the number of first-level gates. By including the largest possible subcubes, the number of inputs to these gates is reduced. The best way to show the procedure is by some examples. In each of the following examples, we shall determine both minimal realizations.

---

[3] R. K. Richards, *Digital Computer Components and Circuits* (Princeton, N.J.: Van Nostrand, 1957), Chap. II. This book also includes many of the earlier hardware realizations.

EXAMPLE 14.   Derive both the minimal-sum-of-products and the minimal-product-of-sums realizations of the following three-variable Boolean function given in algebraic form:

$$f(x_1, x_2, x_3) = \sum (0, 4, 5, 7).$$

The n-cube representation of this function, showing the 1's and 0's separately, with the largest subcubes labeled, is shown in Fig. 2–20. Starting

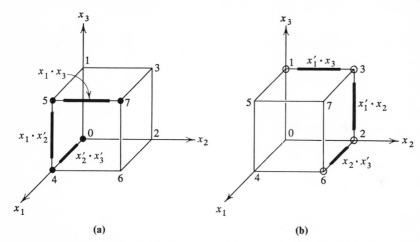

Figure 2–20.   The n-cube representation of $f(x_1, x_2, x_3) = \sum (0, 4, 5, 7)$.

from Fig. 2–20(a) we see that there are four vertices, but as they are not mutually adjacent they cannot be covered by a face. These four points define three edges as shown, but the edge labeled $x_1 \cdot x_2'$ need not be included in the minimal representation. Thus the minimal-sum-of-products form of this function is

$$f(x_1, x_2, x_3) = x_1 \cdot x_3 + x_2' \cdot x_3'.$$

Exactly in the same manner, starting from Fig. 2–20(b), we obtain f' and, by complementing, the minimal product of sums is obtained:

$$f(x_1, x_2, x_3) = (x_1 + x_3') \cdot (x_2' + x_3).$$

The corresponding gate realizations, with the cost of both the expansions and the minimized forms listed, is shown in Fig. 2–21.

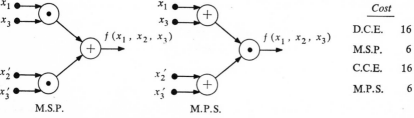

	Cost
D.C.E.	16
M.S.P.	6
C.C.E.	16
M.P.S.	6

Figure 2–21.   Minimal gate realizations of $f(x_1, x_2, x_3) = \sum (0, 4, 5, 7)$.

EXAMPLE 15.   Derive both the M.S.P. and the M.P.S. realizations of the following three-variable Boolean function given in algebraic form:

$$f(x_1, x_2, x_3) = \sum (2, 3, 4, 5, 6, 7).$$

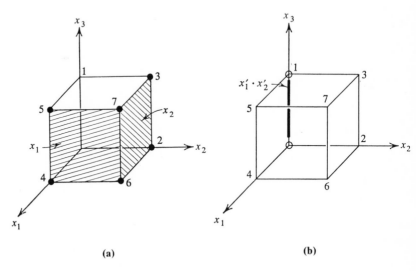

(a)   (b)

Figure 2–22.   The n-cube representation of $f(x_1, x_2, x_3) = \sum (2, 3, 4, 5, 6, 7)$.

In Fig. 2–22(a) are six marked vertices that can be grouped in two sets of four mutually adjacent vertices by including vertices 6 and 7 in both sets. Thus the M.S.P. form of this function is

$$f(x_1, x_2, x_3) = x_1 + x_2.$$

Note that in this example all the subcubes used in the M.S.P. are $(n - 1)$ cubes; thus, this becomes a one-level realization and the two minimal realizations become the same. This is also obtained from Fig. 2–22(b), as f' is represented by the single edge $x_1' \cdot x_2'$. In calculating the cost of this function we find that the cost of D.C.E. is 24, the cost of C.C.E. is 8, and the cost of M.S.P. and M.P.S. is 2.

EXAMPLE 16.   Derive both the M.S.P. and M.P.S. realizations of the following three-variable Boolean function given in algebraic form:

$$f(x_1, x_2, x_3) = \sum (1, 2, 3, 4, 5).$$

Checking the vertices of Fig. 2–23(a), we can see two well-defined edges covering four of the marked vertices and vertex 1 that can be included in either

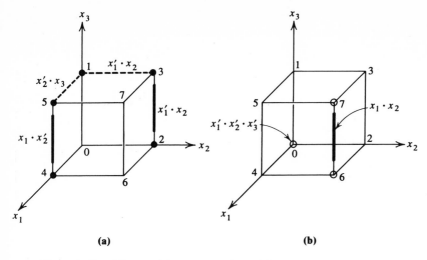

Figure 2–23.   The *n*-cube representation of $f(x_1, x_2, x_3) = \sum (1, 2, 3, 4, 5)$.

one of two vertices. Thus there are two M.S.P. forms for this function, as shown:

$$f(x_1, x_2, x_3) = x_1 \cdot x_2' + x_1' \cdot x_2 + x_1' \cdot x_3$$

or

$$f(x_1, x_2, x_3) = x_1 \cdot x_2' + x_1' \cdot x_2 + x_2' \cdot x_3.$$

The M.P.S. form of this function, as read from Fig. 2–23(b), is

$$f(x_1, x_2, x_3) = (x_1' + x_2') \cdot (x_1 + x_2 + x_3).$$

The corresponding gate realizations are shown in Fig. 2–24.

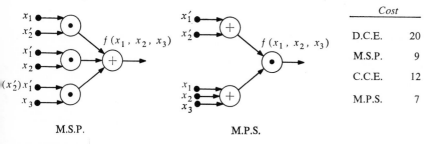

	Cost	
D.C.E.	20	
M.S.P.	9	
C.C.E.	12	
M.P.S.	7	

M.S.P.   M.P.S.

Figure 2–24.   Minimal gate realizations of $f(x_1, x_2, x_3) = \sum (1, 2, 3, 4, 5)$.

EXAMPLE 17.   Derive both the M.S.P. and the M.P.S. realizations of the following three-variable Boolean function given in algebraic form:

$$f(x_1, x_2, x_3) = \sum (0, 2, 3, 4, 5, 6).$$

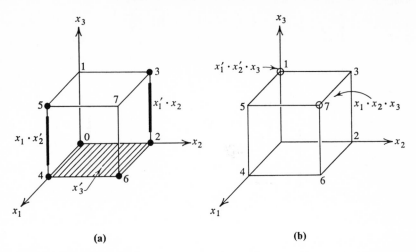

(a)   **(b)**

Figure 2–25.   The n-cube representation of $f(x_1, x_2, x_3) = \sum (0, 2, 3, 4, 5, 6)$.

From Fig. 2–25(a) and (b) we obtain the minimal forms as follows:

$$f(x_1, x_2, x_3) = x_3' + x_1 \cdot x_2' + x_1' \cdot x_2$$

and $$f(x_1, x_2, x_3) = (x_1 + x_2 + x_3') \cdot (x_1' + x_2' + x_3').$$

The corresponding gate realizations are shown in Fig. 2–26.

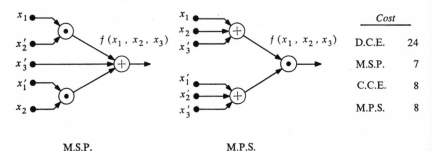

	Cost
D.C.E.	24
M.S.P.	7
C.C.E.	8
M.P.S.	8

M.S.P.   M.P.S.

Figure 2–26.   Minimal gate realization of $f(x_1, x_2, x_3) = \sum (0, 2, 3, 4, 5, 6)$.

From these examples we can see that obtaining the minimal realization is a question of choosing the right subcubes of the n-cube representation. Also, we can see from these examples that both minimal forms have to be derived to make the final results an over-all minimum for the two-level realizations, and that the minimal realizations are not unique.

Another point to be considered is the effect of don't-care conditions; that is, how is the minimization procedure affected when the Boolean function includes undefined points? Such don't-care conditions occur whenever the output is undefined for some specific input combination or when certain input combinations do not occur. As far as minimization is concerned, the causes of the don't-care conditions are not important. The fact remains that at the corresponding vertex of the *n* cube we are free to assign any value or values or leave it uncovered, depending on which will lead to a simpler realization. To see this, consider the following example.

EXAMPLE 18.   Derive both the M.S.P. and the M.P.S. realizations of the following three-variable Boolean function that includes don't-care conditions:

$$f(x_1, x_2, x_3) = \sum (2, 5, 6) \quad \text{and} \quad d(x_1, x_2, x_3) = \sum (1, 3, 4).$$

In Fig. 2–27 the vertices marked × represent don't-care conditions, and

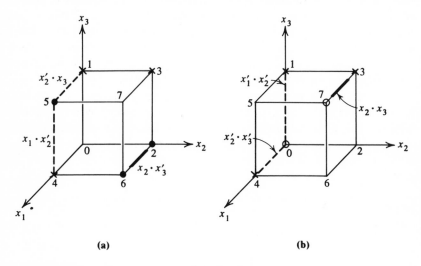

(a)   (b)

Figure 2–27.   The *n*-cube representation of $f(x_1, x_2, x_3) = \sum (2, 5, 6)$ and $d(x_1, x_2, x_3) = \sum (1, 3, 4)$.

two different minimal realizations can be derived from each of the *n* cubes as shown. A possible selection of M.S.P. and M.P.S. is

$$f(x_1, x_2, x_3) = x_2 \cdot x_3' + x_2' \cdot x_3$$

and

$$f(x_1, x_2, x_3) = (x_1 + x_2) \cdot (x_2' + x_3).$$

For this particular choice of subcubes we can see the following assignment of the don't-care conditions: Vertex 1 is left uncovered, vertex 3 is assigned the value 0, and vertex 4 is assigned both values 1 and 0. That is, in the M.S.P. vertex, 4 is assigned the value 1, and in the M.P.S. vertex, 4 is assigned the value 0. Thus the don't-care conditions are only used when they provide further reductions. To illustrate further, let us assume that the don't-care conditions are to be left uncovered. The corresponding minimal functions are

$$f(x_1, x_2, x_3) = x_2 \cdot x_3' + x_1 \cdot x_2' \cdot x_3$$

and $$f(x_1, x_2, x_3) = (x_1 + x_2 + x_3) \cdot (x_1' + x_2' + x_3').$$

2-7. REPRESENTATION OF BOOLEAN FUNCTIONS BY KARNAUGH MAPS

In this section we introduce another graphical representation of Boolean functions. In it, each product of the disjunctive canonical expansion is represented by a square arranged to provide adjacent places for terms that differ in only one variable. The combination of these squares is generally referred to as a *map* or a *logical matrix*. The particular organization of maps used in this book was initiated by Karnaugh[4, 5] and is referred to as a *Karnaugh map*. Actually, this section is to a large extent a review of the sections dealing with Venn diagrams and n cubes, with the addition that here we introduce the organization of maps having as many as six variables.

We shall start with the two-variable Karnaugh map. Because there can be four products in the D.C.E., this map must include four squares, one for each product. The organization of such a map, with the products and the decimal numbers corresponding to the rows of the truth table, is shown in Fig. 2–28.

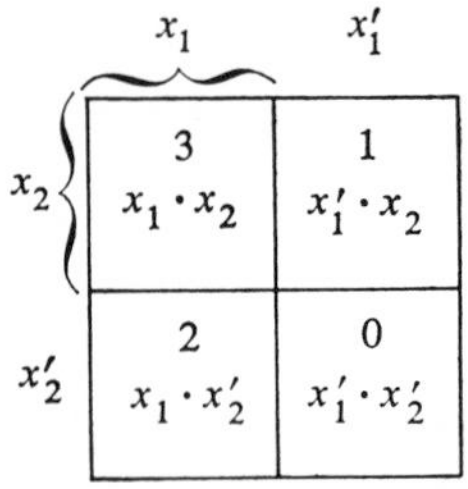

Figure 2–28.   Two-variable Karnaugh map.

In the two-variable Karnaugh map each square must be adjacent to two other squares, as shown in Fig. 2–28. That is, the squares of the Karnaugh map correspond to the vertices of the n cube, and the physical adjacencies of the squares correspond to the edges of the n cube. To see this, in Fig. 2–29(a)

[4] M. Karnaugh, "The Map Method for Synthesis of Combinational Logic Circuits," *Trans. AIEE, Commun. and Electronics,* **72**, 593–599 (1953).

[5] E. W. Veitch, "A Chart Method for Simplifying Truth Functions," *Proc. Computing Machinery,* 1952, pp. 127–133. Presents a map with rows and columns ordered as consecutive binary numbers, not showing the adjacencies.

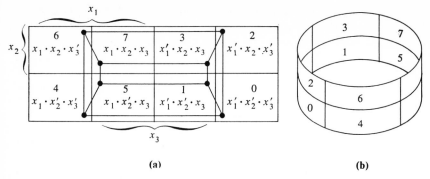

(a)   **(b)**

Figure 2–29.   Three-variable Karnaugh map.

the three-variable Karnaugh map is shown with the edges of a three-cube traced between the corresponding squares.

Thus we can see that two squares are adjacent whenever they have a common edge. Also from Fig. 2–29(a) we can see that squares 2 and 6 should be adjacent, and similarly squares 0 and 4. In other words, the three-variable Karnaugh map should be considered to be drawn on the surface of a cylinder as shown in Fig. 2–29(b). Each square is thus adjacent to three other squares, two horizontally and one vertically.

The next map to be introduced is the four-variable Karnaugh map. This map has sixteen squares corresponding to the vertices of a 4-cube, and each square must be adjacent to four other squares in the map. One organization of a four-variable Karnaugh map is shown in Fig. 2–30.

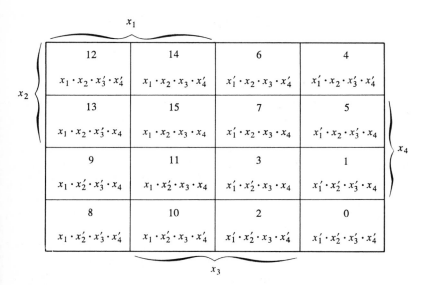

Figure 2–30.   Four-variable Karnaugh map.

In checking the entry in square 0 we see that it must be adjacent to squares 1, 2, 4, and 8. That is, for observing the different adjacencies, this map should be considered to be drawn on the surface of a torus. The best way to observe all the adjacencies is by marking all twenty-four surfaces, that is, the twenty-four different sets of four mutually adjacent squares (Fig. 2–31).

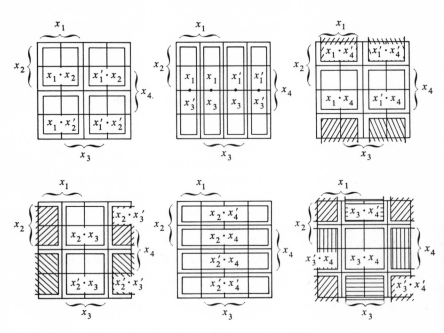

Figure 2–31. Twenty-four surfaces of a four-variable Karnaugh map.

In Fig. 2–32(a) and (b) two possible organizations of five-variable maps are presented. One is obtained by sandwiching two four-variable maps, and the second is made up of two superimposed four-variable maps. Both arrangements show only the algebraic numbers corresponding to the fundamental products.

In obtaining the six-variable Karnaugh map, either of the above two organizations of the sixty-four squares can be used. That is, either four separated four-variable maps can be used, or the sandwiching pattern of the columns of Fig. 2–32(a) can be repeated for the rows. The latter organization is shown in Fig. 2–33.

In Figs. 2–28 through 2–33 the organizations of two- to six-variable Karnaugh maps were introduced. It should be noted that these are particular examples of Karnaugh maps, as in the literature there exist a large number of variations in the organization, especially for more than four variables. In practical use there is not much difference among the various organizations of

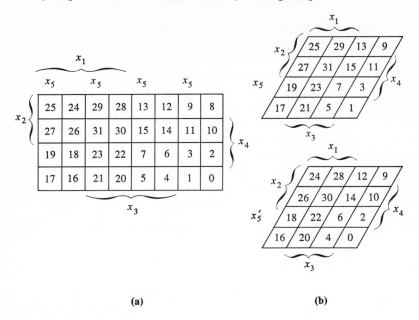

(a)   (b)

Figure 2–32. Two organizations of five-variable Karnaugh maps.

the maps. One may seem more advantageous for certain functions, but really it is only a question of getting more accustomed to one than the other. Also, we introduced maps only up to six variables, as a seven-variable map requires 128 squares, an impractical number.

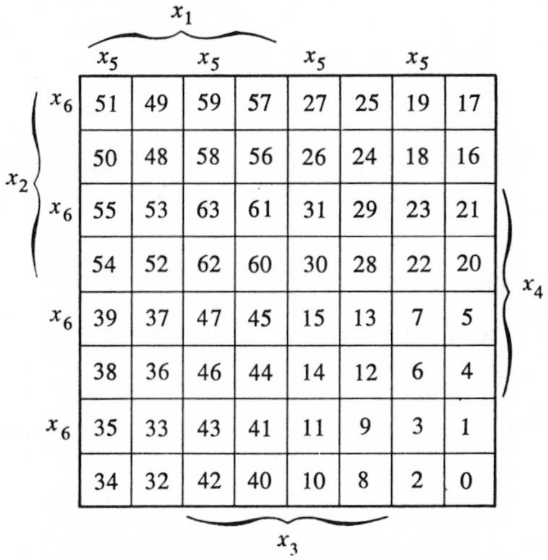

Figure 2–33. Six-variable Karnaugh map.

2–8. SIMPLIFICATION OF BOOLEAN FUNCTIONS WITH KARNAUGH MAPS

The simplification procedure used in Karnaugh-map representation is an exact translation of that used in n-cube representation. We shall use the same terminology; that is, a set of 2^i adjacent squares will be referred to as an i cube. The notation used is to mark by 1, 0, or d the squares of the maps when the specific input combination represents a point where the value of the function is 1, 0, or where a don't-care condition exists.

To restate the basic principles involved in the derivation of a minimal realization we repeat the following two steps used in Section 2–6: (1) choose as few subcubes as possible; (2) choose each subcube as large as possible. Step (1) ensures that the number of first-level gates is reduced as much as possible and step (2) ensures that each of these gates has a minimal number of inputs. To observe the detection of adjacencies in the Karnaugh maps we now introduce a few examples.

EXAMPLE 19. Derive both the minimal-sum-of-products and the minimal-product-of-sums forms of the following four-variable Boolean function:

$$f(x_1, x_2, x_3, x_4) = \sum (3, 4, 7, 11, 12, 15).$$

In Fig. 2–34(a) the six marked squares can be covered by two subcubes as

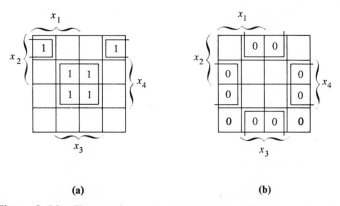

(a)   (b)

Figure 2–34. Karnaugh-map representation of $f(x_1, x_2, x_3, x_4) = \sum (3, 4, 7, 11, 12, 15)$.

shown. Thus the M.S.P. is a two-term function with a cost factor of 7 as follows:

$$f(x_1, x_2, x_3, x_4) = x_3 \cdot x_4 + x_2 \cdot x_3' \cdot x_4'.$$

In Fig. 2–34(b) eight of the ten marked squares can be covered by the two subcubes shown. The remaining two marked squares can be included in two different sets of four mutually adjacent squares. Thus there are two different M.P.S. forms, each with three terms, each having a cost factor of 9. These two minimal functions are

$$f(x_1, x_2, x_3, x_4) = (x_3' + x_4) \cdot (x_3 + x_4') \cdot (x_2 + x_4)$$

or
$$f(x_1, x_2, x_3, x_4) = (x_3' + x_4) \cdot (x_3 + x_4') \cdot (x_2 + x_3).$$

EXAMPLE 20.   Derive both the M.S.P. and the M.P.S. forms of the four-variable Boolean function

$$f(x_1, x_2, x_3, x_4) = \sum (2, 3, 5, 7, 9, 11, 14, 15) .$$

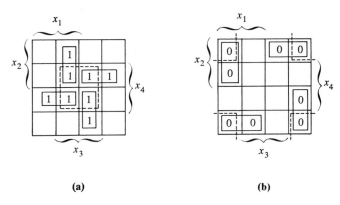

(a)   (b)

Figure 2–35.   Karnaugh-map representation of $f(x_1, x_2, x_3, x_4) = \sum (2, 3, 5, 7, 9, 11, 14, 15)$.

In both parts of Fig. 2–35 there are four marked squares that can only be included in four different sets of two adjacent squares. Also, the resulting four sets of two adjacent squares cover all eight marked squares. Thus the subcube shown by a dashed line, made up of four mutually adjacent squares, need not be included in the minimal realizations, as it does not add uncovered squares. We see that each of the minimal realizations includes four terms having a cost factor of 16. They are

$$f(x_1, x_2, x_3, x_4) = x_1 \cdot x_2 \cdot x_3 + x_1 \cdot x_2' \cdot x_4 + x_1' \cdot x_2 \cdot x_4 + x_1' \cdot x_2' \cdot x_3$$

or $f(x_1, x_2, x_3, x_4) = (x_1 + x_2 + x_3) \cdot (x_1 + x_2' + x_4) \cdot (x_1' + x_2 + x_4)$
$$\cdot (x_1' + x_2' + x_3).$$

EXAMPLE 21.   Derive both the M.S.P. and the M.P.S. forms of the four-variable Boolean function

$$f(x_1, x_2, x_3, x_4) = \sum (3, 6, 12, 15)$$

with the don't-care conditions

$$d(x_1, x_2, x_3, x_4) = \sum (1, 2, 4, 7, 9, 14) .$$

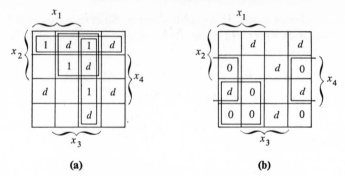

Figure 2–36. Karnaugh-map representation of $f(x_1, x_2, x_3, x_4) = \sum (3, 6, 12, 15)$ with $d(x_1, x_2, x_3, x_4) = \sum (1, 2, 4, 7, 9, 14)$.

From Fig. 2–36(a) we see that the four squares marked 1 can be covered by three sets of four mutually adjacent squares by including some of the squares marked by d. The resulting M.S.P. form includes three terms and has a cost factor of 9. This function is

$$f(x_1, x_2, x_3, x_4) = x_1' \cdot x_3 + x_2 \cdot x_3 + x_2 \cdot x_4'.$$

From Fig. 2–36(b) we can see that five of the six squares marked 0 can be included in two sets of four adjacent squares as shown. The remaining square marked 0 can be included in either one of three sets of four adjacent squares. Thus there are three M.P.S. forms, each of three terms, with a cost factor of 9. These functions are

$$f(x_1, x_2, x_3, x_4) = (x_1' + x_2) \cdot (x_3 + x_4') \cdot (x_2 + x_4)$$

$$f(x_1, x_2, x_3, x_4) = (x_1' + x_2) \cdot (x_3 + x_4') \cdot (x_1 + x_3)$$

and $$f(x_1, x_2, x_3, x_4) = (x_1' + x_2) \cdot (x_3 + x_4') \cdot (x_2 + x_3).$$

EXAMPLE 22.   Derive both the M.S.P. and the M.P.S. forms of the five-variable Boolean function

$$f(x_1, x_2, x_3, x_4, x_5) = \sum (0, 1, 4, 17, 19, 27, 31)$$

with the don't-care conditions

$$d(x_1, x_2, x_3, x_4, x_5) = \sum (5, 10, 11, 16, 23).$$

From Fig. 2–37(a) we obtain a three-term M.S.P. function with a cost factor of 12. That is,

$$f(x_1, x_2, x_3, x_4, x_5) = x_1 \cdot x_4 \cdot x_5 + x_1' \cdot x_2' \cdot x_4' + x_2' \cdot x_3' \cdot x_4'.$$

From Fig. 2–37(b) we can cover fourteen of the squares marked 0 with two sets of eight mutually adjacent squares. The remaining six squares marked 0

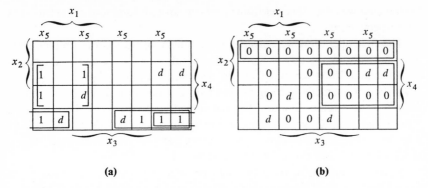

Figure 2–37. Karnaugh-map representation of $f(x_1, x_2, x_3, x_4, x_5) = \sum (0, 1, 4, 17, 19, 27, 31)$ with $d(x_1, x_2, x_3, x_4, x_5) = \sum (5, 10, 11, 16, 23)$.

can now be covered in four different ways, using a set of four and a set of eight mutually adjacent squares. Thus there are four different M.P.S. functions, all with a cost factor of 13. These functions are as follows:

$$f(x_1, x_2, x_3, x_4, x_5) = (x_1 + x_4') \cdot (x_2' + x_4) \cdot \begin{Bmatrix} (x_1' + x_5) \\ \text{or} \\ (x_4' + x_5) \end{Bmatrix} \cdot \begin{Bmatrix} (x_1' + x_2 + x_3') \\ \text{or} \\ (x_1' + x_3' + x_4) \end{Bmatrix}.$$

From these few examples we see that obtaining the minimal realizations with the aid of Karnaugh maps is straightforward. The only requirement is to observe all the possible adjacencies. Although we only included examples of four- and five-variable Karnaugh maps, a little experience makes the simplification of Boolean functions up to six variables become quite simple. But once we reach seven variables this method becomes too cumbersome to have much practical value. Actually, in most cases all paper-and-pencil methods become impractical for more than six variables, and computer methods must be used.

The greatest advantage of the Karnaugh map, or any of the previously introduced graphical representations, is the increased speed of solution. Also, once the mapping is obtained, a set of equivalent expressions can be read directly from the map. This is especially desirable where the simplest realization is not the best for the particular application.

2–9. MANIPULATIONS ON KARNAUGH MAPS

We saw in previous sections that each square of a Karnaugh map can represent either a fundamental product m_i or a fundamental sum M_j. The manipulations described in this section constitute operations on the squares of a Karnaugh map or operations between the corresponding squares of two Karnaugh maps defined by the same variables. In the first case we consider operations on a Boolean function represented by the specific map, and in the second case we consider operations between the two functions represented by the respective maps.

The first operation we consider is the unary operation of complementation. Actually we already executed this operation when we first obtained the complement of the function (f') in the derivation of minimal product of sums. Thus the complement of a logical function is a function that has the value 1 wherever the original function has the value 0 and vice versa. To obtain the same result in a Karnaugh-map representation, the content of each square must be changed accordingly; that is, every entry of 1 in the original map is replaced by a 0 and every 0 is replaced by a 1.

When a logical operation ($*$) is to be defined between two maps in the same variables, each representing a Boolean function (f_1, f_2), it is required to obtain a third map that represents the Boolean function $f_3 = f_1 * f_2$. That is, for each input combination the corresponding square in the resulting map has its value defined by the values of the corresponding squares in the original maps and the rules of the logical operator $*$. Thus the map representing the logical product of two maps has only those of its squares marked 1, where both of the original maps have their squares marked 1. The map representing the logical sum of two maps has those of its squares marked 1 where either or both of the original maps have squares marked 1.

At this point we shall digress and show how the same results can be obtained algebraically. We shall start from the disjunctive canonical expansions of the two functions and let the two original functions be $f_1 = \sum_l m_i$ and $f_2 = \sum_k m_i$, where l and k represent the summations over the points where the functions have the value 1:

(1) The logical product

$$f_1 \cdot f_2 = \left(\sum_l m_i\right) \cdot \left(\sum_k m_i\right),$$

but

$$m_i \cdot m_j = \begin{cases} m_i & \text{if } i = j, \\ 0 & \text{if } i \neq j, \end{cases}$$

because whenever $i \neq j$ there must be at least one variable that appears uncomplemented in one of the fundamental products and complemented in the other, and when $i = j$, $m_i \cdot m_i = m_i$,

$$f_1 \cdot f_2 = \sum_h m_i,$$

where h represents the summations over the points where both of the functions have the value 1.

(2) The logical sum

$$f_1 + f_2 = \left(\sum_l m_i\right) + \left(\sum_k m_i\right) = \sum_g m_i,$$

where g represents the summations over the points where either or both of the functions have the value 1.

Up to this point we have considered completely defined Boolean functions. That is, any given square of the Karnaugh map contains either a 1 or a 0 entry. Whenever don't-care conditions are to be included, the tables of Fig. 2-38 are to be used to define the entries in the resultant map.

·	0	1	d		+	0	1	d		s	s'
0	0	0	0		0	0	1	d		0	1
1	0	1	d		1	1	1	1		1	0
d	0	d	d		d	d	1	d		d	d

Figure 2-38. Rules of operations for Karnaugh maps with don't-care entries.

EXAMPLE 23. The method of obtaining the logical product and logical sums of two Karnaugh maps is shown in Fig. 2-39.

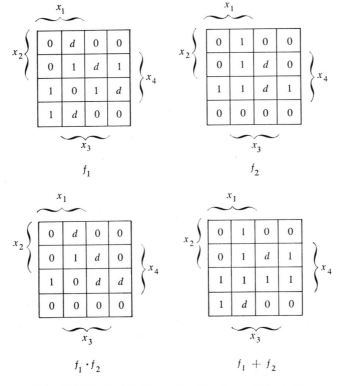

Figure 2-39. Logical operation on Karnaugh maps.

Actually, the inverse processes of the above operations are more useful; that is, given the Karnaugh map of a specific function, it is required to obtain two new maps whose logical combination is the original map. This process is generally referred to as factoring the Karnaugh map. The process can be best seen by example.

EXAMPLE 24.   From Fig. 2–40 we see that $f = f_1 \cdot f_2$; that is,

$$x_1 \cdot x_2' \cdot x_3' + x_1 \cdot x_2' \cdot x_4' + x_1' \cdot x_3 \cdot x_4 + x_2 \cdot x_3 \cdot x_4$$
$$= (x_1 \cdot x_2' + x_3 \cdot x_4) \cdot (x_1' + x_2 + x_3' + x_4').$$

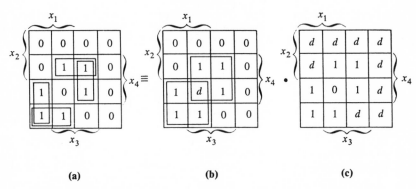

Figure 2–40. Factoring the Karnaugh map of $f(x_1, x_2, x_3, x_4) = \sum (3, 7, 8, 9, 10, 15)$.

In this example f represents the minimal sum of products and has a cost factor of 16. The minimal representations of the two functions f_1 and f_2 have cost factors of 6 and 4, respectively. Thus the factored form of this function has a total cost factor of 12. This further saving was obtained by lifting the restriction to two-level realizations, as the realization corresponding to the factored form is a three-level realization.

EXAMPLE 25.   Factoring the Karnaugh map of Fig. 2–41(a), we reduced the cost factor from 14 to 12 by allowing a third level. (*See next page.*)

With some practice this kind of factorization becomes straightforward. The main problem is that with the Karnaugh maps even an experienced designer cannot synthesize realizations of more than three levels. Also, in most cases, the further minimization introduced by allowing three levels is quite small. But the factorization becomes the only possible method when Karnaugh maps are used in the design of circuits with other than AND and OR gates.[6,7]

[6] M. P. Marcus, Sum Modulo Two ($\oplus$) and Dot Modulo Two ($\odot$) Functions, *IBM Tech. Rep. TR01.01.001.680*, 1962.
[7] G. A. Maley and J. Earle, *The Logic Design of Transistor Digital Computers* (Englewood Cliffs, N.J.: Prentice-Hall, 1963), Chap. 6, pp. 114–159.

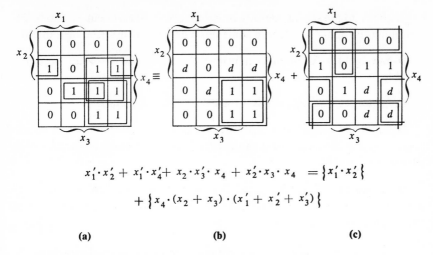

$$x_1' \cdot x_2' + x_1' \cdot x_4' + x_2 \cdot x_3' \cdot x_4 + x_2' \cdot x_3 \cdot x_4 \; = \Big\{ x_1' \cdot x_2' \Big\}$$

$$+ \Big\{ x_4 \cdot (x_2 + x_3) \cdot (x_1' + x_2' + x_3') \Big\}$$

(a)   (b)   (c)

Figure 2–41.   Factoring the Karnaugh map of $f(x_1, x_2, x_3, x_4) =$
$\Sigma\,(0, 1, 2, 3, 5, 7, 11, 13)$.

Read — not responsible for milked

2–10. ALGEBRAIC SIMPLIFICATION OF BOOLEAN FUNCTIONS

The underlying principles of the algebraic method of simplification are the same as those presented in the earlier sections, where graphical methods were introduced. That is, first the largest possible subcubes are obtained, then a minimal subset of these is chosen to include all the input combinations that are defined. Algebraic methods are extremely general, and are introduced to supplement the graphical methods when Boolean functions involving a large number of variables are to be simplified, because it is relatively easy to program them on a computer. But the algebraic methods do not supplant the graphical methods for paper-and-pencil computations when the number of variables is small, as the computation required by the algebraic methods becomes prohibitive for a relatively small number of variables.

In this section the simplification procedure suggested by Quine[8][9] is introduced. This procedure is based on the following two identities:

(1) $\theta \cdot \varphi + \theta = \theta,$

(2) $x \cdot \theta + x' \cdot \varphi = x \cdot \theta + x' \cdot \varphi + \theta \cdot \varphi,$

where θ and φ are either variables or logical products of variables and x is a variable. The first identity is used to drop cubes that are proper subcubes of a

[8] W. V. Quine, "The Problem of Simplifying Truth Functions," *Am. Math. Monthly*, **59**, 521–531 (1952).

[9] W. V. Quine, "A Way to Simplify Truth Functions," *Am. Math. Monthly*, **62**, 627–631 (1955).

larger cube and the second identity is used to obtain new subcubes. But before describing the actual procedure some basic definitions must be introduced.

Definition 11. A *literal* is a primed (complemented) or an unprimed variable.

Definition 12. A *clause* φ is a logical product of literals.

Definition 13. *Implicant.* A clause φ is said to be an implicant of a function f, $\varphi \leq f$, if the assignment of the literals of φ that make φ equal to 1 will also make f equal to 1.

Definition 14. *Prime implicant.* An implicant $\varphi \leq f$ is said to be a prime implicant of f if, by the removal of any one of the literals of φ, φ ceases to be an implicant of f.

To obtain better understanding of these definitions we shall translate them using the n-cube terminology. A clause is thus a subcube of an n cube. An implicant is that subcube whose vertices are all included in the specified function f, and a prime implicant is a maximal subcube that can be included in the representation of the specified function f. Thus, given two implicants θ and φ such that $\theta \neq \varphi$ and $\theta \leq \varphi$, where clause φ is a prime implicant, the clause θ has at least one more literal than φ. In other words, θ represents a proper subcube of φ. As a result of these definitions and the definition of cost (Def. 10), the following theorem can be stated.

Theorem 1. *The minimal-sum-of-products representation of a Boolean function is a sum of prime implicants.*

Proof: Suppose the minimal sum of products is given by $f = \varphi_1 + \varphi_2 + \cdots + \varphi_k$. Each φ_i must be an implicant, and if φ_i is not a prime implicant, a suitable literal of φ_i can be dropped without changing f. But this contradicts the original supposition that f is in its minimal form.

Thus, to carry out the first part of the minimization procedure, the prime implicants must be calculated. In the graphical procedures, this corresponds to the selection of the largest subcubes. Quine developed two procedures for calculating the prime implicants of a given function. Here the second procedure is included in the form of an unproved theorem.[10]

Theorem 2. *Given a Boolean function f, as a sum of implicants, the prime implicants of f are obtained by repeated application of the following two steps:*

[10] The proof of this theorem is given by W. V. Quine, *Am. Math. Monthly,* **62,** 627–631 (1955) and E. W. Samson and B. E. Mills, "Circuit Minimization: Algebra and Algorithms for New Boolean Canonical Expressions," *AFCRC Tech. Rep.* **54–21,** April 1954.

(1)   Drop all obvious superfluities. That is, replace every $\theta \cdot \varphi + \theta$ by θ and $x + x' \cdot \theta$ by $x + \theta$.

(2)   Add new clauses of f; that is, replace every $x \cdot \theta + x' \cdot \varphi$ by $x \cdot \theta + x' \cdot \varphi + \theta \cdot \varphi$,

where x is a literal and θ and φ are clauses.

Note that in this theorem the only restriction on the form of the Boolean function is that it be stated as sum of products. To see the actual computation we introduce as an example the same Boolean function, starting from different expressions in the form of sums of products.

EXAMPLE 26.   Calculate the prime implicants of the three-variable Boolean function $f(x_1, x_2, x_3) = \sum (1, 2, 3, 4, 5, 6)$ starting from each of the following three expressions:

(a) $f(x_1, x_2, x_3) = x_1 \cdot x_3' + x_1' \cdot x_2 + x_2' \cdot x_3.$
(b) $f(x_1, x_2, x_3) = x_1 \cdot x_3' + x_1' \cdot x_3 + x_1 \cdot x_2' \cdot x_3 + x_1' \cdot x_2 \cdot x_3'.$
(c) $f(x_1, x_2, x_3) = x_1' \cdot x_2' \cdot x_3 + x_1' \cdot x_2 \cdot x_3' + x_1' \cdot x_2 \cdot x_3$
$$\qquad\qquad\qquad + x_1 \cdot x_2' \cdot x_3' + x_1 \cdot x_2' \cdot x_3 + x_1 \cdot x_2 \cdot x_3'.$$

(a) $f(x_1, x_2, x_3) = x_1 \cdot x_3' + x_1' \cdot x_2 + x_2' \cdot x_3$

   Step 1: produces no change

   Step 2: adds three new clauses, $x_2 \cdot x_3'$, $x_1 \cdot x_2'$, and $x_1' \cdot x_3$, by combining the clauses $x_1 \cdot x_3' + x_1' \cdot x_2$, $x_1 \cdot x_3' + x_2' \cdot x_3$, and $x_1' \cdot x_2 + x_2' \cdot x_3$, respectively.

   Thus the function now is

   $f(x_1, x_2, x_3) = x_1 \cdot x_3' + x_1' \cdot x_2 + x_2' \cdot x_3 + x_2 \cdot x_3' + x_1 \cdot x_2' + x_1' \cdot x_3.$
   As steps 1 and 2 do not produce any further changes, these six clauses are the prime implicants of the given function.

(b) $f(x_1, x_2, x_3) = x_1 \cdot x_3' + x_1' \cdot x_3 + x_1 \cdot x_2' \cdot x_3 + x_1' \cdot x_2 \cdot x_3'$

   Step 1: produces no change

   Step 2: adds four new nonzero clauses, $x_1 \cdot x_2'$, $x_2 \cdot x_3'$, $x_2' \cdot x_3$, and $x_1' \cdot x_2$, by combining the clauses $x_1 \cdot x_3' + x_1 \cdot x_2' \cdot x_3$, $x_1 \cdot x_3' + x_1' \cdot x_2 \cdot x_3'$, $x_1' \cdot x_3 + x_1 \cdot x_2' \cdot x_3$, and $x_1' \cdot x_3 + x_1' \cdot x_2 \cdot x_3'$, respectively.

   Thus the function now is

   $f(x_1, x_2, x_3) = x_1 \cdot x_3' + x_1' \cdot x_3 + x_1 \cdot x_2' \cdot x_3 + x_1' \cdot x_2 \cdot x_3'$
   $$\qquad\qquad + x_1 \cdot x_2' + x_2 \cdot x_3' + x_2' \cdot x_3 + x_1' \cdot x_2.$$

   Step 1: The two clauses $x_1 \cdot x_2' \cdot x_3$ and $x_1' \cdot x_2 \cdot x_3'$ are dropped, owing to the following combination of clauses; $x_1 \cdot x_2' \cdot x_3 + x_1 \cdot x_2'$ and $x_1' \cdot x_2 \cdot x_3' + x_2 \cdot x_3'$, respectively.

   Thus the function now is

   $f(x_1, x_2, x_3) = x_1 \cdot x_3' + x_1' \cdot x_3 + x_1 \cdot x_2' + x_2 \cdot x_3' + x_2' \cdot x_3 + x_1' \cdot x_2.$
   As further applications of these two steps do not produce other changes, these six clauses are the prime implicants of the given function.

(c) $f(x_1, x_2, x_3) = x_1' \cdot x_2' \cdot x_3 + x_1' \cdot x_2 \cdot x_3' + x_1' \cdot x_2 \cdot x_3 + x_1 \cdot x_2' \cdot x_3'$
$$+ x_1 \cdot x_2' \cdot x_3 + x_1 \cdot x_2 \cdot x_3'$$

Step 1: produces no change

Step 2: adds six new clauses, $x_1' \cdot x_3$, $x_2' \cdot x_3$, $x_1' \cdot x_2$, $x_2 \cdot x_3'$, $x_1 \cdot x_2'$, and $x_1 \cdot x_3'$ by combining the clauses; $x_1' \cdot x_2' \cdot x_3 + x_1' \cdot x_2 \cdot x_3$, $x_1' \cdot x_2' \cdot x_3 + x_1 \cdot x_2' \cdot x_3$, $x_1' \cdot x_2 \cdot x_3' + x_1' \cdot x_2 \cdot x_3$, $x_1' \cdot x_2 \cdot x_3'$ $+ x_1 \cdot x_2 \cdot x_3'$, $x_1 \cdot x_2' \cdot x_3' + x_1 \cdot x_2' \cdot x_3$, and $x_1 \cdot x_2' \cdot x_3' +$ $x_1 \cdot x_2 \cdot x_3'$, respectively. It should be noted that each of these combinations is of the form $x \cdot \theta + x' \cdot \theta$, as step 2 was applied to the canonical expansion. In this case each of the clauses entering into the combinations can be dropped, as $x \cdot \theta + x' \cdot \theta = \theta$.

Thus the function now is

$f(x_1, x_2, x_3) = x_1' \cdot x_3 + x_2' \cdot x_3 + x_1' \cdot x_2 + x_2 \cdot x_3' + x_1 \cdot x_2' + x_1 \cdot x_3'$.
Again, these six clauses are the prime implicants of the given function, as further applications of steps 1 and 2 do not produce other changes.

From this example it can be seen that independent of the particular sum-of-products expression, applying the procedure of Theorem 2 leads to the same set of prime implicants. This result was to be expected, since if the Karnaugh-map representation of a given function is unique, the maximal subcubes are also unique. In other words, the prime-implicant representation of a Boolean function is unique. Because of this, the prime-implicant representation of a Boolean function is sometimes referred to as a *canonical expression*. To obtain a visual picture of the prime implicants in Fig. 2–42, the maximal subcubes of Example 26 are shown.

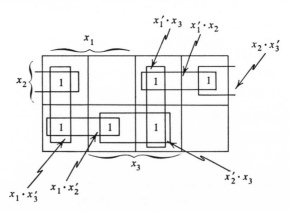

Figure 2–42.   Prime implicants of $f(x_1, x_2, x_3) = \sum (1, 2, 3, 4, 5, 6)$.

The next part of the simplification process is to choose a subset of the prime implicants that satisfies the minimization criteria. Just as in the graphical procedure, this part of the process is divided into two steps. In the first step, the core prime implicants (Def. 15) are selected. This corresponds to the selection of subcubes with a vertex or vertices that are not included in any other subcube. Thus all the core prime implicants have to be included in the representation, to make the function 1 for these input combinations. In the second step the set of core prime implicants is checked for coverage; that is, the core prime implicants are checked to see whether or not they include all the fundamental products of the given function. If the core prime implicants satisfy the coverage requirement, the sum of core prime implicants is the minimal-sum-of-products representation of the given function. Otherwise further prime implicants must be included in the representation. To see how this outline can be executed, the following definition and examples are introduced. Note that in these examples we shall start from the prime-implicants representation of the functions, and their Karnaugh-map representations are included instead of the calculations.

Definition 15. A *core prime implicant* is a prime implicant whose truth, i.e., identity of its literals to 1, does not necessarily make the remainder of the function true.

Note that this definition requires that the clause include at least one fundamental product that is not included in the remainder of the function. To see this, let the function be $f = \varphi + \psi$, where φ is the prime implicant under consideration. If the assignment of literals that makes $\varphi = 1$ also makes $\psi = 1$, then $\varphi \leq \psi$, by Definition 13. In other words, all the fundamental products p_i's included in φ are also included in ψ.

EXAMPLE 27. Derive the minimal-sum-of-products representation of the following Boolean function, given as sum of its prime implicants (and see Fig. 2-43):

$$f(x_1, x_2, x_3, x_4) = x_1 \cdot x_2 \cdot x_4 + x_1' \cdot x_2' \cdot x_3 + x_1 \cdot x_3'.$$

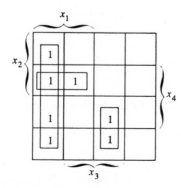

Figure 2-43. Prime implicants of $f(x_1, x_2, x_3, x_4) = \sum (2, 3, 8, 9, 12, 13, 15)$.

To check for core prime implicants each of the clauses is made 1, and the value of the other two clauses is checked for the corresponding assignment of variables.

(1) $x_1 \cdot x_2 \cdot x_4 = 1$ means that $x_1 = x_2 = x_4 = 1$, and for these values $x_1' \cdot x_2' \cdot x_3 + x_1 \cdot x_3' = 0 \cdot 0 \cdot x_3 + 1 \cdot x_3' = x_3'$. Thus $x_1 \cdot x_2 \cdot x_4$ is a core prime implicant.

(2) $x_1' \cdot x_2' \cdot x_3 = 1$ means that $x_1 = x_2 = 0$ and $x_3 = 1$, and for these values $x_1 \cdot x_2 \cdot x_4 + x_1 \cdot x_3' = 0 \cdot 0 \cdot x_4 + 0 \cdot 0 = 0$. Thus $x_1' \cdot x_2' \cdot x_3$ is a core prime implicant.

(3) $x_1 \cdot x_3' = 1$ means that $x_1 = 1$ and $x_3 = 0$, and for these values $x_1 \cdot x_2 \cdot x_4 + x_1' \cdot x_2' \cdot x_3 = 1 \cdot x_2 \cdot x_4 + 0 \cdot x_2' \cdot 0 = x_2 \cdot x_4$. Thus $x_1 \cdot x_3'$ is a core prime implicant.

Since all the prime implicants are core prime implicants, the coverage requirement is satisfied, and the prime-implicant representation is also the minimal-sum-of-products representation.

EXAMPLE 28.   Derive the minimal-sum-of-products representation of the following Boolean function given as the sum of its prime implicants (and see Fig. 2–44):

$$f(x_1, x_2, x_3, x_4) = x_1 \cdot x_2 + x_2 \cdot x_3' + x_2 \cdot x_4 + x_1 \cdot x_3 \cdot x_4' + x_2' \cdot x_3 \cdot x_4'.$$

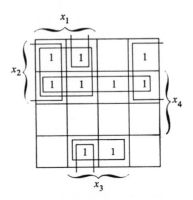

Figure 2–44. Prime implicants of $f(x_1, x_2, x_3, x_4) = \sum (2, 4, 5, 7, 10, 12, 13, 14, 15)$.

Checking each of the prime implicants, we obtain

(1) $x_1 \cdot x_2 = 1$ means that $x_1 = x_2 = 1$, and for these values $x_2 \cdot x_3' + x_2 \cdot x_4 + x_1 \cdot x_3 \cdot x_4' + x_2' \cdot x_3 \cdot x_4' = 1 \cdot x_3' + 1 \cdot x_4 + 1 \cdot x_3 \cdot x_4' + 0 \cdot x_3 \cdot x_4' = 1$. Thus $x_1 \cdot x_2$ is not a core prime implicant.

(2) $x_2 \cdot x_3' = 1$ means that $x_2 = 1$ and $x_3 = 0$, and for these values $x_1 \cdot x_2 + x_2 \cdot x_4 + x_1 \cdot x_3 \cdot x_4' + x_2' \cdot x_3 \cdot x_4' = x_1 \cdot 1 + 1 \cdot x_4 + x_1 \cdot 0 \cdot x_4' + 0 \cdot 0 \cdot x_4' = x_1 + x_4$. Thus $x_2 \cdot x_3'$ is a core prime implicant.

(3) $x_2 \cdot x_4 = 1$ means that $x_2 = x_4 = 1$, and for these values $x_1 \cdot x_2 + x_2 \cdot x_3' + x_1 \cdot x_3 \cdot x_4' + x_2' \cdot x_3 \cdot x_4' = x_1 \cdot 1 + 1 \cdot x_3' + x_1 \cdot x_3 \cdot 0 + 0 \cdot x_3 \cdot 0 = x_1 + x_3'$. Thus $x_2 \cdot x_4$ is a core prime implicant.

(4) $x_1 \cdot x_3 \cdot x_4' = 1$ means that $x_1 = x_3 = 1$ and $x_4 = 0$, and for these values $x_1 \cdot x_2 + x_2 \cdot x_3' + x_2 \cdot x_4 + x_2' \cdot x_3 \cdot x_4' = 1 \cdot x_2 + x_2 \cdot 0 + x_2 \cdot 0 + x_2' \cdot 1 \cdot 1 = 1$. Thus $x_1 \cdot x_3 \cdot x_4'$ is not a core prime implicant.

(5) $x_2' \cdot x_3 \cdot x_4' = 1$ means that $x_2 = x_4 = 0$ and $x_3 = 1$, and for these values $x_1 \cdot x_2 + x_2 \cdot x_3' + x_2 \cdot x_4 + x_1 \cdot x_3 \cdot x_4' = x_1 \cdot 0 + 0 \cdot 0 + 0 \cdot 0 + x_1 \cdot 1 \cdot 1 = x_1$. Thus $x_2' \cdot x_3 \cdot x_4'$ is a core prime implicant.

Thus the sum of core prime implicants is

$$g(x_1, x_2, x_3, x_4) = x_2 \cdot x_3' + x_2 \cdot x_4 + x_2' \cdot x_3 \cdot x_4'.$$

By comparing the two Boolean functions $f(x_1, x_2, x_3, x_4)$ and $g(x_1, x_2, x_3, x_4)$ it is found that $g(x_1, x_2, x_3, x_4)$ does not contain the fundamental product $x_1 \cdot x_2 \cdot x_3 \cdot x_4'$. This fundamental product can be included by adding either one of the remaining two prime implicants. And as the clause $x_1 \cdot x_2$ includes only two literals, this prime implicant is added. Thus the minimal-sum-of-products representation of this function is

$$f(x_1, x_2, x_3, x_4) = x_1 \cdot x_2 + x_2 \cdot x_3' + x_2 \cdot x_4 + x_2' \cdot x_3 \cdot x_4'.$$

In both of these examples the minimal-sum-of-products representation of the Boolean function is unique. But generally this is not the case, and the actual selection of the required subset of prime implicants becomes much more complex. An example of this is the Boolean function of Example 26 (Fig. 2–42). In this example none of the prime implicants is a core prime implicant, and there are two sets of three prime implicants that satisfy the minimality requirement. The actual procedure for the selection of the minimal subset of prime implicants is introduced in Section 2–11, where an extension of Quine's method, Quine and McCluskey's method of simplification, is investigated.

2–11. TABULAR SIMPLIFICATION OF BOOLEAN FUNCTIONS

The simplification procedure described in this section is a systematic translation of Quine's first method.[11] This method was originated by McCluskey[12] and is based on the Boolean identity $x \cdot \varphi + x' \cdot \varphi = \varphi$. The procedure starts from the disjunctive canonical expansion of the n-variable Boolean function, and each fundamental product is designated by the corresponding binary number. The fundamental products are combined according to the above identity whenever possible to obtain clauses with $(n - 1)$ literals.

[11] W. V. Quine, *Am. Math. Monthly*, **59**, 521–531 (1952).

[12] E. J. McCluskey, Jr., "Minimization of Boolean Functions," *Bell System Tech. J.*, **35**, 1417–1444 (1956).

That is, the fundamental products are checked for adjacencies. Then the clauses of $(n - 1)$ literals are combined whenever possible to obtain clauses with $(n - 2)$ literals. This procedure is repeated until we obtain clauses with $(n - i)$ literals that cannot be reduced further. That is, all the sets of 2^i and less mutually adjacent points are obtained, and by dropping all the clauses that entered in the combinations, we obtain the prime implicants as the remaining sets.

If such a combination is possible, a binary number with a dash replacing the corresponding variable is entered in a new column, and the numbers that enter in combination are marked with a check. After all the comparisons are made in the original column of numbers, the same process is repeated in the new column until no newer columns can be obtained. The prime implicants are then obtained by listing all the entries that are not check-marked.

To clarify the procedure, the following example is introduced.

EXAMPLE 29.   Using Quine and McCluskey's method of simplification, obtain the prime implicants of the Boolean function

$$f(x_1, x_2, x_3, x_4) = \sum (0, 1, 2, 3, 11, 13, 15).$$

As a first step, the binary numbers corresponding to the fundamental products are obtained as follows:

$$
\begin{array}{rllll}
(0) & x_1' \cdot x_2' \cdot x_3' \cdot x_4' -\!\!\!- 0 & 0 & 0 & 0 \\
(1) & x_1' \cdot x_2' \cdot x_3' \cdot x_4 -\!\!\!- 0 & 0 & 0 & 1 \\
(2) & x_1' \cdot x_2' \cdot x_3 \cdot x_4' -\!\!\!- 0 & 0 & 1 & 0 \\
(3) & x_1' \cdot x_2' \cdot x_3 \cdot x_4 -\!\!\!- 0 & 0 & 1 & 1 \\
(11) & x_1 \cdot x_2' \cdot x_3 \cdot x_4 -\!\!\!- 1 & 0 & 1 & 1 \\
(13) & x_1 \cdot x_2 \cdot x_3' \cdot x_4 -\!\!\!- 1 & 1 & 0 & 1 \\
(15) & x_1 \cdot x_2 \cdot x_3 \cdot x_4 -\!\!\!- 1 & 1 & 1 & 1 \\
\end{array}
$$

In Fig. 2–45 these binary numbers are grouped according to the number of 1's

		x_1	x_2	x_3	x_4	
I	0	0	0	0	0	✓
II	1	0	0	0	1	✓
	2	0	0	1	0	✓
III	3	0	0	1	1	✓
IV	11	1	0	1	1	✓
	13	1	1	0	1	✓
V	15	1	1	1	1	✓

Figure 2–45.   Fundamental products and Karnaugh-map representation of $f(x_1, x_2, x_3, x_4) = \sum (0, 1, 2, 3, 11, 13, 15)$.

they include. Also given in this figure is the Karnaugh-map representation of this function. Because of this arrangement each element of a group has to be compared only with the elements of the next group. If elements 0 and 1 are compared the result is 000–, as they differ in the fourth bit, and both these entries are check-marked. But element 0 has to be compared with element 2, as they also form an adjacency, that of 00–0. These combinations are executed, and the resulting column of two adjacent vertices and their Karnaugh-map representation is shown in Fig. 2–46.

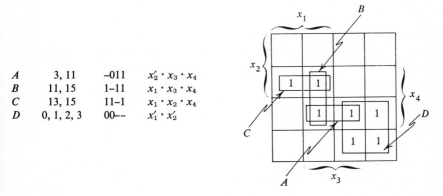

		x_1	x_2	x_3	x_4	
I′	0, 1	0	0	0	–	✓
	0, 2	0	0	–	0	✓
II′	1, 3	0	0	–	1	✓
	2, 3	0	0	1	–	✓
III′	3, 11	–	0	1	1	
IV′	11, 15	1	–	1	1	
	13, 15	1	1	–	1	

Figure 2–46. The 2-cubes and their Karnaugh-map representation of $f(x_1, x_2, x_3, x_4) = \sum (0, 1, 2, 3, 11, 13, 15)$.

Now, to combine any two elements of the new list, it is necessary to use the same identity $x\varphi + x'\varphi = \varphi$. That is, it is required that the dashes occur in the same positions. Thus the elements marked (0, 1) and (2, 3) can be combined to form (0, 1, 2, 3) 00––. Note that the elements (0, 2) and (1, 3) can

A	3, 11	–011	$x_2' \cdot x_3 \cdot x_4$
B	11, 15	1–11	$x_1 \cdot x_3 \cdot x_4$
C	13, 15	11–1	$x_1 \cdot x_2 \cdot x_4$
D	0, 1, 2, 3	00––	$x_1' \cdot x_2'$

Figure 2–47. Prime implicants and Karnaugh-map representation of $f(x_1, x_2, x_3, x_4) = \sum (0, 1, 2, 3, 8, 11, 13, 15)$.

also be combined to form the same clause; thus it is not entered again in the list, but these two entries are to be check-marked, as they are not prime implicants. In this particular example there are no more combinations to be obtained. Thus the unchecked entries are the prime implicants of this function. These entries are now to be translated into clauses. This is done by replacing a 1 in the ith position by x_i and a 0 by x_i', and no literal is included where there is a dash. This is shown in Fig. 2–47, together with the Karnaugh-map representation of the prime implicants.

Thus the prime-implicant representation of this Boolean function is

$$f(x_1, x_2, x_3, x_4) = x_1' \cdot x_2' + x_1 \cdot x_2 \cdot x_4 + x_1 \cdot x_3 \cdot x_4 + x_2' \cdot x_3 \cdot x_4.$$

This, then, is the first part in the simplification-procedure derivation of the prime-implicant representation of a Boolean function. Before considering the second part of the procedure, the relative merits of the two methods, Quine's and Quine and McCluskey's, should first be investigated. The tabular method of Quine and McCluskey is more systematic, thus reducing the number of comparisons to be made, and in addition the actual computations involve only two numbers at a time. On the other hand, the main drawback of this method is that the computations have to be started from the disjunctive canonical expansions. Thus, to use Quine and McCluskey's method, the D.C.E. must first be obtained, which in itself can be a major computation. And even if the function is originally given with some of the prime implicants, they must be recalculated.

Let us now return to the second part of the simplification procedure. We saw in Section 2–10 that in checking for core prime implicants we obtained a partial result, but not the final answer for obtaining a minimal set of prime implicants. To calculate the minimal set of prime implicants, the table of prime implicants is first introduced. In this table the original clauses, the fundamental products, are listed as columns and the prime implicants as rows. Whenever an original clause implies a prime implicant, a cross is placed in the corresponding square. If any column contains only one cross, it means that this original clause is included in only one prime implicant and thus this is a core prime implicant. After obtaining the core prime implicants in this way, all the original clauses included in the core prime implicants have been crossed, leaving only those clauses that must be represented by noncore prime implicants. To see this, consider as an example the prime-implicant table of Example 29.

EXAMPLE 30.   Derive the minimal-sum-of-product representation of the following Boolean function, given the following sum of prime implicants:

$$f(x_1, x_2, x_3, x_4) = x_1' \cdot x_2' + x_1 \cdot x_2 \cdot x_4 + x_1 \cdot x_3 \cdot x_4 + x_2' \cdot x_3 \cdot x_4.$$

This example has seven fundamental products and four prime implicants.

			ORIGINAL CLAUSES						
PRIME IMPLICANTS			0	1	2	3	11	13	15
A	3, 11	$x_2' \cdot x_3 \cdot x_4$				X	X		
B	11, 15	$x_1 \cdot x_3 \cdot x_4$					X		X
C	13, 15	$x_1 \cdot x_2 \cdot x_4$						X	X
D	0, 1, 2, 3	$x_1' \cdot x_2'$	X	X	X	X			

Figure 2–48.   Prime-implicant table of $f(x_1, x_2, x_3, x_4) = \sum (0, 1, 2, 3, 11, 13, 15)$.

The prime-implicant table is as shown in Fig. 2–48. In this example the clauses C and D are seen to be core prime implicants and they cover all but the fundamental product 11. This fundamental product can be included by adding either one of the prime implicants A or B. As both these clauses have the same number of literals, either one of them can be used in the minimal representation. Thus the minimal representations are the sum of prime implicants A, C, and D or B, C, and D. In other words, the minimal-sum-of-products representations of this function are

$$f(x_1, x_2, x_3, x_4) = x_1' \cdot x_2' + x_1 \cdot x_2 \cdot x_4 + x_2' \cdot x_3 \cdot x_4$$

or $$f(x_1, x_2, x_3, x_4) = x_1' \cdot x_2' + x_1 \cdot x_2 \cdot x_4 + x_1 \cdot x_3 \cdot x_4.$$

The cost factor of each of these functions is 11.

In this example the choice of prime implicants is quite simple, which is not generally the case. When this becomes more complex, an algebraic method has to be used. This is shown by an example.

EXAMPLE 31.   Derive the minimal-sum-of-products representation of the Boolean function

$$f(x_1, x_2, x_3, x_4) = \sum (3, 4, 5, 6, 7, 8, 10, 11, 12).$$

The computation and the table of prime implicants are given in Fig. 2–49. In this example there is only one core prime implicant (a) and after the inclusion of this implicant there remain five original clauses (3, 8, 10, 11, 12)

	x_1	x_2	x_3	x_4
4	0	1	0	0	√
8	1	0	0	0	√
3	0	0	1	1	√
5	0	1	0	1	√
6	0	1	1	0	√
10	1	0	1	0	√
12	1	1	0	0	√
7	0	1	1	1	√
11	1	0	1	1	√

	x_1	x_2	x_3	x_4	
4, 5	0	1	0	–	√
4, 6	0	1	–	0	√
4, 12	–	1	0	0	ⓑ
8, 10	1	0	–	0	ⓒ
8, 12	1	–	0	0	ⓓ
3, 7	0	–	1	1	ⓔ
3, 11	–	0	1	1	ⓕ
5, 7	0	1	–	1	√
6, 7	0	1	1	–	√
10, 11	1	0	1	–	ⓖ

	x_1	x_2	x_3	x_4	
4, 5, 6, 7	0	1	–	–	ⓐ

			ORIGINAL CLAUSES								
PRIME IMPLICANTS			3	4	5	6	7	8	10	11	12
a	4, 5, 6, 7	$x_1' \cdot x_2$		X	X	X	X				
b	4, 12	$x_2 \cdot x_3' \cdot x_4'$		X							X
c	8, 10	$x_1 \cdot x_2' \cdot x_4'$						X	X		
d	8, 12	$x_1 \cdot x_3' \cdot x_4'$						X			X
e	3, 7	$x_1' \cdot x_3 \cdot x_4$	X					X			
f	3, 11	$x_2' \cdot x_3 \cdot x_4$	X							X	
g	10, 11	$x_1 \cdot x_2' \cdot x_3$							X	X	

Figure 2–49. Determination of prime implicants and prime-implicant table of $f(x_1, x_2, x_3, x_4) = \sum (3, 4, 5, 6, 7, 8, 10, 11, 12)$.

that must be included by other prime implicants. The algebraic method to be used can be described by the following three statements:

(1) To include any original clause it is necessary to include any one of the prime implicants that this clause implies. For example, to include clause (3) either of the prime implicants e or f must be chosen $(e + f)$.

(2) To include any two original clauses it is required that a combination of one or more prime implicants be included that covers these clauses. For example, to include clauses (3) and (4) any one of the four combinations, e and a, or e and b, or f and a, or f and b, of prime implicants must be included. Represented algebraically, this condition is $(e + f) \cdot (a + b)$.

(3) To include all the original clauses, statement (2) is extended. That is, the corresponding algebraic expression is

$$(e + f) \cdot (a + b) \cdot (a) \cdot (a) \cdot (a + e) \cdot (c + d) \cdot (c + g) \cdot (f + g) \cdot (b + d),$$

and by reducing the obvious superfluities we obtain

$$a \cdot (e + f) \cdot (f + g) \cdot (c + d) \cdot (c + g) \cdot (b + d)$$
$$= (a \cdot e \cdot f + a \cdot f + a \cdot f \cdot g + a \cdot e \cdot g) \cdot (c + c \cdot g + d \cdot c + d \cdot g)$$
$$\cdot (b + d)$$
$$= (a \cdot f + a \cdot e \cdot g) \cdot (b \cdot c + c \cdot d + b \cdot d \cdot g + d \cdot g)$$
$$= a \cdot b \cdot c \cdot f + a \cdot c \cdot d \cdot f + a \cdot d \cdot f \cdot g + a \cdot b \cdot c \cdot e \cdot g$$
$$+ a \cdot d \cdot c \cdot e \cdot g + a \cdot d \cdot e \cdot g.$$

Thus we obtain four different combinations of four prime implicants and one of five prime implicants that can be used in the representation of the Boolean function. To obtain the cost factor of each representation, the number of literals of the prime implicants is added to the number of prime implicants in the representation. In this example (a) has two literals and the other prime implicants have three literals; thus all the realizations of four prime implicants have cost factors of $2 + 3 + 3 + 3 + 4 = 15$, and the realization with five prime implicants has the cost factor $2 + 3 + 3 + 3 + 3 + 5 = 19$. Note that in the same manner as the Karnaugh-map method this procedure leads to all the parallel minimal realizations of a Boolean function.

To complete this section it remains to include two additional cases in this method, the inclusion of don't-care conditions and the procedure for minimal product of sums.

When don't-care conditions are to be included, the procedure for obtaining the prime implicants is the same as before, assuming these vertices as original clauses. The only difference is in the second part of the simplification procedure. In preparing the prime implicant tables, the don't-care conditions are left out, both as original clauses and as prime implicants whenever there is a prime implicant made up entirely of don't-care conditions. The reason for this is that the don't-care conditions are included only to provide maximal subcubes, but they do not have to be included in the representation. To see this, consider the following example.

EXAMPLE 32. Derive the minimal-sum-of-products representation of the following Boolean function:

$$f(x_1, x_2, x_3, x_4) = \sum (0, 3, 4, 7, 8, 12, 15)$$

with the don't-care conditions

$$d(x_1, x_2, x_3, x_4) = \sum (5, 13, 14).$$

The computation of prime implicants and the table of prime implicants is

	x_1 x_2 x_3 x_4	
	0 0 0 0 0	√
	4 0 1 0 0	√
	8 1 0 0 0	√
	3 0 0 1 1	√
d	5 0 1 0 1	√
	12 1 1 0 0	√
	7 0 1 1 1	√
d	13 1 1 0 1	√
d	14 1 1 1 0	√
	15 1 1 1 1	√

	x_1 x_2 x_3 x_4	
0, 4	0 – 0 0	√
0, 8	– 0 0 0	√
4, 5	0 1 0 –	√
4, 12	– 1 0 0	√
8, 12	1 – 0 0	√
3, 7	0 – 1 1	ⓔ
5, 7	0 1 – 1	√
5, 13	– 1 0 1	√
12, 13	1 1 0 –	√
12, 14	1 1 – 0	√
7, 15	– 1 1 1	√
13, 15	1 1 – 1	√
14, 15	1 1 1 –	√

	x_1 x_2 x_3 x_4	
0, 4, 8, 12	– – 0 0	ⓐ
4, 5, 12, 13	– 1 0 –	ⓑ
5, 7, 13, 15	– 1 – 1	ⓒ
12, 13, 14, 15	1 1 – –	ⓓ

	PRIME IMPLICANTS		ORIGINAL CLAUSES						
			0	3	4	7	8	12	15
a	0, 4, 8, 12	$x_3' \cdot x_4'$	X		X		X	X	
b	4, 5, 12, 13	$x_2 \cdot x_3'$			X			X	
c	5, 7, 13, 15	$x_2 \cdot x_4$				X			X
d	12, 13, 14, 15	$x_1 \cdot x_2$						X	X
e	3, 7	$x_1' \cdot x_3 \cdot x_4$		X		X			

Figure 2–50. Determination of prime implicants and prime-implicant table of $f(x_1, x_2, x_3, x_4) = \sum (0, 3, 4, 7, 8, 12, 15)$ and $d(x_1, x_2, x_3, x_4) = \sum (5, 13, 14)$.

given in Fig. 2–50. From the table of prime implicants the following two realizations are read off: $a \cdot c \cdot e$ and $a \cdot d \cdot e$. Both of these are minimal with the cost factor of $2 + 2 + 3 + 3 = 10$. Written as sum of clauses these realizations are

$$f(x_1, x_2, x_3, x_4) = x_3' \cdot x_4' + x_2 \cdot x_4 + x_1' \cdot x_3 \cdot x_4$$

and $$f(x_1, x_2, x_3, x_4) = x_3' \cdot x_4' + x_1 \cdot x_2 + x_1 \cdot x_3 \cdot x_4.$$

To obtain the minimal-product-of-sums representation of a Boolean function, the dual procedure is used. That is, the vertices where the value of the function is 0, and the vertices corresponding to the don't-care conditions, are included in the original list. From then on the computation is exactly the same as in the procedure used for obtaining the minimal sum of products. The result is the M.S.P. representation of the negated function (f'), which is then negated to obtain the M.P.S. representation. To see this, consider the following example.

EXAMPLE 33.   Derive the minimal-product-of-sums representation of the Boolean function of Example 32. The 0's of this function are at the vertices (1, 2, 6, 9, 10, 11). The computations and the table of prime implicants are given in Fig. 2–51.

		x_1	x_2	x_3	x_4	
	1	0	0	0	1	√
	2	0	0	1	0	√
d	5	0	1	0	1	√
	6	0	1	1	0	√
	9	1	0	0	1	√
	10	1	0	1	0	√
	11	1	0	1	1	√
d	13	1	1	0	1	√
d	14	1	1	1	0	√

	x_1	x_2	x_3	x_4	
1, 5	0	–	0	1	√
1, 9	–	0	0	1	√
2, 6	0	–	1	0	√
2, 10	–	0	1	0	√
5, 13	–	1	0	1	√
6, 14	–	1	1	0	√
9, 11	1	0	–	1	$\textcircled{c}$
9, 13	1	–	0	1	√
10, 11	1	0	1	–	$\textcircled{d}$
10, 14	1	–	1	0	√

	x_1	x_2	x_3	x_4	
1, 5, 9, 13	–	–	0	1	$\textcircled{a}$
2, 6, 10, 14	–	–	1	0	$\textcircled{b}$

			ORIGINAL CLAUSES					
	PRIME IMPLICANTS		1	2	6	9	10	11
a	1, 5, 9, 13	$x_3' \cdot x_4$	X			X		
b	2, 6, 10, 14	$x_3 \cdot x_4'$		X	X		X	
c	9, 11	$x_1 \cdot x_2' \cdot x_4$				X		X
d	10, 11	$x_1 \cdot x_2' \cdot x_3$					X	X

Figure 2–51.   Determination of prime implicants and prime-implicant table of $f'(x_1, x_2, x_3, x_4) = \sum (1, 2, 6, 9, 10, 11)$ and $d(x_1, x_2, x_3, x_4) = \sum (5, 13, 14)$.

From the table of prime implicants, two minimal realizations, each of a cost factor of $2 + 2 + 3 + 3 = 10$, corresponding to the combinations of prime implicants $a \cdot b \cdot c$ and $a \cdot b \cdot d$ are obtained. These are

$$f'(x_1, x_2, x_3, x_4) = x_3' \cdot x_4 + x_3 \cdot x_4' + x_1 \cdot x_2' \cdot x_4$$

and $\qquad f'(x_1, x_2, x_3, x_4) = x_3' \cdot x_4 + x_3 \cdot x_4' + x_1 \cdot x_2' \cdot x_3.$

And to obtain the minimal-product-of-sums representations, these functions are complemented. The resulting functions are

$$f(x_1, x_2, x_3, x_4) = (x_3 + x_4') \cdot (x_3' + x_4) \cdot (x_1' + x_2 + x_4')$$

and $$f(x_1, x_2, x_3, x_4) = (x_3 + x_4') \cdot (x_3' + x_4) \cdot (x_1' + x_2 + x_3').$$

Actually, these functions can be obtained directly from the prime-implicant table by listing the complemented prime implicants, that is, by translating the binary numbers representing a prime implicant, as follows. Each binary number represents a sum of literals with a 0 in the ith position replaced by x_i and a 1 by x_i'.

Note that although the inclusion of don't-care conditions was introduced in this section, all the discussion applies equally well to the material of Section 2–10. This is especially true as the difference in the procedure arises only in the selection of minimal sets of prime implicants. This is also true with respect to the computation of minimal product of sums; that is, by a suitable translation, Quine's method of simplification can be used.

2–12. MULTIPLE-OUTPUT COMBINATIONAL CIRCUITS

The general form of combinational circuits has multiple outputs as defined by Definition 2. In previous sections the simplification procedures considered only circuits with a single output. With present tools, the multiple-output circuits can only be designed as a set of separate single-output circuits. But when a circuit having more than one output is required, it is frequently possible to combine or share part of the circuitry among several of the outputs, thus reducing the cost factor of the over-all circuit. In this section the cost factor of Definition 10 is used; that is, the circuits are restricted to two-level logical realizations in the sum-of-products or product-of-sums form.

The procedure used in this section is an extension of Quine and McCluskey's simplification procedure. In this procedure the prime implicants of each function and of the common terms of every possible combination of these functions are obtained. The resulting prime implicants are then listed in a combined table of prime implicants from which the combined cost factor of the over-all circuit is determined. This procedure is illustrated with an example.

EXAMPLE 34.   Derive the minimal-sum-of-products representation of the three-output combinational circuit defined by the following three Boolean functions:

$$f_1(x_1, x_2, x_3) = \sum (0, 4, 6, 7),$$

$$f_2(x_1, x_2, x_3) = \sum (0, 3, 5, 7),$$

$$f_3(x_1, x_2, x_3) = \sum (0, 3, 4, 6).$$

The minimal-sum-of-products realizations of these functions separately is

$$f_1(x_1, x_2, x_3) = x_1 \cdot x_2 + x_2' \cdot x_3',$$
$$f_2(x_1, x_2, x_3) = x_1' \cdot x_2' \cdot x_3' + x_1 \cdot x_3 + x_2 \cdot x_3,$$
$$f_3(x_1, x_2, x_3) = x_1' \cdot x_2 \cdot x_3 + x_1 \cdot x_3' + x_2' \cdot x_3'.$$

The total cost factor of these three representations is $6 + 10 + 10 = 26$. But as clause $x_2' \cdot x_3'$ is included in both f_1 and f_3, by realizing it only once the cost factor can be reduced by 2. Actually, this cost factor can be further reduced by the following procedure.

First, the prime implicants of the original functions must be calculated. These are

$f_1 = \sum (0, 4, 6, 7)$

	x_1	x_2	x_3	
0, 4	–	0	0	✓
4, 6	1	–	0	✓
6, 7	1	1	–	Ⓗ

$f_2 = \sum (0, 3, 5, 7)$

	x_1	x_2	x_3	
0	0	0	0	✓
3, 7	–	1	1	⒡
5, 7	1	–	1	⒢

$f_3 = \sum (0, 3, 4, 6)$

	x_1	x_2	x_3	
3	0	1	1	✓
0, 4	–	0	0	✓
4, 6	1	–	0	✓

The different products of these functions with their prime implicants are

$f_1 \cdot f_2 = \sum (0, 7)$

	x_1	x_2	x_3	
0	0	0	0	✓
7	1	1	1	⒠

$f_1 \cdot f_3 = \sum (0, 4, 6)$

	x_1	x_2	x_3	
0, 4	–	0	0	⒞
4, 6	1	–	0	⒟

$f_2 \cdot f_3 = \sum (0, 3)$

	x_1	x_2	x_3	
0	0	0	0	✓
3	0	1	1	⒝

$f_1 \cdot f_2 \cdot f_3 = \sum (0)$

	x_1	x_2	x_3	
0	0	0	0	⒜

Note that these prime implicants were calculated as outlined in Section 2–11. The actual computations were omitted to save space. The next step is to construct a prime-implicant table that will lead to the minimal solution. The basic idea of this minimization is to share as much as possible the first-level logical blocks, that is, to use as much as possible the prime implicants of the products. Thus whenever there is a prime implicant that implies both a function and a product, it is included only in the product part of the prime-implicant table. The columns of the table are arranged in groups, one group for each function. The different prime-implicant representations of each function are computed in the same manner as in Section 2–11. These are then checked for the representation that provides greatest over-all simplification. The combined prime-implicant table of this example is shown in Fig. 2–52.

It should be observed that the original clauses of a product prime implicant

ORIGINAL CLAUSES

FUNCTIONS	PRIME IMPLICANTS	0	4	6	7	0	3	5	7	0	3	4	6
f_1	h 6, 7 $x_1 \cdot x_2$			X	X								
f_2	g 5, 7 $x_1 \cdot x_3$							X	X				
	f 3, 7 $x_2 \cdot x_3$						X		X				
$f_1 \cdot f_2$	e 7 $x_1 \cdot x_2 \cdot x_3$				X				X				
$f_1 \cdot f_3$	d 4, 6 $x_1 \cdot x_3'$		X	X								X	X
	c 0, 4 $x_2' \cdot x_3'$	X	X							X		X	
$f_2 \cdot f_3$	b 3 $x_1' \cdot x_2 \cdot x_3$						X				X		
$f_1 \cdot f_2 \cdot f_3$	a 0 $x_1' \cdot x_2' \cdot x_3'$	X				X				X			

Figure 2–52. Combined prime-implicant table of Example 34.

are marked in each of the functions included in the product. Using the algebraic method for calculating the minimal set of prime implicants, we obtain the following combinations:

$$f_1 = (a + c) \cdot (c + d) \cdot (d + h) \cdot (e + h)$$
$$= (a \cdot d + c) \cdot (d \cdot e + h)$$
$$= \underline{a \cdot d \cdot e + a \cdot d \cdot h + c \cdot d \cdot e + c \cdot h},$$

$$f_2 = a \cdot (b + f) \cdot g \cdot \cancel{(e + f + g)}$$
$$= a \cdot g \cdot (b + f)$$
$$= \underline{a \cdot b \cdot g + a \cdot f \cdot g},$$

$$f_3 = (a + c) \cdot b \cdot \cancel{(c + d)} \cdot d$$
$$= b \cdot d \cdot (a + c)$$
$$= \underline{a \cdot b \cdot d + b \cdot c \cdot d}.$$

In checking these possible realizations it can be seen that f_1 can be represented four different ways and f_2 and f_3 can each be represented in two different ways. That is, the over-all circuit can be represented $4 \times 2 \times 2 = 16$ different ways. To obtain the cost factor of an over-all realization, the products representing the specific prime implicants used in the realization of each function are multiplied algebraically. The result is a set of letters raised to some power, where each letter represents a prime implicant that must be realized by a first-level gate, and the power to which each letter is raised represents the number of second-level gates to which this prime implicant is connected. Thus the total cost of the first-level gates is the sum of literals included in the prime implicants represented by these letters. The total cost of the second-level gates is given by the sum of the powers to which these letters are raised. For example, if the realization corresponding to the first combination is to be considered, the cost factor is computed from the product $(a \cdot d \cdot e) \cdot (a \cdot b \cdot g) \cdot (a \cdot b \cdot d) = a^3 \cdot b^2 \cdot d^2 \cdot e \cdot g$. That is, there are five first-level gates with respective cost factors of 3, 3, 2, 3, and 2. As the sum of the powers is $3 + 2 + 2 + 1 + 1 = 9$, the cost of the second-level gates is 9. Thus the total cost factor of this representation is $3 + 3 + 2 + 3 + 2 + 9 = 22$. The products and the cost factors of the 16 different realizations of this circuit are as follows:

(111)	$a^3b^2d^2eg$	$9 + 3 + 3 + 2 + 3 + 2$	$= 22$
(112)	$a^2b^2cd^2eg$	$9 + 3 + 3 + 2 + 2 + 3 + 2$	$= 24$
(121)	a^3bd^2efg	$9 + 3 + 3 + 2 + 3 + 2 + 2$	$= 24$
(122)	a^2bcd^2efg	$9 + 3 + 3 + 2 + 2 + 3 + 2 + 2$	$= 26$
(211)	$a^3b^2d^2gh$	$9 + 3 + 3 + 2 + 2 + 2$	$= 21$
(212)	$a^2b^2cd^2gh$	$9 + 3 + 3 + 2 + 2 + 2 + 2$	$= 23$
(221)	a^3bd^2fgh	$9 + 3 + 3 + 2 + 2 + 2 + 2$	$= 23$
(222)	$a^2bcdfgh$	$9 + 3 + 3 + 2 + 2 + 2 + 2 + 2$	$= 25$
(311)	$a^2b^2cd^2eg$	$9 + 3 + 3 + 2 + 2 + 3 + 2$	$= 24$
(312)	$ab^2c^2d^2eg$	$9 + 3 + 3 + 2 + 2 + 3 + 2$	$= 24$
(321)	a^2bcd^2efg	$9 + 3 + 3 + 2 + 2 + 3 + 2 + 2$	$= 26$
(322)	abc^2d^2efg	$9 + 3 + 3 + 2 + 2 + 3 + 2 + 2$	$= 26$
(411)	a^2b^2cdgh	$8 + 3 + 3 + 2 + 2 + 2 + 2$	$= 22$
(412)	ab^2c^2dgh	$8 + 3 + 3 + 2 + 2 + 2 + 2$	$= 22$
(421)	$a^2bcdfgh$	$8 + 3 + 3 + 2 + 2 + 2 + 2 + 2$	$= 24$
(422)	abc^2dfgh	$8 + 3 + 3 + 2 + 2 + 2 + 2 + 2$	$= 24$

In this list the three digits in parentheses represent the combinations of prime implicants used in the specific realization. From this list the minimal circuit has a cost factor of 21 and the first column is 211. That means that in the realization of f_1 the second combination of prime implicants is used and in the realization of f_2 and f_3 the first combination of prime implicants is used. That is,

$$
\begin{aligned}
f_1(x_1, x_2, x_3) &= x_1' \cdot x_2' \cdot x_3' + x_1 \cdot x_3' + x_1 \cdot x_2 & (a \cdot d \cdot h), \\
f_2(x_1, x_2, x_3) &= x_1' \cdot x_2' \cdot x_3' + x_1' \cdot x_2 \cdot x_3 + x_1 \cdot x_3 & (a \cdot b \cdot g), \\
f_3(x_1, x_2, x_3) &= x_1' \cdot x_2' \cdot x_3' + x_1' \cdot x_2 \cdot x_3 + x_1 \cdot x_3' & (a \cdot b \cdot d).
\end{aligned}
$$

Note that the cost of each separate realization is increased but the over-all cost is reduced, because of the sharing of some of the first-level gates. The corresponding gate realization is shown in Fig. 2–53.

From this example it can be seen that the procedure for obtaining minimal multiple-output circuits is straightforward. Whenever there are don't-care conditions, they are included in exactly the same manner as in Section 2–11. In obtaining the combinations of the different functions, the relations $0 \cdot d = 0$, $1 \cdot d = d$, and $d \cdot d = d$ are used, as shown in Fig. 2–38 in Section 2–9. The major drawback of this method and of the other methods appearing in the literature is that they restrict all the functions to a single form, sum of products

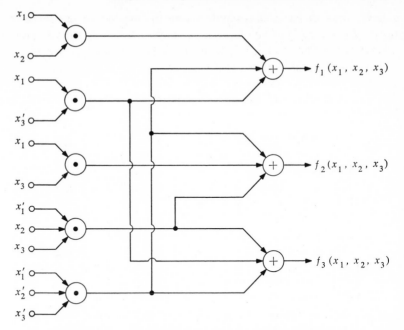

Figure 2–53.   Minimal gate realization of Example 34.

or product of sums, without considering the possibility of a mixed representation. There are two basic variations of this method. One transforms the
m n-input function into an $(m + n)$-input single-output function,[13] and
another tags the fundamental products that represent the different functions.[14]

2-13. OTHER TWO-LEVEL LOGICAL
REALIZATIONS

In previous sections procedures were introduced to derive minimal
Boolean expressions in the sum-of-products and product-of-sums forms. These
realizations are possible, because every n-variable Boolean function can be
represented in one of these forms, assuming that both the variables and their
complements are available. Such a form is generally referred to as a *nondegenerate form*. That is, given the multiple-input AND and OR gates, they can
be combined in two nondegenerate forms: AND-to-OR and OR-to-AND,
corresponding to sum of products and product of sums, respectively. By
including also the multiple-input N-AND and N-OR gates as defined in Section

[13] D. E. Muller, "Application of Boolean Algebra to Switching Circuit Design and to
Error Detection," *IRE Trans. Electron. Computers*, 3, 6–12 (1954).
[14] T. C. Bartee, "Computer Design of Multiple-Output Networks," *IRE Trans.
Electron. Computers*, 10, 21–30 (1961).

2–4, there are eight nondegenerate two-level logical forms. To show these realizations we shall use the following notation. Let sum of products $\equiv \sum p_i$, product of sums $\equiv \prod s_j$, and the general two-level multiple-input gate realizations be as shown in Fig. 2–54.

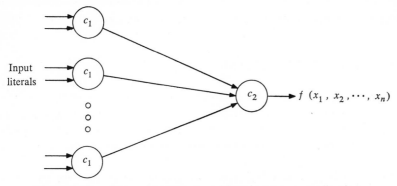

Figure 2–54.   General two-level multiple-input gate realization.

In this figure c_1 represents a first-level gate and c_2 represents the second-level gate. In Fig. 2–55 the list of the eight nondegenerate two-level forms with their

Input Literals	c_1	c_2	$f(x_1, x_2, \ldots, x_n)$
Literals of p_i	AND	OR	$\sum p_i$
Literals of s_j	OR	AND	$\prod s_j$
Literals of p_i	N-AND	N-AND	$\sum p_i$
Literals of s_j	N-OR	N-OR	$\prod s_j$
Complemented literals of p_i	N-OR	OR	$\sum p_i$
Complemented literals of s_j	N-AND	AND	$\prod s_j$
Complemented literals of p_i	OR	N-AND	$\sum p_i$
Complemented literals of s_j	AND	N-OR	$\prod s_j$

Figure 2–55.   List of nondegenerate two-level logical forms with AND, OR, N-AND, and N-OR multiple-input gates.

respective input literals is shown. To show that any one of these realizations is a nondegenerate form, it is enough to show that it can be translated into $\sum p_i$ or $\prod s_j$. From the definition of the multiple-input N-AND gate,

$$T(x_1, x_2, \ldots, x_n) = (x_1 \cdot x_2 \cdot \cdots \cdot x_n)' = x_1' + x_2' + \cdots + x_n'.$$

And from Fig. 2–55, the N-AND-to-N-AND realization is expressed

$$f(x_1, x_2, \ldots, x_n) = T[T(\text{literals of } p_i)]$$
$$= T[\text{sum of complemented literals of } p_i]$$
$$= T[p_i']$$
$$= \sum p_i.$$

The proof of nondegeneracy of each of the last five combinations in Fig. 2–54 is left as a homework problem.

These representations are becoming more important today as N-AND and N-OR gates become widely used, owing to their simple implementations with transistors. But at the same time, the restriction to two-level logic is quite arbitrary when transistors are used, because the gates can be used as amplifiers. The two-level restriction in transistors is only imposed in extremely fast operations, when the delay through a gate becomes a main factor.

2–14. CONCLUDING REMARKS

In this chapter some of the basic problems that arise in the design of combinational circuits were discussed. In the beginning the translation of the verbal definition to a set of logical functions was introduced. This was done very briefly, because once the exact verbal definition is obtained, the translation becomes straightforward. The main problem is to obtain this exact definition, and since this is largely governed by the specific application for which the circuit is to be designed, this problem was not investigated.

The second step of the design procedure, the translation of the logical function into a set of interconnected gates, was next introduced. In presenting this part of the procedure, two main points became apparent. First, every logical function can always be realized by a set of gates that forms a functionally complete set of operators. Second, there is no way of telling without trial which functionally complete set of operators will lead to a minimal gate realization of a specific logical function. It should be stated that the second point is not so important as it might seem, because in the design of any large system the first decision is the choice of the hardware to be used. This restricts the number of different gates that are available to the logical designer. The third problem that arises in this step is the actual design of the minimal gate realization; that is, given the set of connectives that are to be used, the logical designer must to a great extent rely on a bag of tricks to obtain a realization that uses a minimal number of gates.

In Section 2–4 the class of n-input logical gates was introduced to provide the basic building blocks of the minimal-cost realization. Also in this section the threshold gate was introduced, with the majority gate as a subclass. Even though the threshold gate is probably the largest potential advance in switching theory in the last 10 years, this material was covered very briefly. The reason is that the required theory is largely in the research stage, and there are only a few experimental systems that use threshold gates as basic building blocks.

In the second part of this chapter two different graphical representations were introduced, the n cube to provide the nomenclature and the Karnaugh map for actual use in the simplification of Boolean functions. To obtain a minimization procedure a very specific cost factor was defined. Actually, there are other minimization problems when either the definition of the cost factor or the restrictions on the form of the circuit are changed. As an example, the same cost factor can be used, but restrictions might be changed to allow more than two-level circuits or to reduce the number of inputs that can be applied to any one gate. To return to the simplification procedures presented, it can be seen that Karnaugh maps are the simplest to use for paper-and-pencil computations. But for more than six variables they become much too complex to be of much use, and in this case a computer must be used to simplify a Boolean function using one of the algebraic methods described in the last few sections.

Note that the simplification criteria described in this chapter become inapplicable in many designs. For example, many circuits are designed to satisfy some reliability criteria. This is generally done by including redundant elements, so that the over-all circuit will perform correctly even when some of the individual elements fail. Or whenever bilateral switching devices such as relay contacts are used, the minimal circuit generally is a bridge network that requires a completely different simplification procedure. A list of research papers covering these design aspects is given in Appendix I.

A sampling of basic papers that deal with the more generalized aspects of combinational circuits is given in the footnotes to this chapter. A second set of papers that cover some of the more specialized parts is presented in Appendix I. A few of the books that can be used as references are

S. H. Caldwell. *Switching Circuits and Logical Design.* New York: Wiley, 1958. This is one of the first textbooks on switching-circuit theory and provides an excellent coverage of combinational-circuit design, oriented mainly toward the design of contact networks.

M. P. Marcus. *Switching Circuits for Engineers.* Englewood Cliffs, N.J., Prentice-Hall, 1962. This is a very well organized book providing an applied approach to combinational-circuit design.

R. E. Miller. *Switching Theory* (Vol. 1: Combinational Circuits). New York: Wiley, 1965. This book provides some of the most complete coverage of combinational-circuit design. The approach is highly abstract in most places. This is an excellent reference book for the student interested in doing further research on a particular topic.

PROBLEMS

1. Obtain the truth-table representation and derive the algebraic representations of each of the following four-input (x_1, x_2, x_3, x_4) and three-output (z_1, z_2, z_3) circuits:

    (a) The three outputs of the circuit are defined as follows: $z_1 = 1$ if and only if three or more inputs are 1, $z_2 = 0$ if and only if $x_1 = x_2$ and $x_3 \neq x_1$, and $z_3 = 1$ if and only if any three of the inputs are equal.

  (b) The four inputs x_1, x_2, x_3, and x_4 are divided into two groups x_1x_2 and x_3x_4. Each group represents a number from 0 to 3 in binary notation. The three outputs z_1, z_2, and z_3 represent the sum of these two numbers in binary notation.

  (c) The four inputs x_1, x_2, x_3, and x_4 represent a decimal digit X in binary notation, $0 \le X \le 9$. The three outputs z_1, z_2, and z_3 are a decimal digit Z in binary notation defined as follows:

$$Z = X \qquad \text{whenever } 0 \le X \le 4, \text{ and}$$
$$Z = 9 - X \qquad \text{whenever } 5 \le X \le 9.$$

Note: The numbers in brackets in Problems 2, 3, and 4 are the number of logical gates required in the realization of the respective Boolean functions.

2. Obtain a simple gate realization of the following two-variable Boolean functions:

  (a) $f_a(p, q) = p' \cdot q + p \cdot q'$,
  (b) $f_b(p, q) = p' \cdot q' + p \cdot q$.

  Use the following functionally complete sets of logical connectives:

  (A) SHEFFER-STROKE [4, 5],
  (B) IMPLIES (assume that 0 is available) [4, 5].

3. Obtain a simple gate realization of the following three-variable Boolean functions:

  (a) $f_a(x, y, z) = x \cdot (y + z') + y' \cdot z$,
  (b) $f_b(x, y, z) = (x \cdot y + z) \cdot (x + y \cdot z)'$,
  (c) $f_c(x, y, z) = (x + y \cdot z) \cdot [x' + (y \cdot z)']$.

  Use the following sets of logical connectives:

  (A) AND, OR, and NOT [3, 3, 5],
  (B) EXCLUSIVE-OR and AND [5, 4, 2],
  (C) BUT-NOT and NOT [4, 2, 7].

4. The truth table and the block diagram shown in Fig. 2–56 represent a

X	Y	S	C
0	0	0	0
0	1	1	0
1	0	1	0
1	1	0	1

Figure 2–56.   Truth table and block diagram of a half-adder.

half-adder. Obtain a simple gate realization of the above-defined half-adder using the following set of logical connectives:

(A) AND, OR, and NOT [4],
(B) EXCLUSIVE-OR and AND [2],
(C) SHEFFER-STROKE [5],
(D) NEITHER-NOR [5].

5. Assume a normalized threshold gate as defined in Definition 7. By trial and error, obtain the values of m_0, m_1, and m_2 required to make this gate represent a two-input gate of the following types:

(a) AND gate;
(b) OR gate;
(c) SHEFFER-STROKE gate;
(d) NEITHER-NOR gate;
(e) IMPLIES gate;
(f) BUT-NOT gate.

Minimize $\sum_{i=0}^{2} |m_i|$ for each of the above gates.

6. Assume a normalized threshold gate as defined in Definition 7. Obtain the set of 2^n inequalities corresponding to each of the following three-variable Boolean functions:

(a) $f(x_1, x_2, x_3) = x_1' \cdot x_2 + x_1' \cdot x_3' + x_2 \cdot x_3'$;
(b) $f(x_1, x_2, x_3) = x_2' \cdot (x_1' + x_3)$;
(c) $f(x_1, x_2, x_3) = x_1 \cdot x_2' + x_2 \cdot x_3'$.

Whenever possible solve these inequalities by trial and error. Minimize $\sum_{i=0}^{3} |m_i|$.

7. Obtain the 3-cube and the three-variable Karnaugh-map representations of the following three-variable Boolean functions:

(a) $f(x, y, z) = x \downarrow (y \downarrow z)$;
(b) $f(x, y, z) = x \oplus y \oplus (x + y)$;
(c) $f(x, y, z) = x \Leftrightarrow z \Leftrightarrow (y' \cdot z)$;
(d) $f(x, y, z) = x \cap [y \rightarrow (x/y)]$;
(e) $f(x, y, z) = (x \oplus y) \downarrow (y + x \cdot z)$;
(f) $f(x, y, z) = (z/x) \cap [(x' \Leftrightarrow z) + y]$.

8. Using the Karnaugh-map method derive the minimal-sum-of-products and the minimal-product-of-sums forms of the five-variable Boolean function $f(v, w, x, y, z)$ that has the value 1 whenever the binary number represented by the five-input variables (v, w, x, y, z) is not divisible by 2 or 5. Assume that 0 is divisible by both 2 and 5.

9. Using the Karnaugh-map method, derive the minimal-sum-of-products and the minimal-product-of-sums forms of the following Boolean functions:

(a) $f(x_1, x_2, x_3, x_4) = \sum (0, 4, 5, 7, 8, 12, 14, 15)$,
(b) $f(x_1, x_2, x_3, x_4) = \prod (15, 14, 10, 9, 6, 4, 2)$,
(c) $f(x_1, x_2, x_3, x_4) = \sum (0, 2, 4, 6, 7, 8, 12, 13, 15)$,
(d) $f(x_1, x_2, x_3, x_4, x_5) = \prod (30, 26, 22, 21, 18, 17, 12, 8, 7)$,
(e) $f(x_1, x_2, x_3, x_4) = \sum (2, 5, 6, 9, 13, 14)$,
$\quad d(x_1, x_2, x_3, x_4) = \sum (0, 7, 8, 10, 15)$,
(f) $f(x_1, x_2, x_3, x_4) = \sum (1, 4, 6, 8, 11, 12)$,
$\quad d(x_1, x_2, x_3, x_4) = \sum (2, 5, 13, 15)$,
(g) $f(x_1, x_2, x_3, x_4, x_5) = \prod (30, 29, 16, 14, 11, 10, 9, 8, 6, 3)$,
$\quad d(x_1, x_2, x_3, x_4, x_5) = \sum (5, 11, 13, 30, 31)$.

10. Using Quine's method, derive the prime implicants and the core prime implicants of the following Boolean functions:

(a) $f(x, y, z, w) = y' \cdot w + x \cdot y' \cdot w' + x' \cdot y \cdot w + x' \cdot y' \cdot z'$;
(b) $f(x, y, z, w) = x \cdot w' + z' \cdot w' + x \cdot y \cdot w + x \cdot y' \cdot z + x' \cdot y' \cdot z$;
(c) $f(x, y, z, w, v) = x \cdot y + x' \cdot y' + w \cdot v' + x \cdot y \cdot z + y' \cdot z \cdot v$
$$+ x \cdot z \cdot w \cdot v.$$

11. Using Quine and McCluskey's method, obtain the minimal-product-of-sums representation of the Boolean functions of Problem 10.
12. Using Quine and McCluskey's method, derive the minimal-sum-of-products and minimal-product-of-sums representations of the Boolean functions of Problem 9.
13. Using Quine and McCluskey's method, derive the minimal-sum-of-products representation of the following multiple-output circuits:

(a) $f_1(x_1, x_2, x_3) = \sum (3, 4, 5, 6, 7)$,
$\quad f_2(x_1, x_2, x_3) = \sum (0, 3, 4, 5)$,
$\quad f_3(x_1, x_2, x_3) = \sum (0, 6, 7)$.

(b) $f_1(w, x, y, z) = (w \downarrow z)/y$,
$\quad f_2(w, x, y, z) = \sum (1, 3, 5, 7, 8, 12)$,
$\quad f_3(w, x, y, z) = \prod (1, 2, 3, 5, 6, 7, 9, 11, 13, 15)$.

(c) $\begin{cases} f_1(w, x, y, z) = \sum (0, 2, 10, 11), \\ d_1(w, x, y, z) = \sum (3, 8), \end{cases}$
$\quad \begin{cases} f_2(w, x, y, z) = \sum (0, 2, 3, 11), \\ d_2(w, x, y, z) = \sum (1, 10), \end{cases}$
$\quad \begin{cases} f_3(w, x, y, z) = \sum (0, 1, 2, 4), \\ d_3(w, x, y, z) = \sum (10). \end{cases}$

(d) $\begin{cases} f_1(w, x, y, z) = \sum(1, 5, 7, 9, 14), \\ d_1(w, x, y, z) = \sum(3, 13, 15), \end{cases}$
$\begin{cases} f_2(w, x, y, z) = \sum(7, 9, 13, 14), \\ d_2(w, x, y, z) = \sum(1, 12, 15), \end{cases}$
$\begin{cases} f_3(w, x, y, z) = \sum(1, 5, 12), \\ d_3(w, x, y, z) = \sum(3, 13, 15). \end{cases}$

14. Using Quine and McCluskey's method, derive the minimal-product-of-sums representations of the multiple-output circuits of Problem 13.

15. Using the notation of Section 2–13, complete the proof of the list in Fig. 2–55. That is, prove the following five identities:

(a) $D[D(\text{literals of } s_j)] = \prod s_j$;
(b) $\sum [D(\text{complemented literals of } p_i)] = \sum p_i$;
(c) $\prod [T(\text{complemented literals of } s_j)] = \prod s_j$;
(d) $T[\sum (\text{complemented literals of } p_i)] = \sum p_i$;
(e) $D[\prod (\text{complemented literals of } s_j)] = \prod s_j$.

CHAPTER

3

Asynchronous Sequential Circuits

3-1. INTRODUCTION

A sequential switching circuit is defined in Section 2–3, Definition 3, as a switching circuit whose outputs are determined both by the present inputs and the past sequence of inputs. Thus some information about the past history has to be stored in such a circuit. This stored information is generally referred to as the *internal state of the circuit*. With this in mind, a sequential circuit can always be represented by the block diagram of Fig. 3–1.

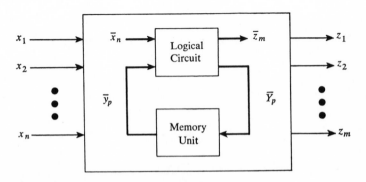

Figure 3–1. Generalized representation of an n-input, m-output sequential circuit.

In Fig. 3–1 the following notations are used:

$\bar{x}_n = x_1, x_2, \ldots, x_n$ is an n-tuple representing the n binary inputs of the circuit,

$\bar{z}_m = z_1, z_2, \ldots, z_m$ is an m-tuple representing the m binary outputs of the circuit,

$\bar{Y}_p = Y_1, Y_2, \ldots, Y_p$ is a p-tuple defining the next internal state of the circuit,

$\bar{y}_p = y_1, y_2, \ldots, y_p$ is a p-tuple representing the present internal state of the circuit.

$\bar{Y}_p$ and $\bar{y}_p$ are generally referred to as *secondary variables*.

This transformation is a theoretical concept, and it is not necessary for a given physical realization that this separation between the logical circuits and memory unit be possible. This separation is theoretically possible, because any information about the past input sequence can be contained in the p tuple, $\bar{y}_p$. Thus the behavior of a sequential circuit can now be described by the following two sets of Boolean functions:

$$z_i = F_i(\bar{x}_n, \bar{y}_p) \quad \text{for } i = 1, 2, \ldots, m,$$
$$Y_j = G_j(\bar{x}_n, \bar{y}_p) \quad \text{for } j = 1, 2, \ldots, p.$$

In other words, the behavior of an n-input and m-output sequential switching circuit can be described by a set of $(m + p)$ Boolean functions in $(n + p)$ variables. That is, by increasing the number of functions by p and the number of variables by p, a sequential switching circuit is transformed into a combinational switching circuit with p memory units. The purpose of this chapter and the next is to describe the procedures used to obtain this transformation and to reduce the number of secondary variables, that is, to reduce the number p.

The above discussion applies to sequential switching circuits in general. But these systems are divided into two main classes, depending on the timing of their signals. These two classes of sequential switching circuits are defined as follows.

Definition 1. A *synchronous sequential switching circuit* is a sequential system whose behavior can be defined from the knowledge of its signals at well-defined instants of time.

That is, the behavior of a synchronous sequential switching circuit is governed by the values of its signals at well-defined predetermined instants of time, and is unaffected by their values between these instants.

Definition 2. An *asynchronous sequential switching circuit* is a sequential system whose behavior depends upon the order in which its variables change.

That is, the behavior of asynchronous sequential switching circuits has to be defined in a time continuum, and the values or changes of its signals are not related to any specific instants of time.

In this chapter we shall restrict our discussion to asynchronous systems, and synthesis procedures will be developed by first introducing an analysis example. The first person to formalize the theory of sequential systems was Huffman,[1] and his papers will serve as the basis of this chapter, with later developments introduced whenever they are applicable. Two other basic investigators whose ideas are used extensively in this chapter are Mealy[2] and Moore.[3]

The theory of sequential systems is based on the recognition of a time delay between the input and output of a memory element. This is true in any hardware realization; for example, consider the times to energize and de-energize in relays, the rise and decay times in transistors, and the flux build-up and decay times in magnetic hardwares. To obtain a better understanding of the memory unit, the following two widely used memory units are defined.

Definition 3.   A *set-reset memory unit* is a two-input (S, R) and a single-output (y) device, shown in Fig. 3–2, whose behavior is defined as follows:

(a)   The output y of the memory unit is 1 if the set signal is 1, and this state is held even after the set signal becomes 0.

(b)   The output y of the memory unit is 0 if the reset signal is 1, and this state is held even after the reset signal becomes 0.

(c)   Only one of the input signals, set or reset, is to be 1 at any given time.

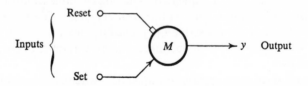

Figure 3–2.   Block-diagrammatic representation of a set-reset memory unit.

Actually, there are several variations of this basic memory unit, some of which will be defined later. Examples of set-reset memory units are the flip-flop connections in vacuum-tube and transistor logic, and a relay circuit with separate energizing and holding paths in relay logic.

[1] D. A. Huffman, "The Synthesis of Sequential Switching Circuits," *J. Franklin Inst.*, **257** (3), 161–190 (1954); and **257** (4), 275–303 (1954). A clear and excellent paper mainly oriented toward the design of relay sequential circuits.

[2] G. H. Mealy, "Method for Synthesizing Sequential Circuits," *Bell System Tech. J.*, **34**, 1045–1079 (1955). Considers the design of both synchronous and asynchronous systems.

[3] E. F. Moore, "Gedanken-Experiments on Sequential Machines," *Automata Studies Ann. Math.*, **34**, 129–153 (1956). Represents a theoretical investigation of the general properties of sequential systems.

Definition 4. A *transition memory unit* is a single-input (Y) and single-output (y) device, shown in Fig. 3–3, whose behavior is defined as follows:

If the excitation of the ith memory element is Y_i, then after some time Δt_i the state, that is, the output, takes on the value of the input.

Input or excitation $Y_i \longrightarrow M_i \longrightarrow y_i$ Output or state

Figure 3–3. Block-diagrammatic representation of a transition memory unit.

An example of such a memory unit is any device that transmits a signal, as there is a finite delay in all physical circuits. Concrete examples are delay lines or the operation delay of an electromagnetic relay. In this chapter we largely restrict our discussion to transition memory units, since this results in a slightly simpler design procedure, and the translation to an S-R memory unit is quite straightforward.

At this point, before introducing the analysis and synthesis procedures of asynchronous sequential switching circuits, we shall diverge and introduce the basic ideas of relay contact networks. This is done to relate the analysis procedure to a specific hardware realization, thus making it more concrete. Relay contact networks were chosen because they are the easiest to visualize and because they bring to light most of the problems that appear in the general design of sequential switching circuits.

3–2. BASIC DEFINITIONS AND PROPERTIES OF RELAY CONTACT NETWORKS

In this section no attempt is made to give an exhaustive description of relay contact networks.[4] Only those basic definitions are introduced that are necessary for the description of relay sequential circuits.

Definition 5. A *contact* is the abbreviated term for a contact pair, that is, two springs which can either touch or not, thus establishing or destroying an electrical path between two points.

In this presentation the presence and absence of a path are denoted, respectively, by the constants 1 and 0 of a two-valued Boolean algebra. The contacts themselves, generally denoted by lower-case letters, can be actuated

[4] F. E. Hohn, *Applied Boolean Algebra: An Elementary Introduction,* Second Edition, (New York: Macmillan 1966), Chap. I, pp. 1–70, provides a very clear and basic exposition of the properties of relay contact networks.

either by a switch or a relay, generally denoted by a capital letter. In each case the same actuator can have more than one pair of contacts. In practice, these contacts are designed as MAKE or BREAK contacts, depending upon whether they open or close when the actuator is de-energized or in the off position. The notations used in literature to represent these contacts are shown in Fig. 3–4.

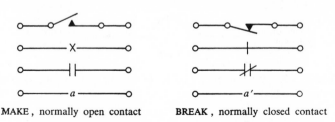

MAKE , normally open contact   BREAK , normally closed contact

Figure 3–4.   Notations of MAKE and BREAK contacts.

In practical contact networks, a third kind of contact is used. It is a combination of the above two contacts, called a TRANSFER contact, and is made up of three springs. This kind of contact can be of two types, either MAKE BEFORE BREAK or BREAK BEFORE MAKE, as shown schematically in Fig. 3–5.

MAKE BEFORE BREAK   BREAK BEFORE MAKE

Figure 3–5.   Schematic representation of TRANSFER contacts.

Given a network of interconnected contacts, the behavior of the resulting circuit can be studied with the help of a two-valued Boolean algebra. To see this, let us first consider the two simplest possible interconnections of n contacts. Given a set of n contacts, $x_1, x_2, \ldots, x_n$, which is connected in series between two points, there is a path between these two points if and only if all these contacts are closed. That is, the series interconnection of contacts corresponds to the AND operation in a two-valued Boolean algebra. Also, given a set of n contacts, $x_1, x_2, \ldots, x_n$, connected in parallel between two points, there exists a path between these two points whenever one or more contacts are closed. That is, the parallel interconnection of contacts corresponds to the OR operation in a two-valued Boolean algebra. In general, when the Boolean function describing the behavior of a contact network between two specified points is to be obtained, all possible paths between these two points have to be summed (OR operation) and each path is the product (AND operation) of the contacts (primed or unprimed) encountered in traversing this path.

The statements of the above paragraph can be formalized with the help of the following definitions.

Definition 6.   A *contact network* is a set of interconnected elements with a Boolean variable associated with each element. The Boolean variable is unprimed if the element represents a MAKE contact and is primed if the element represents a BREAK contact.

Definition 7.   A *path* P_{ij} is a set of elements that provides a possible connection between the specified points i and j.

Definition 8.   A *path product* p_{ij} is the Boolean product of the variables associated with the elements of a path P_{ij}.

Definition 9.   A *switching function* F_{ij} is that Boolean function of the contact variables which has the value 1 whenever there is an electric path between points i and j, the value 0 whenever there is no such path; $F_{ij} = \sum_k p_{ij}^{(k)}$ where the summation is a Boolean summation extending over all paths between points i and j.

In deriving the switching function F_{ij}, only those paths P_{ij} need be considered that include each element only once, as we are interested in the path products and in Boolean algebra $a \cdot a \cdot x = a \cdot x$. These definitions could have been simplified by using the nomenclature and the concepts of graph theory. A detailed presentation of contact networks using these concepts, which discusses the strong relationships that exist between contact networks and conventional networks, is given by Seshu and Reed.[5]

To see the mechanics of this procedure for calculating switching functions representing the behavior of contact networks, consider the following example.

EXAMPLE 1.   Obtain the switching function F_{14} of the contact network shown both diagrammatically and schematically in Fig. 3–6.

From Fig. 3–6(a) the paths P_{14} that do not include an element twice listed according to the points that they connect are 124, 1254, 1354, and 13524. The corresponding path products are $x' \cdot w'$, $x' \cdot y \cdot z$, $x \cdot y' \cdot z$, and $x \cdot y' \cdot y \cdot z$. The corresponding switching function F_{14} is

$$F_{14}(X, Y, Z, W) = x' \cdot w' + x' \cdot y \cdot z + x \cdot y' \cdot z.$$

From Fig. 3–6(b) it can be seen that this network is realized with two transfer contacts (X, Y) and two contact pairs (Z, W), requiring $3 + 3 + 2 + 2 = 10$ springs altogether. Note that the transfer contact of relay X is a MAKE BEFORE BREAK type. This was required so that the electrical path between points 1 and

[5] S. Seshu and M. B. Reed, *Linear Graphs and Electrical Networks* (Reading, Mass.: Addison-Wesley, 1961), Chap. 9, pp. 227–267. An excellent survey of the application of graph theory to the theory of switching functions.

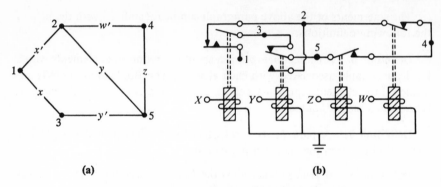

(a)   (b)

Figure 3–6.   Contact network of Example 1.

4 would not be broken momentarily when the input combination $x' \cdot y' \cdot z \cdot w'$ changed to $x \cdot y' \cdot z \cdot w'$ or vice versa. The transfer contact of relay Y need not be of the same type, since its contacts are not in paths where the electrical path between points 1 and 4 has to be maintained when relay Y changes state. This was introduced only to show one example of the practical problems that arise in the realization of contact networks. A detailed discussion of these problems is presented by Keister, Ritchie, and Washburn.[6]

Actually, in using Boolean algebra for the description of the behavior of contact networks, we tacitly assumed some idealizations of these devices. These idealizations are

(1)   Whenever a contact is closed, it has zero resistance and whenever a contact is open, it has infinite resistance.
(2)   A contact is always either open or closed.
(3)   All normally open contacts of a relay are open or closed simultaneously, and the same is true for all normally closed contacts.
(4)   When the normally open contacts of a relay are open its normally closed contacts are closed and conversely.

Many of these idealizations have to be overcome in the actual realization of a contact network. An example of this is the use of the MAKE BEFORE BREAK transfer contact of the above example. Another major problem is the minimization of contact networks. In contact networks the cost factor is defined to be the number of springs required in a realization and the distribution of the contacts between the different relays. This cost factor has nothing in common with the cost factor defined in Chapter 2.

[6] W. Keister, A. E. Ritchie, S. H. Washburn, *The Design of Switching Circuits* (Princeton, N.J., Van Nostrand, 1951), Chaps. 4, 5, and 6. Uses the hindrance-function notation; that is, the presence of a path is denoted 0 and the absence of a path is denoted 1.

3–3. ANALYSIS OF ASYNCHRONOUS SEQUENTIAL SWITCHING CIRCUITS

In this section the analysis procedure suggested by Huffman[7] is investigated. To obtain better understanding, a relay realization is assumed with transition memory devices. In this case the general block diagram can be redrawn as shown in Fig. 3–7.

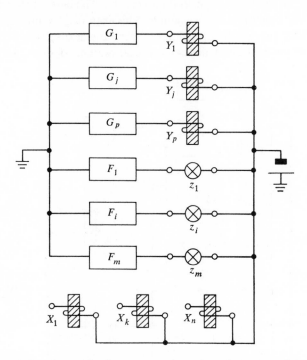

Figure 3–7.   Generalized representation of a relay sequential circuit with transition memories.

The variables and units of Fig. 3–7 are

$X_1, \ldots, X_k, \ldots, X_n$ are the n primary (input) relays,
$Y_1, \ldots, Y_j, \ldots, Y_p$ are the p secondary (memory) relays,
$z_1, \ldots, z_i, \ldots, z_m$ are the m output lamps.

The excitations of the memory relays are given by the Boolean functions

$$Y_j = G_j(x_1, x_2, \ldots, x_n, y_1, y_2, \ldots, y_p) \qquad j = 1, 2, \ldots, p.$$

[7] D. A. Huffman, *J. Franklin Inst.*, **257** (3), 161–190 (1954); **257** (4), 275–303 (1954).

The outputs, which in Fig. 3–7 are the lighting of the lamps z_i, are given by

$$z_i = F_i(x_1, x_2, \ldots, x_n, y_1, y_2, \ldots, y_p) \qquad i = 1, 2, \ldots, m.$$

These $m + p$ $(n + p)$-variable Boolean functions can be represented by a truth table of 2^{n+p} rows and $(m + p)$ columns. Such a truth table contains all the information about the given circuit. The purpose of this section is to provide procedures to decipher the information contained in such a truth table. This is done by rearranging and breaking up the information into a set of tables that bring out the pertinent information. The best way to show these tables and their analysis is by an example. This example, Example 2, shown in Fig. 3–8, is used repeatedly throughout this and the next section to clarify the basic ideas of the analysis. This is an artificial example designed to bring out

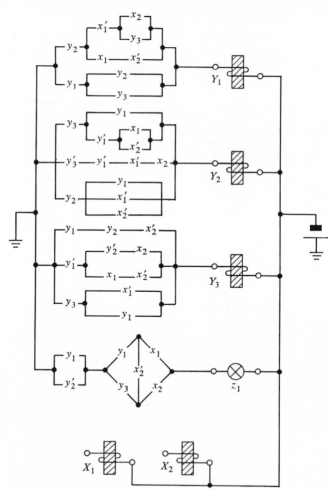

Figure 3–8. Circuit diagram of Example 2.

most of the problems and thus does not satisfy the design restrictions of later sections.

EXAMPLE 2.   The excitation functions describing the behavior of the three secondary relays and the output function of the circuit of Fig. 3–8 are as follows:

$$Y_1 = y_2 \cdot (x_1 \cdot x_2' + x_1' \cdot x_2 + y_3 \cdot x_1') + y_1 \cdot (y_2 + y_3),$$
$$Y_2 = y_3 \cdot (y_1 + y_1' \cdot x_1 + y_1' \cdot x_2') + y_1' \cdot y_3' \cdot x_1' \cdot x_2 + y_2 \cdot (y_1 + x_1' + x_2'),$$
$$Y_3 = y_1 \cdot y_2 \cdot x_2' + y_1' \cdot (y_2' \cdot x_2 + x_1 \cdot x_2') + y_3 \cdot (y_1 + x_1'),$$
$$z_1 = (y_1 + y_2') \cdot \{y_1 \cdot x_1 + y_3 \cdot (x_1 + x_2)\}.$$

Instead of the truth-table representation of this circuit, the information is represented in two matrices. One describes the internal behavior of the circuits used to represent the excitation functions and is referred to as a *Y matrix*. Another describes the output behavior of the circuit used to represent the output function; it is referred to as *Z matrix*. These matrices have 2^n columns, corresponding to the 2^n possible combinations of the n primary (input) variables, and 2^p rows, corresponding to the 2^p possible combinations of the p secondary (memory) variables.

Note that in Fig. 3–9 the arrangement of the rows and columns of the Y matrix are not ordered according to the binary numbers that represent the variables. Rather, the matrix is arranged in such a way that the transition between any two adjacent rows or columns is obtained by the change of one variable only. This organization of the matrix is a slight variation of the

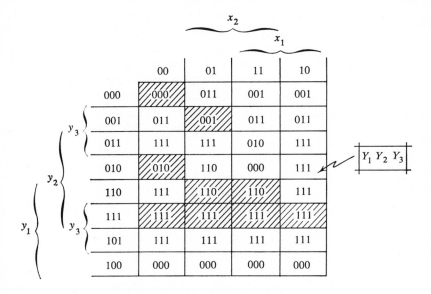

Figure 3–9.   The Y matrix of Example 2.

Karnaugh map, as can be seen from the assignment of variables. The Z matrix of this example is shown in Fig. 3–10.

$$x_1 \, x_2$$

	00	01	11	10
000	0	0	0	0
001	0	1	1	1
011	0	0	0	0
$y_1 \, y_2 \, y_3$ 010	0	0	0	0
110	0	0	1	1
111	0	1	1	1
101	0	1	1	1
100	0	0	1	1

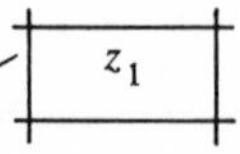

z_1

Figure 3–10. The Z matrix of Example 2.

In the remainder of this section we shall consider only the internal behavior of the circuit as defined by the Y matrix. First the meaning of a specific entry in the Y matrix has to be checked. Suppose the entries in a specific row $y_1 y_2 y_3$ are to be considered; then the present states of the memory relays are given by the values of $y_1 y_2 y_3$ of this row, as the value of y_i represents the state of the contacts of relay Y_i. Each of the entries of this row represents the next state of the memory relays under the influence of the specified input values $x_1 x_2$. That is, if in the specified entry the excitation function $Y_i = 1$, the ith memory relay will become (or remain) energized, and if $Y_i = 0$, the ith memory relay will become (or remain) de-energized. Thus whenever in a specific row there is an entry such that $y_1 y_2 y_3 = Y_1 Y_2 Y_3$, this square represents a *stable state*. These squares are referred to as stable states because the values of the excitation functions are such that no memory relay has to change state, and the over-all circuit will remain unchanged upon reaching these states until the input is changed. These states are shown as shaded squares in the excitation matrix of Fig. 3–9. The next question is how to classify the other squares of the excitation matrix. This can best be done by observing the internal behavior of the circuit, which we shall do next.

Let us assume that the circuit is in the stable state defined by the co-ordinates $00/000$ $(x_1 x_2/y_1 y_2 y_3)$ that has the values $Y_1 Y_2 Y_3 = 000$, and suppose the input is changed to 10. This leads to the square with the co-ordinates $10/000$, thus producing the excitations 001, which will lead, after some time delay Δt, to a change of memory outputs such that $y_1 y_2 y_3 = 001$.

Thus after Δt the circuit is at the square characterized by the coordinates 10/001, which, in turn, produces the excitation 011. After another Δt the square 10/011 with the entry 111 is reached, which, in turn, leads to the stable state defined by the coordinates 10/111. These changes can be summarized in a diagram as shown in Fig. 3–11.

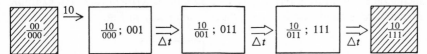

Figure 3–11.   Example of a transition path between two stable states.

Checking the above example, it can be seen that starting from a stable state another stable state is reached through three intermediate steps. In this example, at each intermediate step only one excitation function changes from the previous step. Such an intermediate square is generally referred to as an *unstable state*.

As another example, consider starting from the same stable state 00/000, and observing the transitions due to a change in input to 01. Because of the input change the square 01/000 with the entries 011 is reached. That is, the excitation of two secondary relays is changed and the timing of these changes becomes important. In this case there are three possibilities: If the secondary relay Y_3 changes state first, this leads to the stable state 01/001. On the other hand, if the secondary relay Y_2 changes state first, this leads to the unstable state 01/010, which, in turn, leads to the stable state 01/110. And if both secondary relays change state at exactly the same time, this leads to the unstable state 01/011, which, in turn, leads to the stable state 01/111. These transitions are shown diagrammatically in Fig. 3–12.

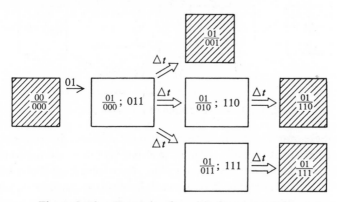

Figure 3–12.   Example of a critical race condition.

In this example there is an unstable state that requires changes in the states of more than one secondary relay; thus the transition from such a state depends on which relay changes first. Such a state is referred to as a *race state*.

As shown in Fig. 3–12, the stable state that is reached in this example depends on the secondary relay that changes first; thus such a race condition is referred to as a *critical* or *nonsafe race*.

In contrast to the above example, there can be race conditions whose outcome does not depend on which of the secondary relays changes state first. Such a race condition is referred to as a *safe* or *noncritical race*. An example of such a race condition is shown diagrammatically in Fig. 3–13.

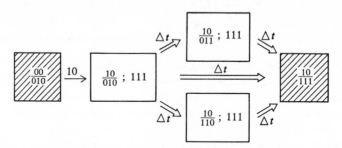

Figure 3–13.   Example of a safe race condition.

Another possible result of a transition from a stable state under the influence of an input change is exhibited by a *buzzer circle*. Here the circuit enters a sequence of unstable states which it cannot leave, as these unstable states provide transitions that lead into each other. An example of a buzzer circle is shown diagrammatically in Fig. 3–14.

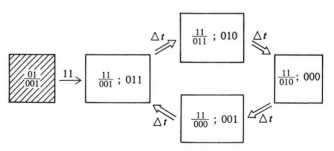

Figure 3–14.   Example of a buzzer circle.

From these examples it can be seen that the transitions due to the changes in the secondary relays are all contained in a single column, and the transitions due to an input change are along a row. Also, from these examples it becomes obvious that critical races are to be avoided, because the outcome of a specific change becomes uncertain and the system is not deterministic any more. Thus in the design of practical circuits only safe races are allowed, or the secondary relays are specially selected so that there is no doubt about which relay will change first. Actually in this chapter we shall mainly consider Huffman's design procedure, where all races are to be avoided. In these examples we only considered races caused by changes of the secondary relays, but the same race conditions can be present because of changes of primary relays. To avoid races of the primary relays, the basic assumption is made that only one input may be changed at any time. This is the reason for the special arrangement of the columns and the rows of the matrices used in the analysis. In the analysis, another assumption was implied—that the changes of input signals are placed far enough apart in time so that the circuit can reach equilibrium, that is, a stable state, before the next input change is applied.

As seen from the above discussion, there are three kinds of internal states in a sequential system. A quick classification of the internal states can be obtained with the *transition-index matrix* or τ *matrix*. The τ matrix is based on the *transition* or *instability index*, defined as follows:

Definition 10. The *transition*, or *instability index* τ_i is a variable associated with the transition memory device Y_i, which has the value 1 whenever the memory changes state. That is, $\tau_i = y_i \oplus Y_i$, where $\oplus$ stands for the exclusive or operation.

Thus when $\tau_i = 0$, the ith memory element will not change state, as its excitation has the value of its state; that is, $Y_i = y_i$. And when $\tau_i = 1$, the ith memory element will change state as $Y_i \neq y_i$. These transition indices are arranged in a table to form the τ matrix. This matrix has the same organization as the excitation matrix, having as its entries the transition indices of the particular states. The states can be characterized according to the number of 1's in the τ-matrix, as follows:

(1) If $\tau_1 \tau_2 \cdots \tau_p = 00 \cdots 0$, this entry represents a *stable state*. No memory element has to change state, as there are no 1's in the entry.

(2) If $\tau_1 \tau_2 \cdots \tau_i \cdots \tau_p = 00 \cdots 1 \cdots 0$, this entry represents an *unstable state*. The ith memory element has to change state, as there is only one number 1 at the ith place in this entry.

(3) If $\tau_1 \tau_2 \cdots \tau_i \cdot \tau_j \cdots \tau_p = 00 \cdots 1 \cdot 1 \cdots 0$, this entry represents a *race state*, as two or more memory elements have to change state, there being two or more 1's in this entry.

Figure 3–15 represents the τ matrix of Example 2, and it can be seen that classification of the internal states becomes obvious. Also, it is simple to identify which, if any, of the relays has to change its state. But the τ matrix is lacking some information. This can be seen from the following statements:

(1) The τ matrix only indicates race conditions, without specifying whether the race condition is safe or critical.

(2) The τ matrix does not show whether or not the sequential system contains a buzzer circle.

(3) The τ matrix shows only the instability condition of a specific internal state without indicating where it leads, that is, whether it leads to a stable state, a race state, or a buzzer circle.

$x_1 x_2$

	00	01	11	10
000	000 (Stable)	011 (Race)	001	001
001	010	000 (Stable)	010	010
011	100	100	001	100
010	000 (Stable)	100	010	101 (Race)
110	001	000 (Stable)	000 (Stable)	001
111	000 (Stable)	000 (Stable)	000 (Stable)	000 (Stable)
101	010	010	010	010
100	100	100	100	100

$y_1 y_2 y_3$ (row labels)

Legend:
- Stable (hatched ///)
- Unstable (plain box)
- Race (cross-hatched \\\)

Figure 3–15. The τ matrix of Example 2.

Note that the preceding information can be computed from the τ matrix, because $\tau_i = y_i \oplus Y_i$; thus $Y_i = y_i \oplus \tau_i$. That is, the Y matrix can be computed from the τ matrix, but the problem is to obtain this information in a form that is easy to recognize. To obtain this, the *flow table* is introduced. This table is organized in the same format as the excitation matrix. Each stable state is assigned a number and is encircled to show that it represents a stable state. Each unstable state is given the number of the stable state it leads to, or

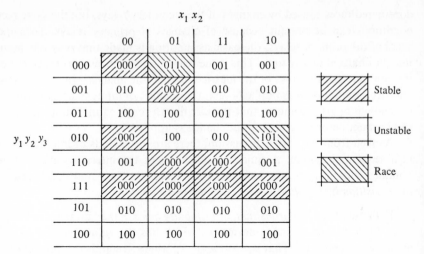

$x_1 x_2$

	00	01	11	10
000	①	4, 7, 2		9
001	6	②		9
011	6	7		9
010	③	4		9, 9, 9
110	6	④	⑤	9
111	⑥	⑦	⑧	⑨
101	6	7	8	9
100	1	4, 7, 2	B	9

$y_1 y_2 y_3$ (row labels)

Figure 3–16. Flow table of Example 2.

is denoted by B if it leads to a buzzer circle, or is assigned the numbers representing the race state into which it leads. And each race state is characterized by the numbers of stable states or buzzer circles to which it may lead. The existence of a buzzer circle is denoted by a closed circle, showing the transitions among the different states included in the specified buzzer. The flow table of Example 2 is shown in Fig. 3–16.

From Fig. 3–16 it can be seen that the internal changes are all contained in one column, because they do not involve changes in the input. Also, the changes from one column to another have to be initiated from a stable state if we assume that input changes occur only after the system reaches equilibrium. Thus, given a stable state as the initial state and given a specified input change, with the help of the flow table it is very simple to see the final state the system reaches under the influence of this input change. The flow table only indicates the initial and final states; it does not show the actual path of transitions between these two states. To show the complete path of transitions between two equilibrium states, the *transition diagram* is introduced. In this diagram the transitions between states are shown by arrows. The transition diagram of Example 2 is shown in Fig. 3–17.

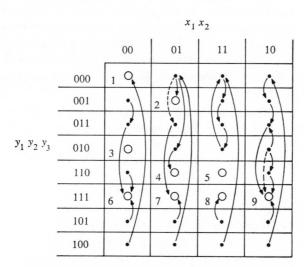

Figure 3–17.   Transition diagram of Example 2.

Note that in Fig. 3–17 there are dashed arrows leaving each race state. These arrows represent transitions that require more than one relay to change state. The transition diagram also shows the longest possible path that can exist between any two stable states, thus providing the required information about the timing of input changes.

In this section we have seen that the behavior of a sequential system is completely defined by the excitation and output matrices, with the excitation matrix containing all the information about the internal behavior of the system. And we have shown that the information included in the Y matrix can be represented in three tables: the τ matrix, the flow table, and the transition diagram, each containing partial information. These representations become especially important in the inverse procedure, that is, in the synthesis of asynchronous sequential circuits. In the synthesis procedure the flow table is obtained first, and from it a transition diagram is derived. From the transition diagram the Y matrix is computed, either directly or from the τ matrix, which is generally computed first for complex systems.

3–4. THE p-CUBE REPRESENTATION OF SEQUENTIAL SYSTEMS

The p-cube representation[8] is a graphical translation of the Y matrix. A p-dimensional cube is associated with the p memory elements, with each vertex of the p cube representing a row in the Y matrix. In contrast to the transition diagram, in the p-cube representation the transitions caused by input changes are emphasized. The best way to present the procedure involved in obtaining the p cube is by an example. Example 2 of Section 3–3 will be used. As this example (shown in Fig. 3–8) has three secondary relays, a three-dimensional cube is required for the representation. In the p-cube representation, shown in Fig. 3–18, the cube is spread flat for the sake of clarity.

We shall start from the first row of the excitation matrix, that is, from the row labeled $y_1 y_2 y_3 = 000$.

(1) Under the influence of the input combination $x_1 x_2 = 00$, the excitation remains $Y_1 Y_2 Y_3 = 000$. This is represented by a self-loop of vertex 000, marked 00.

(2) Under the influence of the input combination $x_1 x_2 = 01$, the excitation becomes $Y_1 Y_2 Y_3 = 011$. This is represented by a path along a diagonal of the p cube between vertices 000 and 011, marked 01, and oriented toward vertex 011.

(3) Under the influence of the input combination $x_1 x_2 = 11$, the excitation becomes $Y_1 Y_2 Y_3 = 001$. This is represented by a path along an edge of the p cube between vertices 000 and 001, marked 11, and oriented toward vertex 001.

(4) Under the influence of the input combination $x_1 x_2 = 10$, the excitation becomes $Y_1 Y_2 Y_3 = 001$. This is represented by a path along an edge of the p cube between vertices 000 and 001, marked 10, and oriented toward vertex 001.

[8] In the literature this representation is generally referred to as the *n-cube representation*. Here the name *p cube* is used, to distinguish it from the *n*-cube representation in combinational switching circuits. This representation was first introduced in an intuitive way by W. Keister, A. E. Ritchie, and S. H. Washburn in *The Design of Switching Circuits* (Princeton, N.J., Van Nostrand, 1951).

Executing these steps for each of the rows of the Y matrix, the *p*-cube representation of Example 2 is obtained as shown in Fig. 3–18.

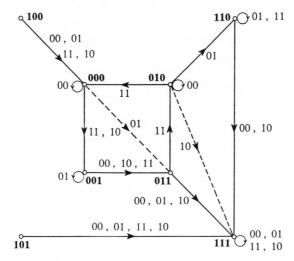

Figure 3–18.   The *p*-cube representation of Example 2.

From this it can be seen that each vertex of the p cube has the following two meanings: It represents the state of the memory, $y_1y_2y_3$, for the side of the arrow that leaves the vertex; and it represents the excitation of the memory, $Y_1Y_2Y_3$, for the side of the arrow that enters the vertex.

The next question is how to read the information included in the *p*-cube representation. This is done by observing the directions and the geometry of the arrows representing the transitions. In checking these arrows, it can be seen that they are of three types:

(1) An arrow, marked $\bar{x}^i$, that forms a self-loop around a vertex $\bar{y}^j$. As no excitation function changes, this represents a stable state, corresponding to the stable state at the coordinates $\bar{x}^i/\bar{y}^j$ of the Y matrix.

(2) An arrow, marked $\bar{x}^i$, from vertex $\bar{y}^j$ to vertex $\bar{y}^l$ connecting these two vertices along an edge of the p cube. Because the arrow is along an edge of the p cube, only one excitation function changes, representing an unstable state corresponding to the unstable state at the coordinates $\bar{x}^i/\bar{y}^j$ of the Y matrix.

(3) An arrow, marked $\bar{x}^i$, from vertex $\bar{y}^j$ to vertex $\bar{y}^k$ connecting these two vertices along a diagonal of the p cube. Because the arrow is along a diagonal of the p cube, at least two excitation functions have to change; this represents a race state corresponding to the race state at the coordinates $\bar{x}^i/\bar{y}^j$ of the Y matrix.

We see that the geometry of the arrows completely defines the classification of the internal states, and the directions of the arrows indicate the transitions between the internal states. For example, consider case 2. The arrow marked $\bar{x}^i$ connecting the two vertices $\bar{y}^j$ and $\bar{y}^l$ means that the unstable state $\bar{x}^i/\bar{y}^j$ leads to the state $\bar{x}^i/\bar{y}^l$. We still must check the race states to see whether the race conditions are safe or critical. This is done in exactly the same manner as in the Y matrix; that is, the different possible operating conditions are assumed and checked to see what equilibrium states are reached under these conditions. To see this, the pertinent part of the p cube is reproduced in Fig. 3–19.

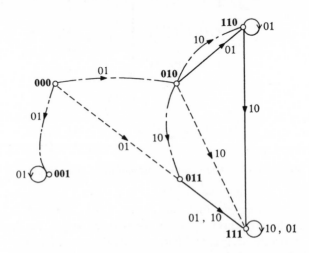

Figure 3–19.   Partial p-cube representation of Example 2.

First we check the arrow marked 10 between vertices 010 and 111. If both secondary relays change state exactly at the same time, the vertex 111 is reached, and, since this vertex has a self-loop marked 10, the stable state 10/111 is the equilibrium state for this path. On the other hand, if one of the secondary relays changes state first, either vertex 110 or vertex 011 is reached. As none of these two vertices has a self-loop marked 10, the excitation functions have to change again, and as both these vertices have arrows marked 10 leading to vertex 111 that has a self-loop marked 10, the stable state 10/111 is the equilibrium state for both these paths. Thus this diagonal represents a safe race condition between the vertices 010 to 111 under the influence of the input combination 10.

Considering now the second race condition shown in Fig. 3–19, that is, the arrow marked 01 between the vertices 000 and 011, we can see that there are three different stable states that can be reached. If both secondary relays change state at exactly the same time, vertex 011 is reached, which in turn leads to the stable state 01/111 at vertex 111. If the secondary relay Y_3 changes state first, the stable state 01/001 at vertex 001 is reached. If the secondary relay Y_2 changes state first, the vertex 010 is reached, which in turn leads to the stable state 01/110 at vertex 110. Thus this diagonal represents a critical race condition. From these two examples it can be seen that both safe and critical races are represented in the same manner. Thus in the p-cube representation all the diagonal transitions have to be investigated to see whether they represent safe or critical races. Actually, with Huffman's design criteria we are not concerned with the question of whether the races are safe or critical, because races are not allowed.

Another condition that remains to be investigated is the detection of a buzzer circle as represented in the p-cube representation. Since a buzzer circle is obtained when there is a set of states that lead into each other, in the p-cube representation the presence of a buzzer circle is represented by a closed loop of transitions, all in the same direction, obtained under the influence of the same input conditions. In Example 2 there is a buzzer circle under the influence of input combination 11, including the vertices 000, 001, 011, and 010 of the p cube.

From this presentation it can be seen that the p-cube representation is an exact graphical translation of the Y matrix. As a further step, the outputs of the sequential system can be associated with the transitions to include all the information in both the Y and Z matrices. At this point it should be pointed out that although some papers refer to the p-cube representation as a state diagram, this is not so, as a state diagram (as shown in Section 3–5) does not contain the information in such detailed form. In the synthesis procedure the state-diagram representation is usually the first step of design, and the p-cube representation is generally used much later in the procedure, being one of the final steps of the design.

3–5. STATE-DIAGRAM REPRESENTATION OF SEQUENTIAL SYSTEMS

Just as the p-cube representation is the graphical translation of the excitation matrix, the state diagram is the graphical translation of the flow table. In the state-diagram representation a stable state is denoted by a circle. The circles are connected by directed arrows representing transitions between two states under the influence of the specified input combination. The state diagram was first introduced by Kutti,[9] but in this presentation the more exact state-diagram representations of Mealy[10] and Moore[11] will be used. These

[9] A. K. Kutti, "On a Graphical Representation of the Operating Regime of Circuits," in *Sequential Machines: Selected Papers*, edited by E. F. Moore (Reading, Mass.: Addison-Wesley, 1964), pp. 228–235. This is a translation of the paper "O Graficheskoni Izobrazhenii Rabochego Rezhima Skhem," which appeared in *Tr. Leningr. Eksperim. Elektroteknicheskoĭ Lab.*, **8**, 11–18 (1928).

[10] G. H. Mealy, *Bell System Tech. J.*, **34**, 1045–1079 (1955).

[11] E. F. Moore, *Ann. Math.*, **34**, 129–153 (1956).

two state diagrams differ mainly in the representation of the outputs associated with the sequential system. We shall first introduce Mealy's state diagram, as it is more appropriate to use in the analysis procedure. Moore's state diagram is introduced next, as it is simpler to obtain from the verbal definition of the problem, and thus it is generally used as the first step in the synthesis procedure.

In Mealy's state diagram each circle can represent one or more stable states, depending on the number of self-loops associated with it. Also, with each directed arrow representing a transition, an output is associated. To see this, a simple example of Mealy's state diagram is shown in Fig. 3–20.

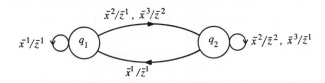

Figure 3–20.   Example of Mealy's state diagram.

To obtain the verbal description of the system represented by the state diagram of Fig. 3–20, we shall start by assuming that the system is in general internal state q_1, represented by the circle q_1. If the input combination $\bar{x}^1$ is now applied, the system remains in q_1 and the output combination $\bar{z}^1$ is obtained. If the input combination $\bar{x}^2$ or $\bar{x}^3$ is applied, the system changes state, entering the general internal state q_2, and the output combinations $\bar{z}^1$ and $\bar{z}^2$ are obtained. If we assume that the system is in the general internal state q_2, this is represented by the circle q_2. If the input combinations $\bar{x}^2$ and $\bar{x}^3$ are now applied, the system remains in state q_2 and the output combinations $\bar{z}^2$ and $\bar{z}^1$ are obtained. If the input combination $\bar{x}^1$ is applied, the system changes state, entering the general internal state q_1, and the output combination $\bar{z}^1$ is obtained.

Note that when referring to one of the circles, the term *general internal state* has been used. This is to show that one of these circles may represent more than one stable state. Henceforth, the general term *state* or *stable state* will be used both for such a multiple stable state and for a single stable state.

Generally it is quite cumbersome to manipulate such a graphical representation. To overcome this, a table called the *transition table* is constructed. There are the same number of rows as the number of stable states, and there are two sets of columns corresponding to the different input combinations, where the next state and next outputs are entered. The transition-table representation of the state diagram of Fig. 3–20 is shown in Fig. 3–21.

To return to the analysis procedure, the Mealy's state diagram of Example 2 will now be developed. For each row of the Y matrix a circle is assigned in

PRESENT STATE	NEXT STATE			NEXT OUTPUT		
	$\bar{x}^1$	$\bar{x}^2$	$\bar{x}^3$	$\bar{x}^1$	$\bar{x}^2$	$\bar{x}^3$
q_1	q_1	q_2	q_2	$\bar{z}^1$	$\bar{z}^1$	$\bar{z}^2$
q_2	q_1	q_2	q_2	$\bar{z}^1$	$\bar{z}^2$	$\bar{z}^1$

Figure 3–21. Transition table of the state diagram of Fig. 3–20.

which there is one (or more) stable state. Such a circle is assigned the number corresponding to the binary number represented by the values of $y_1 y_2 y_3$ of this row. In our example there are five circles, marked 0, I, II, VI, and VII. (Roman numerals are used to distinguish between these states and the stable states in the flow table.) Also, separate circles are included for each of the buzzer circles of the system. These circles are connected by arrows representing the transitions between the states. Each arrow is marked $\bar{x}^i/\bar{z}^j$, where $\bar{x}^i$ represents the input combination under whose influence this transition is being made and $\bar{z}^j$ represents the final output combination that is obtained when the system enters the specified state. To see this we start with the first row of the Y matrix of Example 2, which contains the stable state 00/000. As this is a stable state and the entry in the Z matrix corresponding to these coordinates is 0, there is a self-loop marked 00/0 associated with this circle. Under the influence of the input combination 10, the stable state 10/111 is reached. The output corresponding to these coordinates in the Z matrix is 1. Thus an arrow, 10/1, is drawn from circle 0 to circle VII. Under the influence of the input combination 01, there is a critical race condition leading to the stable states 01/001, 01/110, and 01/111. The outputs associated with these states are 1, 0, and 1, and there are three dashed arrows 01/1, 01/0, and 01/1 from circle 0 to circles I, VI, and VII. The input combination 11 is not investigated here, as this would require a change in two input variables, there being only one stable state in this row under the influence of the input combination 00. By executing the same steps for each of the rows containing one or more stable states, the state diagram of Fig. 3–22 is obtained.

Note that this state diagram does not contain all the information about the system analyzed. Only the transitions between stable states are shown, without specifying the unstable states that are passed. Also, only the final output combination is shown. For example, when the transition between stable states 00/000 and 10/111 is executed, the sequence of outputs obtained is 0, 0, 1, 0, 1. In checking Fig. 3–22 it can be seen that there are two double circles, circles 0 and II. These circles are referred to as *initial states*. This name is used because once the system has left any one of these states it cannot return to it, as all the arrows are leaving the circles. Note that circle VII has only arrows entering it, so once the system enters such a state it can never leave it. Such a state is generally referred to as a *final* or *terminal state*.

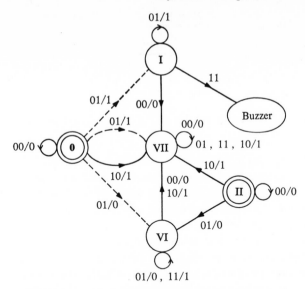

Figure 3–22. Mealy's state diagram for Example 2.

The transition table corresponding to Mealy's state-diagram representation of Example 2 is shown in Fig. 3–23.

PRESENT STATE	NEXT STATE				NEXT OUTPUT			
	00	01	11	10	00	01	11	10
0	0	I, VI, VII	——	VII	0	1, 0, 1	——	1
I	VII	I	B	——	0	1	——	——
II	II	VI	——	VII	0	0	——	1
VI	VII	VI	VI	VII	0	0	1	1
VII	VII	VII	VII	VII	0	1	1	1

Figure 3–23. Transition table of Example 2.

Note that the dashes that occur in the transition table correspond to the input combinations that cannot occur, under the assumption that only one input variable can change at any given time.

Now we define Moore's state diagram. In this representation each circle can represent one or more stable states that have the same output combinations associated with them. This requirement of having the same output is added because in this state diagram the outputs are associated with the internal states and not with the transitions. The directed arrows represent transitions between states under the influence of a specified input combination. To see this, a simple example of Moore's state diagram is shown in Fig. 3–24.

The verbal description of such a state diagram is done in exactly the same manner as for Mealy's state diagram. For example, suppose the system is in

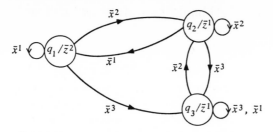

Figure 3–24. Example of Moore's state diagram.

state q_1; then it has an output combination $\bar{z}^2$. Under the influence of the input combination $\bar{x}^1$, the system remains in state q_1 with output $\bar{z}^2$. And under the influence of the input combinations $\bar{x}^2$ and $\bar{x}^3$, the system changes state, entering state q_2 with output $\bar{z}^1$ and state q_3 without output $\bar{z}^1$, respectively.

The transition table corresponding to Moore's state diagram has to be modified, owing to the change in the representation of the output. This is done by using only one column to represent the outputs instead of a set of columns, as the output depends only on the state of the system. The transition-table representation of the above state diagram is shown in Fig. 3–25.

PRESENT STATE	NEXT STATE			PRESENT OUTPUT
	$\bar{x}^1$	$\bar{x}^2$	$\bar{x}^3$	
q_1	q_1	q_2	q_3	$\bar{z}^2$
q_2	q_1	q_2	q_3	$\bar{z}^1$
q_3	q_3	q_2	q_3	$\bar{z}^1$

Figure 3–25. Transition table of the state diagram of Fig. 3–24.

Note that Moore's and Mealy's state diagrams become equivalent if all the transitions in Mealy's state diagram which enter a given state have the same output associated with them. In general, when a translation from Mealy's state diagram to Moore's state diagram is sought, it will require the splitting of some states. That is, given a sequential system represented in both state diagrams, Moore's state diagram will generally have more states. To see the exact difference between these two state diagrams, the functional description of the sequential systems is used. In Mealy's state diagram, the next state (excitation) depends on the present state (memory outputs) and the input combinations. The same is true for the outputs. Thus the functional description of the circuit is the same as described in Section 3–1; that is,

$$z_i = F_i(\bar{x}_n, \bar{y}_p) \qquad \text{for } i = 1, 2, \ldots, m,$$
$$Y_j = G_j(\bar{x}_n, \bar{y}_p) \qquad \text{for } j = 1, 2, \ldots, p.$$

In Moore's state diagram, the same holds true for the memory excitations, but the outputs depend only on the state of the system. That is, the functional description of this circuit is

$$z_i = \Phi_i(\bar{y}_k) \qquad \text{for } i = 1, 2, \ldots, m,$$
$$Y_j = \Gamma_j(\bar{x}_n, \bar{y}_k) \qquad \text{for } j = 1, 2, \ldots, k.$$

In the literature other forms of state diagrams are also defined. These state diagrams will require other changes in the functional descriptions of the sequential systems. Most of these state diagrams have much more limited scope because they were introduced to deal with particular types of sequential systems; for this reason they are not included in this presentation.

To return to the analysis procedure, when the Moore's-state-diagram representation of a system is to be obtained, there are two general ways to define the stable states. One is to define as many states for a given row of the Y matrix as there are stable states with different associated outputs. For example, if we consider Example 2, then for the row 111 of the Y matrix two states are to be associated, one representing the stable state 00/111 with the output 0 and the second representing the stable states 01/111, 11/111, and 10/111 with the output 1. The second possibility is to represent each stable state of the system separately. In our presentation, the second approach is used, as we are interested in Moore's state diagram primarily as a design step, and this format is easier to obtain from the verbal definition of a problem. For this assignment of states, Moore's state diagram becomes an exact translation of the flow table, and we shall now present this state diagram of Example 2 without further discussion (Fig. 3–26).

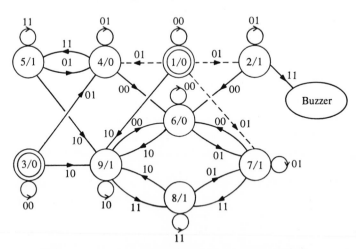

Figure 3–26.   Moore's state diagram of Example 2.

Note that in the state diagram of Fig. 3–26 there are two states marked by double circles. These states are initial states, just as in Mealy's state diagram. Note also that there is a final state in Mealy's state diagram but there is not such a state in Fig. 3–26. This is so because the four states 6/0, 7/1, 8/1, and 9/1 of Fig. 3–26 are represented by the single general state VII in Fig. 3–22. In Fig. 3–26 the same numbering of states is used as in the flow table, and only the transitions caused by allowable input combinations are shown. The transition table describing Moore's state diagram of Example 2 is shown in Fig. 3–27.

PRESENT STATE	NEXT STATE				PRESENT OUTPUT
	00	01	11	10	
1	1	2, 4, 7	--	9	0
2	6	2	B	--	1
3	3	4	--	9	0
4	6	4	5	--	0
5	--	4	5	9	1
6	6	7	--	9	0
7	6	7	8	--	1
8	--	7	8	9	1
9	6	--	8	9	1

Figure 3–27.   Transition-table representation of Example 2.

A transition table such as the one shown in Fig. 3–27, where there is only one stable state in each row, is generally referred to as a *primitive transition table*. And to make it similar to Huffman's flow table, the entry in the next-state column that has the same number as its row, is encircled to indicate that this is the stable state of the row.

3–6. INTRODUCTION TO ASYNCHRONOUS SEQUENTIAL CIRCUIT SYNTHESIS

In this section we investigate some of the basic problems that arise in the synthesis procedure. To do this, a simple asynchronous sequential circuit is designed using the tools developed in the previous sections. The problem to be designed is defined as follows.

EXAMPLE 3.   The circuit to be designed has two inputs and a single output. The two inputs (x_1, x_2) are push-button switches that make contact when activated, and they can be activated only one at a time. With these switches the decimal numbers 1 and 2 are associated. The output (L) is a lamp that shows if the accumulated number obtained by pressing the push-button switches is even or odd. Suppose the lamp to be an even indicator.

It is obvious that this is a sequential circuit, as there can be two different outputs for the same input combinations. For example, suppose the accumulated number is odd, with the lamp off. Now if the push-button switch x_1 is depressed, the accumulated number becomes even and the lamp is switched on. If the same switch x_1 is depressed again, the accumulated number becomes odd and the lamp is switched off. The first step of synthesis is to translate the verbal specifications of the problem into a state diagram. In most cases it is simpler to start from Moore's state diagram, where the outputs are associated with the present memory states. Also, it is generally simpler to start with a state diagram that has one stable state associated with each circle, so that all the arrows entering a circle have the same input combinations associated with them. Thus in considering the above example there are three allowable input combinations, 00, 01, and 10, and as the output can be changed by each of these inputs, the state diagram must include six circles. These circles are numbered as shown in Fig. 3–28. To obtain the transitions among these circles, the behavior of the system has to be investigated.

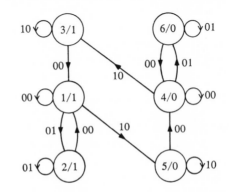

PRESENT	NEXT STATE				PRESENT
STATE	00	01	11	10	OUTPUT
1	①	2	--	5	1
2	1	②	--	--	1
3	1	--	--	③	1
4	④	6	--	3	0
5	4	--	--	⑤	0
6	4	⑥	--	--	0

Figure 3–28. State diagram and primitive transition table of Example 3.

Suppose the system is in state 1, that is, in the circle marked 1/1. This means that the accumulated number is even, because the output is 1 and the previous input combination to the system was 00, as this circle has a self-loop 00. Now if the input combination 01 is applied, the accumulated number remains even and the system enters state 2, represented by circle 2/1. After the system enters this state the next input combination is predetermined; it must be 00, since both push buttons cannot be activated at the same time. And under the influence of the input combination 00 there is a transition from state 2 to state 1. On the other hand, if the system is in state 1 and the input combination 10 is applied, the accumulated number becomes odd and the system enters state 5, represented by circle 5/0. Again the next input combination must be 00, producing the transition between states 5 and 4. The remainder of the transitions are obtained in exactly the same manner, starting from the assumption that the system is in state 4. The resulting state diagram and its transition table are shown in Fig. 3–28.

In checking the primitive transition table of Fig. 3–28 it can be seen that it has six rows. And since bivalued memory devices are used, three secondary relays are required to distinguish between the six rows as $2^2 < 6 < 2^3$. But looking at the transition table we see that adding the uncircled entry 5 in row 2 and column 10 changes nothing, because the input 10 cannot occur when the system is in state 2. This enables us to combine rows 1 and 2 into one row. In a similar manner, by adding the uncircled entry 3 in row 6 and column 10, rows 4 and 6 can be combined into one row. By this procedure, referred to as *row merging*, the number of rows of the transition table is reduced to four. And as $2^2 = 4$, we may be able to implement this circuit using only two secondary relays. The resulting reduced transition table and state diagram are shown in Fig. 3–29.

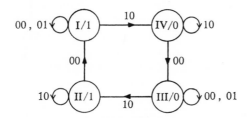

PRESENT STATE	NEXT STATE				PRESENT OUTPUT
	00	01	11	10	
I(1, 2)	①	②	--	5	1
II(3)	1	--	--	③	1
III(4, 6)	④	⑥	--	3	0
IV(5)	4	--	--	⑤	0

Figure 3–29. Reduced state diagram and transition table of Example 3.

Before considering the next step in the synthesis procedure, it should be noted that the rows of the primitive transition table can also be combined in a different manner. For example, rows 2 and 3 can be combined and then rows 5 and 6. The resulting transition table also has only four rows, but all its next-state entries outside column 11 are filled. The transition table shown has two undefined entries in column 01. These are don't-care conditions when the excitation functions are defined, and can be used to simplify the resulting

Boolean functions. Thus, whenever possible, the combinations of rows are made in such a way as to leave as many undefined entries as possible.

To return to the synthesis procedure, the next step is to assign present memory-state values ($y_1 y_2$) to these rows. This assignment has to be made in such a way that whenever there are to be transitions between rows, these rows are adjacent. As seen from the state diagram in this case, this is already achieved if physically adjacent rows are assigned adjacent values of $y_1 y_2$. The next question is where to assign the value $y_1 y_2 = 00$. This is generally assigned to a row that has a stable state under the influence of the input combination 00, so that no memory unit must change state when the system is switched on. Thus in the present example we can assign the value 00 to either row I or row III. There is an implied assumption in the way this assignment is made. That is, if row I is assigned the value 00, it implies that 0 is assumed to be an even number, as the accumulated number is 0 when the system is switched on. In the same manner, if row III is assigned the value 00, it is assumed that 0 is an odd number. We shall assume that 0 is even and use the following assignment of rows: I = 00, II = 01, III = 11, and IV = 10.

To obtain the Y matrix the circled entries of the transition table are assigned the same values as the value of the rows, because these represent stable states. The uncircled entries are assigned the values of the rows where the same entries appear circled, because these represent unstable states that lead into those rows. Also, in this example there is no need to derive a Z matrix, as the outputs depend only on the internal states; that is, the outputs are only functions of the memory states. Thus the excitation matrix and output vector of this example are as shown in Fig. 3–30. From these tables the

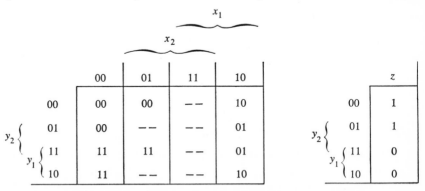

Figure 3–30.   The Y matrix and Z vector of Example 3.

Boolean functions representing the excitations of the two secondary relays and the output lamp are calculated. These functions are

$$Y_1 = x_1' \cdot y_1 + x_1 \cdot y_2',$$
$$Y_2 = x_1 \cdot y_2 + x_1' \cdot y_1,$$
$$z = y_1'.$$

The corresponding circuit diagram is shown in Fig. 3–31, where it can be

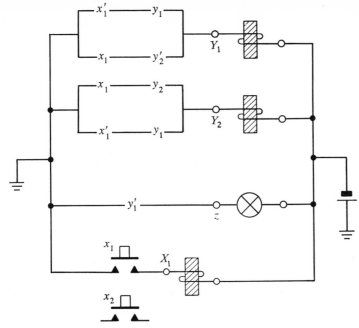

Figure 3–31.   Circuit diagram of Example 2.

seen that the push-button switch x_2 need not be connected. This result was expected, as x_2 is associated with the decimal number 2; thus whenever it is activated it will not change the output.

Even from this simple example we can see some of the problems involved in the synthesis procedure. The major problem is to obtain the first step, that is, the translation of the verbal specification of the problem into a state diagram. The second thing that can be seen from this example is the way in which the complex synthesis procedure is carried out in a number of simpler steps. In this simple example we used four basic steps: obtaining the state-diagram representation of the problem, reducing the number of states, calculating the excitation matrix and the output matrix, and deriving the circuit diagrams from these matrices. In Section 3–7 we shall consider in more detail the general problems involved in these steps.

3–7. SCHEMATIC OUTLINE OF THE SYNTHESIS PROCEDURE

This section is introduced to provide an over-all picture of the design procedure. As stated earlier, Huffman's synthesis procedure is developed in this chapter. As a first step we list the basic assumptions of Huffman's procedure that were introduced in the analysis procedure presented before. These assumptions are

(1) Only one binary input variable may be changed at a time.
(2) Sufficient time must be allowed between input changes for the sequential system to reach a stable state.
(3) No races are allowed; this means that only one memory unit can be unstable at any given time. Such a sequential system is generally referred to as a *totally sequential system.*
(4) No buzzer circles are allowed.

Note that the first assumption is a restriction on the input variables of the system and has to be considered in the first step of synthesis when the translation from the verbal specification to the state-diagram representation of a problem is obtained. The second assumption is a restriction on the timing of the input signals and affects the synthesis procedure only indirectly, by restricting the number of unstable states that can be introduced in a transition chain between two stable states. The last two assumptions are restrictions on the excitations of the memory units and have to be considered in the assignment of memory states. Both these assumptions apply only for the defined entries of the Y matrix; that is, the don't-care entries can be filled in such a way as to simplify the Boolean function, because the system will not reach these states under the prescribed input combinations.

The actual synthesis procedure is essentially a reversal of the analysis procedure outlined before. The over-all synthesis procedures starting from the verbal specification to the final circuit diagram can be divided into the following four steps:

(1) Obtain a state-diagram representation of the problem.
(2) Reduce the number of states of the state diagram obtained in step (1).
(3) Obtain an assignment of the memory states of the reduced state diagram.
(4) Derive the excitation and output matrices and design the corresponding combinational circuit.

Each of these steps will be considered in detail in the next few sections, but it seems appropriate to make a few preliminary remarks now. To do this, we shall consider briefly each step.

Step (1). In the translation of the verbal specifications into a state diagram, Moore's state diagram with a single stable state per circle is generally used. In this translation it is not necessary to recognize all the equivalent states, as their reduction is attempted at a later stage, but recognizing some of them can reduce the over-all complexity. The main difficulty encountered in this step is that the translation is a trial-and-error procedure that requires some experience to obtain. The result of this step is a Moore's state diagram and the corresponding primitive transition table.

Step (2). The purpose of this step is to reduce the number of rows of the primitive transition table to obtain a reduced transition table. This reduction is done in two parts. In the first part the states of the primitive transition table are checked for equivalences. Note that after eliminating the equivalences the resulting transition table is still a primitive transition table. In the second part of the reduction procedure, the rows of the primitive transition table are combined, whenever there is no contradiction, to obtain a new transition table with fewer rows. This procedure is referred to as *merging* and the resulting transition table is called a *reduced* or *condensed transition table*. The rows of the condensed flow table can have more than one stable state. Generally the condensed transition table cannot be represented by a Moore's state diagram, as rows with different outputs can be merged, and a Mealy's state diagram is required to represent the condensed transition table.

Step (3). In this step the rows of the condensed transition table are assigned binary numbers representing the present states of the memory units. This is done by first embedding Mealy's state diagram of step (2) in a p cube in such a way that all the transitions are along the edges of the p cube, to avoid race conditions. By associating a memory output variable with each unit vector of the p cube, the memory assignment corresponding to the vertices of the p cube is obtained. This embedding ensures the required adjacencies, but it does not define uniquely the assignment of the states of the memory units. Generally the assignment of the origin $(00\cdots 0)$ to a specific row of the transition table is implied by the verbal specification of the problem. In this presentation the unit vectors of the p cube are associated with the memory units at random. Actually this freedom of associating a memory unit with a unit vector of the p cube can be used to simplify the resulting Boolean function, as will be indicated briefly at the end of Chapter 4. The result of this step is a transition table having associated with each of its rows a p bit binary number, and a Mealy's state diagram embedded in a p cube, showing all the transitions among the states.

Step (4). In this step the transitions between the different rows of the condensed transition tables are shown by arrows and then the rows of the tables rearranged to correspond to the organization of the matrices used in the analysis. The result of this is a transition diagram. From the transition diagram the Y matrix is obtained, either directly or by first obtaining the τ matrix. Note that the second set of columns of the transition table of step (3) corresponds to a partially filled Z matrix. These columns of the transition tables are only partially filled because only those entries are defined that correspond to a stable state. To obtain the Z matrix the entries corresponding to unstable states have to be defined. Generally these entries are assigned the output values of the stable states to which the corresponding unstable state leads. This definition of outputs is used so that the system will not have transient false outputs when there is a transition between two stable states. The Boolean functions are derived from the excitation and output matrices so obtained. The last step of synthesis is to obtain the combinational circuits corresponding to these functions. When set and reset memory devices are to be used, the excitation functions must be modified slightly. These memory devices and gate realizations of the combinational circuits will be discussed later.

Note that in this synthesis procedure the main emphasis was placed on reduction of the rows of the transition table. That is, the only reduction that was considered was the reduction in the number of required memory devices, but this reduction generally will result in more complex Boolean functions for the excitations and outputs. Thus this reduction is not necessarily a reduction of the over-all cost of the system. The only simplification of the Boolean functions that is considered here consists of filling in the don't-care conditions in the excitation and output matrices.

In the next four sections each of these steps will be considered in detail. To further illustrate these steps, two examples are solved. Also, whenever required, additional examples are included to bring out specific points. The two basic examples solved in continuation are as follows.

EXAMPLE 4. Simplified manual switchboard. It is required to design the control circuit between two telephone receivers (A, B). The word statement of this problem is as follows: Lifting one of the receivers closes its switch and turns its lamp on at the operator's board. The lamp remains lighted until either the second receiver is lifted or the first receiver is closed first. After both receivers are lifted, if either one of them is replaced, the lamp associated with the other receiver lights up. If both of the receivers are replaced, both lamps light up and remain so until the operator turns them off with the operator switch (O). The lamps associated with the receivers are denoted L_A and L_B.

EXAMPLE 5. Reversible counter modulo-four. The device to be designed has two lamps, L_1 and L_2, which in binary notation can represent the decimal numbers 0, 1, 2, and 3. The box also contains two pushbutton switches, one marked ADVANCE (x_1) and the other marked REVERSE (x_2). The operation of the system is defined as follows. When the advance push button is depressed, $x_1x_2 = 10$, the output indicator advances by one; that is, $0 \to 1 \to 2 \to 3 \to 0$. When the reverse push button is depressed, $x_1x_2 = 01$, the output indicator is decreased by one; that is, $0 \to 3 \to 2 \to 1 \to 0$. Only one of the push-button switches can be activated at a given time; thus between any two activations of the inputs, the input combination becomes $x_1x_2 = 00$ and the output remains the same, as determined by the previous input combination.

3–8. SYNTHESIS PROCEDURE, STEP 1 (STATE DIAGRAM)

In this part of the procedure a Moore's state diagram is to be obtained with a single stable state per circle. As this is a trial-and-error procedure, we shall start at once with our examples.

EXAMPLE 4 (*continued, I*). As a first step the inputs and the outputs are ordered so they can be referred to as the corresponding *n* tuple and *m* tuple. The orderings used in this example are *A, B, O,* and L_A, L_B. To start the state-diagram representation of the system, it is assumed that all the inputs and outputs are 0; that is, the system is in a state that has an output combination 00 and has a self-loop marked 000. Let us denote this state by a circle 1/00. Starting from this state the behavior of the system is analyzed, assuming the different allowable input combinations. From this state we can reach the state 4/00, when both receivers are lifted, by the states 2/10 or 3/01, depending upon where the operation was initiated. Note that according to the definition of the problem, a receiver can be returned before the other receiver is lifted. This is represented by a transition 000 from either one of the states 2/10 or 3/01 to the state 1/00. From state 4/00, the state representing both receivers being returned 7/11 can be reached by the way of states 5/01 or 6/10, depending upon which receiver is returned first.

When the system is in one of the states 5/01 or 6/10, that is, one of the receivers is returned while the other receiver is still lifted, there can be two interpretations of the verbal specifications. One interpretation is that if the returned receiver is lifted again, the system should return to state 4/00. The other interpretation is that if one of the receivers was returned, the other receiver must be returned before any other changes can be made. This second interpretation is assumed here, and thus from states 5/01 and 6/10 there can be transition only to state 7/11 under the influence of the input combination 000. Once state 7/11 is reached, the operator switches off both lamps by the operator's switch, and state 8/00 is reached. When the operator's switch is switched off, the system returns to the original state 1/00. This state-diagram

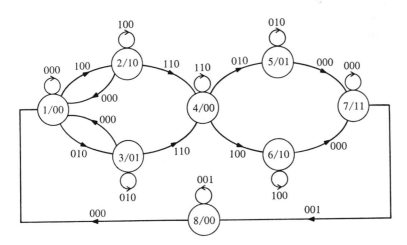

Figure 3–32. Moore's-state-diagram representation of simplified manual switchboard.

representation of the problem is shown in Fig. 3–32. The corresponding
primitive transition table is given in Fig. 3–33.

PRESENT STATE	NEXT STATE								OUTPUTS	
	000	001	011	010	110	111	101	100	L_A	L_B
1	①	--	--	3	--	--	--	2	0	0
2	1	--	--	--	4	--	--	②	1	0
3	1	--	--	③	4	--	--	--	0	1
4	--	--	--	5	④	--	--	6	0	0
5	7	--	--	⑤	--	--	--	--	0	1
6	7	--	--	--	--	--	--	⑥	1	0
7	⑦	8	--	--	--	--	--	--	1	1
8	1	⑧	--	--	--	--	--	--	0	0

Figure 3–33. Primitive transition table for simplified manual switchboard.

Note that in the primitive transition table of Fig. 3–33 there are three
columns, 011, 111, and 101, in the next-state section without any entries.
These columns represent the input combinations which cannot occur.

EXAMPLE 5 (*continued, I*).   To start constructing Moore's state diagram,
we assume the ordering of the input push buttons, ADVANCE and REVERSE
(x_1, x_2), and the two output lights (L_1, L_2). We begin analyzing the system
behavior assuming that all inputs and outputs are 0; that is, the system is in
circle 1/00 having self-loop 00. Now if the ADVANCE push button is depressed,
$x_1x_2 = 10$, the system reaches the state represented by circle 2/01 with self-
loop 10. The next input combination is now prescribed as $x_1x_2 = 00$, this
being represented by a transition into circle 3/01 with self-loop 00. Repeated
activation and deactivation of the ADVANCE push button will take the system
through states 4/10, 5/10, 6/11, and 7/11. When the ADVANCE push button is
depressed again, the system reaches state 8/00, and the release of this push
button, $x_1x_2 = 00$, provides transition into the starting state 1/00.

To check the behavior of the system when the REVERSE push button is
depressed, we start with the system in state 1/00. The input combination
$x_1x_2 = 01$ takes the system to state 9/11, the next input combination, $x_1x_2 = 00$, must take the system to a circle that has output 11 and self-loop 00. Such a
circle is the state 7/11. In the same manner, there must be three additional
states for the transitions under the influence of the input combination
$x_1x_2 = 01$ among the states that are reached by the input combinations
$x_1x_2 = 00$. These states are 10/10, 11/01, and 12/00. The corresponding state
diagram and primitive-transition-table representation of this problem are
shown in Figs. 3–34 and 3–35.

Note that in the Moore's-state-diagram representation of asynchronous
sequential systems, whenever there is an arrow marked $\bar{x}^i$ that leads to a
circle, there is a self-loop marked by the same input combination $\bar{x}^i$. This was

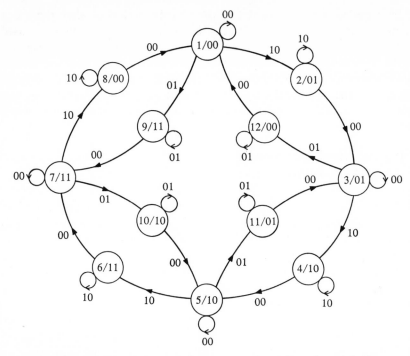

Figure 3–34. Moore's-state-diagram representation of modulo-four counter.

PRESENT STATE	NEXT STATE				OUTPUTS	
	00	01	11	10	L_1	L_2
1	①	9	--	2	0	0
2	3	--	--	②	0	1
3	③	12	--	4	0	1
4	5	--	--	④	1	0
5	⑤	11	--	6	1	0
6	7	--	--	⑥	1	1
7	⑦	10	--	8	1	1
8	1	--	--	⑧	0	0
9	7	⑨	--	--	1	1
10	5	⑩	--	--	1	0
11	3	⑪	--	--	0	1
12	1	⑫	--	--	0	0

Figure 3–35. Primitive-transition-table representation of modulo-four counter.

to be expected, because the system can change state only when there is a change in the input variables. Thus, when a Moore's state diagram is used to represent an asynchronous sequential system, the self-loops corresponding to arrows that enter a circle need not be shown because they are implied by these arrows, and only those self-loops need be shown explicitly that do not correspond to transitions to that specific general state. The latter can occur when a circle of the state diagram includes more than a single stable state.

3–9. SYNTHESIS PROCEDURE, STEP 2
(STATE MINIMIZATION)

In this section we consider some of the methods for reducing the number of rows of the primitive transition table. That is, we seek an equivalent transition table that has fewer rows than the original primitive transition table. Equivalent is meant in the sense that the reduced transition table should describe the behavior of the system in exactly the same manner as the original transition table. This reduction is performed to reduce the number of memory devices required in the synthesis.

Checking the primitive transition tables of the synthesis examples we see that Example 4 has a primitive transition table with eight rows; that is, the realization of this example requires at least three memory units. The primitive transition table of Example 5 has twelve rows; that is, the realization of this example requires at least four memory units. In general, given a transition table with l rows, where $2^{p-1} < l \le 2^p$, it requires p secondary variables to encode the rows of this table. But, this in itself will not ensure that all the transitions are along an edge in the p-cube representation, and in some cases the number of secondary variables must be increased to obtain all the transitions along an edge to avoid race conditions. Thus the realization of such an l-row transition table requires at least p memory units.

Before considering the concepts of transition-table reduction, let us see what is involved. In Section 3–1 the Boolean functions associated with a sequential system were defined as

$$z_i = F_i(\bar{x}_n, \bar{y}_p) \qquad \text{for } i = 1, 2, \ldots, m,$$
$$Y_j = G_j(\bar{x}_n, \bar{y}_p) \qquad \text{for } j = 1, 2, \ldots, p.$$

Associating with each of these Boolean functions a cost factor c_{zi} and c_{Yj}, the over-all cost factor C of a sequential circuit can now be defined as

$$C = \sum_{i=1}^{m} c_{zi} + \sum_{j=1}^{p} c_{Yj} + Kp,$$

where K is the cost factor of a memory unit. Thus by reducing the number of memory units the number of variables in each Boolean function is reduced; in addition, the number of excitation functions and the total memory cost is reduced. On the other hand, this reduction will generally increase the complexity of the remainder functions, and thus it may increase the cost factor of each function. In most cases reducing the number of memory units reduces the over-all cost factor C of a sequential circuit. However, depending on the value associated with K, there can be a point where further reduction of the number of memory units results in an increase in the over-all cost factor C. In our presentation we shall assume that the value of K is large enough that the latter condition does not occur. Note that the row reduction of a transition table should be to an integral power of two (2^p); otherwise the complexity of the Boolean functions may be increased without reducing the number of required memory units.

This row reduction is performed in two parts. In the first part the rows of the primitive transition table are checked for equivalence. In the second part the rows of a reduced primitive transition table are combined to obtain rows with multiple stable states. Each of these procedures will be considered in detail.

To check for equivalent states or what is sometimes referred to as *indistinguishability*, the following definition is used.

Definition 11. *Equivalent states.* A state q_i of a sequential circuit M is said to be *equivalent* to state q_j of M if and only if every input sequence applied to M when it has q_i as the initial state (starting state) produces the same output sequence as it would when it has q_j as the initial state.

The above definition means that there is no way for an outside observer to distinguish between two such states. The equivalence relationship between states can be of two forms, as shown by the following two definitions.

Definition 12. *Simple equivalence.* States $q_i, q_j, \ldots, q_l$ of the sequential circuit M are said to be *simply equivalent* if and only if the corresponding rows $i, j, \ldots, l$ of the primitive transition table differ only in one column, the column of the circled entries.

Thus the simple equivalence relationship requires that there be a set of rows of the primitive transition table that are identical in the uncircled and undefined entries and the outputs.

Definition 13. *Multiple equivalence.* States S_i of the sequential circuit M are said to be *multiply equivalent* if there is a chain of sets of states $S_1, S_2, \ldots, S_t$ such that the equivalence of states belonging to set S_i implies the equivalence of states in S_{i-1} for $2 \leq i < t$ and the equivalence of states in S_1 implies equivalence of states in S_t.

Thus, in the case of multiple equivalent states, the next-state entries, whenever defined, of the rows in a given set need not be the same. The requirement for a set of states to be multiply equivalent is that the uncircled entries in the different columns belong to another set of multiply equivalent states.

Both these types of equivalences occur if in deriving the state diagram of a problem we do not recognize that we have returned to a previous state. To see this we shall now consider an example, as shown by the primitive transition table of Fig. 3–36.

EXAMPLE 6.   Check for equivalences the primitive transition table of Fig. 3–36.

PRESENT STATE	NEXT STATE 00	01	11	10	PRESENT OUTPUT
1	①	5	--	9	0
2	3	②	6	--	0
3	③	2	--	9	0
4	④	10	--	--	0
5	1	⑤	6	--	0
6	--	10	⑥	8	1
7	--	10	⑦	8	1
8	4	--	7	⑧	1
9	1	--	6	⑨	0
10	3	⑩	7	--	0

Figure 3–36.   Primitive transition table of Example 6.

To check for equivalences the rows of the primitive transition table are compared pairwise. For any pair of rows to represent two equivalent states a requirement is that their outputs be the same and that both have circled entries in the same column. Such rows are called *probably equivalent rows*, and in our example they are (1, 3), (1, 4), (2, 5), (2, 10), (3, 4), (5, 10), and (6, 7). Each of these pairs must be checked to see if they are equivalent. For example, for states 1 and 3 to be equivalent it is required that the uncircled entries be equivalent, that is, that pair (2, 5) be an equivalent pair. These latter rows are called *implied pairs*. To obtain a complete check of equivalences, the probably equivalent pairs of rows are listed in a table, as shown in Fig. 3–37. With each of these pairs the implied pair of rows is also listed. If they do not imply any

PROBABLY EQUIVALENT	IMPLIED PAIRS
1, 3	(2, 5)
1, 4	X
2, 5	(1, 3)
2, 10	(6, 7)
3, 4	X
5, 10	(1, 3), (6, 7)
6, 7	✓

Figure 3–37.   Equivalence table of Example 6.

other pair, then a check mark is placed against these pairs, as they represent a pair of simply equivalent states, and if there is a contradiction, that is, there is an undefined entry in one row where there is an uncircled entry in the other row, an X is placed against these pairs of probably equivalent rows. Such a completed table is shown in Fig. 3–37.

To complete the check for equivalences, the rows of the equivalence table marked with an X and the rows that contain an implied pair that does not appear somewhere in the left column are eliminated. Thus in Fig. 3–37 the rows (1, 4) and (3, 4) of the equivalence table are crossed out. As the elimination of a row eliminates a probable pair, that is, an implied pair, the equivalence table must be reinspected until no more rows are eliminated. In the above example, because there are no more rows to be eliminated, the remainder of the rows represent equivalent pairs of states. These equivalent pairs are (1, 3), (2, 5), (2, 10), (5, 10), and (6, 7). Note that three pairs of equivalent states include the states 2, 5, and 10, and each one of these states is equivalent to the other two states; thus they form a set of three equivalent states. Now the primitive transition table of Fig. 3–36 can be remapped into a six-row primitive transition table. By mapping the states $(1, 3) \rightarrow 1$, $(2, 5, 10) \rightarrow 2$, $(4) \rightarrow 3$, $(6, 7) \rightarrow 4$, $(8) \rightarrow 5$, and $(9) \rightarrow 6$, the primitive transition table of Fig. 3–38 is obtained.

PRESENT STATE	NEXT STATE				PRESENT OUTPUT
	00	01	11	10	
1	①	2	--	6	0
2	1	②	4	--	0
3	③	2	--	--	0
4	--	2	④	5	1
5	3	--	4	⑤	1
6	1	--	4	⑥	0

Figure 3–38. Reduced primitive transition table of Example 6.

Note that the reduction of the transition table by recognizing the above equivalence relationships produces a primitive transition table, a transition table having one stable state for each row. In addition, the resulting state diagram is still a Moore's state diagram, because the outputs are associated with the present states. Actually, all these equivalences could be avoided by noting them in the derivation of the state-diagram representation. In practice it is simpler to recognize only the most obvious equivalences in the derivation of the state diagram and to check the transition table for equivalences.

The second part of the procedure for reducing a transition table is called *row merging*, assigning more than one stable state to each row. This assignment is accomplished by combining the entries of two or more rows of a primitive transition table into one row. In row merging, just as in detecting equivalent states, the only requirement is that no change of the system be detectable by an outside observer. In other words, the system obtained by row merging should be indistinguishable from the original system. Thus the following statement can be made about two rows that can be merged: *Any two rows of the transition table that have no conflicting next-state entries can be merged into one row.* To obtain a procedure for row merging, the above statement can be broken up into the following two rules:

Rule 1.   Two rows of the transition table may be merged if the next-state numbers appearing in corresponding columns of each row are alike or if one of the rows contains an unspecified entry.
Rule 2.   When circled and uncircled entries of the same state are to be combined, the resulting entry is circled.

In checking these two rules it can be seen that they satisfy the above statement, because they only allow the merging of rows that have no contradiction. Note that in row merging nothing was said about the outputs associated with a given row, because at this point Moore's state diagram generally becomes inadequate for representing the system. This happens when two rows with different outputs are merged, and in this case the outputs will be associated with the transitions; that is, a Mealy's state diagram is required to represent the system. Thus to represent the outputs, the transition table must now have 2^n columns, corresponding to all the possible combinations of the n input variables, and its entries are the outputs associated with the stable states. The best way to see the problems involved in row merging is by considering an example. We shall continue the reduction of the transition table of Example 6.

EXAMPLE 6 (*continued, I*).   By row merging, reduce the number of rows of the reduced primitive transition table as shown in Fig. 3–38.

In checking this table note that we can merge the pairs of rows (1, 2), (1, 6), (2, 4), (2, 6), (3, 4), (3, 5), and (4, 5). As a first step we choose arbitrarily to merge rows (1, 2) and (4, 5). The resulting transition table is a four-row table, and because rows with the same outputs are merged, the resulting system can still be represented by a Moore's state diagram. This transition table is shown in Fig. 3–39. Note that this transition table represents a minimal-state Moore system because no more rows having the same output can be merged. On the other hand, the rows of this table can be further reduced, as it is possible to merge the rows (I, IV) and (II, III). The resulting Mealy's transition table is shown in Fig. 3–40.

In checking the output part of Fig. 3–40 there are three outputs defined in each row corresponding to the three stable states, and a dash corresponding to the unstable state. If these dashes are considered as don't-care conditions, this can produce temporary false outputs. For example, if in the second row

PRESENT STATE	NEXT STATE 00	01	11	10	PRESENT OUTPUT
I-1, 2	①	②	4	6	0
II-3	③	2	--	--	0
III-4, 5	3	2	④	⑤	1
IV-6	1	--	4	⑥	0

Figure 3–39. Minimal Moore's-transition-table representation of Example 6.

the dash is assigned the value 1, then if there is a transition from stable state 3 to stable state 2 under the influence of the input combination 01, there will be a temporarily false output 1. If such transient outputs are to be avoided, these undefined spaces should be assigned the output values of the states reached from the corresponding unstable states. This is a generalized procedure for the avoidance of temporarily false outputs, and not all don't-care output conditions need be specified accordingly. For example, the dash in the first row can be retained as a don't-care condition because it will never lead to a temporarily false output.

PRESENT STATE	NEXT STATE 00	01	11	10	NEXT OUTPUT 00	01	11	10
a-1, 2, 6	①	②	4	⑥	0	0	--	0
b-3, 4, 5	③	2	④	⑤	0	~~0~~	1	1

Figure 3–40. Minimal Mealy's-transition-table representation of Example 6.

In obtaining the transition table of Fig. 3–40, we started by merging rows at random. To obtain a better understanding of the row-merging procedure, we shall use the same example but merge different pairs first. For example, by merging rows (1, 6), (2, 4), and (3, 5) the three-row transition table of Fig. 3–41 is obtained.

PRESENT STATE	NEXT STATE 00	01	11	10	NEXT OUTPUT 00	01	11	10
I'-(1, 6)	①	2	4	⑥	0	0	--	0
II'-(2, 4)	1	②	④	5	0	0	1	1
III'-(3, 5)	③	2	4	⑤	0	0	1	1

Figure 3–41. Transition-table representation of Example 6.

Checking this transition table we see that it cannot be reduced any further, as none of its rows can be merged. Thus, from this example, it can be seen that the order in which the rows are merged is important, because the results of the first merger was a two-row transition table and the second merger resulted in a three-row transition table. This is due to the fact that merging generally is a nontransitive binary relation. This nontransitive relationship occurs when two rows that have undefined entries at different columns are merged, because in this case by the merging of these two rows the undefined entries are assigned the values of the defined entries in the other row. Actually, given a completely defined table (a complete column may be empty, as this shows only an invalid input combination), the order of merging is unimportant, as in this case merging is a transitive binary relation. In general, for a set of rows to be merged into one row it is required that every pair of rows of this set be capable of merging. As an aid in the merging of rows of a primitive transition table, a *merger diagram*, as defined by Caldwell,[12] is used.

A merger diagram is obtained by representing each row of the primitive transition table by a point that is given the number of the corresponding row. Whenever any two rows of the primitive transition table can be merged, a line is connected between the two corresponding points of the merger diagram. The merger diagram of the transition table of Fig. 3–38 is shown in Fig. 3–42.

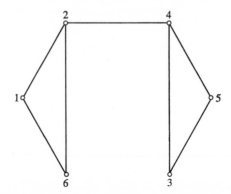

Figure 3–42.   Merger diagram of Example 6.

From this merger diagram it can be seen that by merging rows 2 and 4 all the other lines connected to these points must be disconnected, because there is no set of points capable of being merged pairwise that also includes these two points and another point. On the other hand, if rows 1 and 2 are merged first, row 6 can be merged with the resulting row, because these three points form a set of rows in which every pair of rows is capable of being merged. The merg-

[12] S. H. Caldwell, *Switching Circuits and Logical Design* (New York: Wiley, 1958), p. 475.

ings that produce the condensed transition tables of Figs. 3–40 and 3–41 can be shown on the merger diagram as in Fig. 3–43.

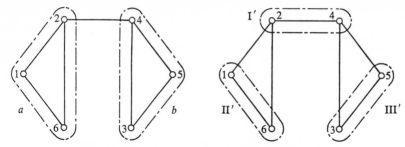

Figure 3–43. Two possible mergers of Example 6.

Now that we have the required background for reducing the primitive transition table, let us return to our original examples of synthesis and derive the condensed transition tables and the corresponding state-diagram representations.

EXAMPLE 4 (*continued, II*).   Checking the primitive transition table of the simplified manual switchboard, as shown in Fig. 3–33, there are only two pairs of probably equivalent states, (2, 6) and (3, 5). The pair (2, 6) is not equivalent, because in column 110 row 2 has the entry 4 and row 6 has no entry in this column. And the pair (3, 5) implies the nonequivalent pair (1, 7). Thus this table does not contain equivalences. The next step is to check for mergers. To do this, the merger diagram is first obtained, as shown in Fig. 3–44. From the merger diagram we see that the rows of the primitive transition table can be combined into two sets of four rows, with each set capable of being merged into one. The corresponding condensed transition table and Mealy's state diagram are shown in Figs. 3–45 and 3–46.

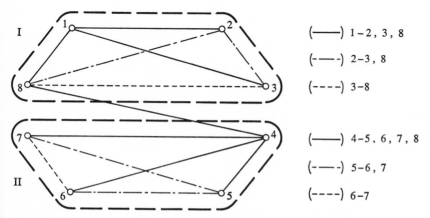

Figure 3–44.   Merger diagram of simplified manual switchboard.

PRESENT STATE	NEXT STATES								NEXT OUTPUTS							
	000	001	011	010	110	111	101	100	000	001	011	010	110	111	101	100
I-1, 2, 3, 8	①	⑧	--	③	4	--	--	②	00	00	--	01	00	--	--	10
II-4, 5, 6, 7	⑦	8	--	⑤	④	--	--	⑥	11	00	--	01	00	--	--	10

Figure 3–45. Condensed transition table of simplified manual switchboard.

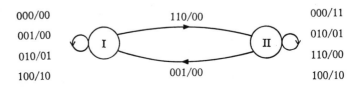

000/00   110/00   000/11
001/00   010/01
010/01 I   II 110/00
100/10   001/00   100/10

Figure 3–46. Minimal Mealy's state diagram of simplified manual switchboard.

EXAMPLE 5 (*continued, II*). Checking the primitive transition table of the modulo-four counter, as shown in Fig. 3–35, there are no probably equivalent states, and thus this table does not contain equivalences. To check for mergers, the merger diagram as shown in Fig. 3–47 is derived. From this merger diagram we can merge four pairs of rows. The resulting condensed transition table and minimal Moore's state diagram are shown in Figs. 3–48 and 3–49.

I 1 ○   2 ○————○ 11 II

III 3 ○   4 ○————○ 10 IV

V 5 ○   6 ○————○ 9 VI

VII 7 ○   8 ○————○ 12 VIII

Figure 3–47. Merger diagram of modulo-four counter.

Note that in this example the Moore's-state-diagram representation is used. This was done because in obtaining the condensed transition table only rows with the same output can be merged. Actually, there should be no difference even if Mealy's state diagram is used, if the assignment of the undefined entries in the output part of the transition table is made accordingly. Note that in making the assignment of the undefined outputs, the only requirement was to avoid temporarily false outputs when there is a transition. In this case since all the stable states of a specific row have the same outputs, if all the undefined outputs of such a row are assigned the same output values, the above requirement will be automatically satisfied. By making the output assignment described above, each row in the output part of Mealy's transition

PRESENT STATE	NEXT STATES				OUTPUTS	
	00	01	11	10	L_1	L_2
I-1	①	9	--	2	0	0
II-2, 11	3	⑪	--	②	0	1
III-3	③	12	--	4	0	1
IV-4, 10	5	⑩	--	④	1	0
V-5	⑤	11	--	6	1	0
VI-6, 9	7	⑨	--	⑥	1	1
VII-7	⑦	10	--	8	1	1
VIII-8, 12	1	⑫	--	⑧	0	0

Figure 3–48. Reduced transition table of modulo-four counter.

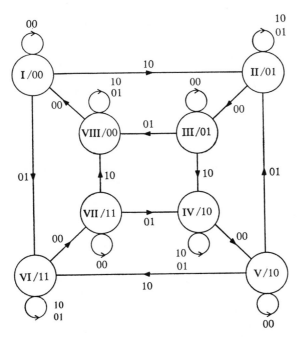

Figure 3–49. Minimal Moore's state diagram of modulo-four counter.

table will have the same output. In other words, when the Boolean functions representing the outputs are derived, they will be independent of the input variables. That is, each $z_i = F_i(\bar{y}_p)$, which brings us back to a Moore's type of system.

3–10. SYNTHESIS PROCEDURE, STEP 3
(SECONDARY STATE ASSIGNMENT)

In this step each row of the condensed transition table is assigned a p-digit binary number representing the present state. This assignment is made according to Huffman's design criterion, that is, avoiding all race conditions. From the analysis we know that this corresponds to embedding the minimal state diagram into a corresponding p cube in such a way that all the transitions are along the edges of the p cube. To illustrate the procedure and show some of the problems that arise, we shall examine both the synthesis examples of the previous sections and some specially designed examples.

EXAMPLE 4 (*continued, III*).   In this example the condensed transition table has only two rows; in other words, only one memory unit is required for its realization. Thus there cannot be any race conditions, and the memory-state assignment becomes arbitrary. The only requirement is that the memory units be unexcited when the system is originally switched on. In this example that means that row 1 of the primitive transition table, Fig. 3–33, should have the value $y = 0$ assigned to it, and as this row was merged into row I of the condensed transition table, Fig. 3–45, row I is assigned this value. Thus for obtaining the excitation and output matrices, the assignment $I \equiv 0$ and $II \equiv 1$ is used.

EXAMPLE 5 (*continued, III*).   In this example the condensed transition table has eight rows, and thus the realization of this circuit requires at least three memory units to assign the different memory states for these rows. The eight circles of the reduced state diagram are thus associated with the eight vertices of a 3-cube in such a way that the transitions between pairs of vertices are along the edges of the 3-cube. In this example the embedding process is obvious, as can be seen from Fig. 3–49, because the minimal state diagram is drawn as a flattened 3-cube. The first step of the assignment is the choice of the starting state. Checking the primitive transition table, Fig. 3–35, we see that when the system is switched on it is in state 1. Therefore, as this row is merged into row I of the reduced transition table, row I is assigned the memory state 000. The next step is to decide on a specific orientation of the 3-cube and accordingly assign the memory states. An example of such an orientation is shown in Fig. 3–50.

Note that this is one of six possible orientations of the 3-cube that can be used for the assignments. In this presentation the choice of a specific assignment is made at random, although this freedom in the assignment of memory states can sometimes be used to obtain simpler combinational circuits. For example, the above assignment yields excitation functions having the cost factors $Y_1 = 16$, $Y_2 = 21$, and $Y_3 = 16$. On the other hand, the assignment

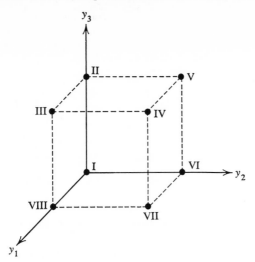

Figure 3–50. Memory-state assignment of modulo-four counter.

that results by interchanging y_1 and y_2 in Fig. 3–50 yields excitation functions having the cost factors $Y_1 = 16$, $Y_2 = 25$, and $Y_3 = 24$.

Actually, in both these examples we were very fortunate. Example 4 required only one memory unit, so there was no possibility of race conditions, and Example 5 could be embedded exactly into a 3-cube. Also note that in these two examples every transition between two states of the embedded state diagram is between two stable states. That is to say, a transition involves exactly one unstable state, and is thus obtained by the change of only one memory unit. Such a system is referred to as a *single-step-transition system*. In general, such an exact fit very seldom occurs, and we must resort to *multiple-step-transition systems*. These are systems in which the transitions between two stable states can take the system through a set of vertices of the p cube that does not represent a stable state for that particular input combination. To see the ideas involved in the design of circuits with multiple-step transitions, we shall introduce a few examples. In these examples we shall assume that the starting state is always state 1.

EXAMPLE 7. Obtain a memory-state assignment for the sequential system defined by the reduced transition table and the corresponding state diagram, as shown in Fig. 3–51.

The transition table of this example has three rows and thus requires two secondary variables to encode them. In other words, the state-diagram representation of the above system must be embedded in a 2-cube. This can be done only when another row is added to the transition table. The addition of a row can be done in two ways, either by adding an unstable state in the path of a transition, that is, a row that has an uncircled entry, or by row

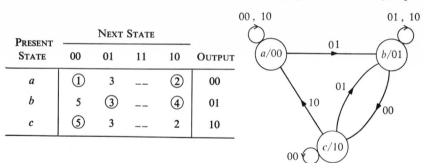

PRESENT STATE	NEXT STATE				OUTPUT
	00	01	11	10	
a	①	3	--	②	00
b	5	③	--	④	01
c	⑤	3	--	2	10

Figure 3–51. Reduced transition table and minimal Moore's state diagram of Example 7.

splitting, the opposite of row merging. An example of each of these possibilities is shown in Fig. 3–52.

To obtain the system represented in Fig. 3–52(a), row d, including the unstable state 2, is added. This is done to provide a two-step transition between rows c and a under the influence of the input combination 10, thus enabling the state-diagram representation to be embedded in a 2-cube with all the transitions along the edges. Note that, although row d includes only an

PRESENT STATE	NEXT STATE				OUTPUT
	00	01	11	10	
a	①	3	--	②	00
b	5	③	--	④	01
c	⑤	3	--	2	10
d	–	--	--	2	–0

(a)

PRESENT STATE	NEXT STATE				OUTPUT
	00	01	11	10	
a′	①	3	--	2	00
b′	5	③	--	④	01
c′	⑤	3	--	2	10
d′	1	-3-	--	②	00

(b)

Figure 3–52. Two possible four-row representations of Example 7.

unstable state, a partially defined output must be associated with this row to avoid temporary false outputs. As state 1, the starting state, is included in row a, this row is assigned the secondary variable combination 00, and then the following two memory assignments can be used: $a \equiv 00$, $b \equiv 01$, $c \equiv 11$, and $d \equiv 10$; or $a \equiv 00$, $b \equiv 10$, $c \equiv 11$, and $d \equiv 01$.

To obtain the system represented in Fig. 3–52(b), row a is split into two rows, a' and d'. This is done by using a procedure inverse to row merging. That is, a circled entry of the original row is entered as a circled entry in one row and as an uncircled entry in the other row, and every uncircled entry in the original row is entered as uncircled entries in both rows. The uncircled entries of the resulting rows are checked to see whether they are required, that is, whether they can be reached from the stable states of that row. In the above example the uncircled entry 3 in row d' can be omitted, because the stable state 2 of this row is reached by the input combination 10 and cannot be followed by an input combination 01. Note that the result of this particular row splitting is a single-step transition system. Just as in the case of Fig. 3–52(a), there can be two memory assignments that satisfy all the requirements. These assignments are $a' \equiv 00$, $b' \equiv 01$, $c' \equiv 11$, and $d' \equiv 10$; or $a' \equiv 00$, $b' \equiv 10$, $c' \equiv 11$, and $d' \equiv 01$.

EXAMPLE 8.   Obtain a memory-state assignment for the sequential system defined by the reduced transition table and the corresponding state diagram, as shown in Fig. 3–53.

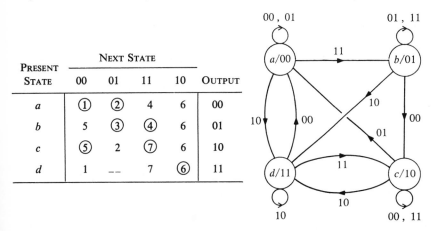

Figure 3–53.   Reduced transition table and minimal Moore's state diagram of Example 8.

The transition table of Fig. 3–53 has four rows, so at least two secondary variables are required to encode these rows. Checking the state-diagram representation, it can be seen that it is impossible to embed it in a 2-cube, because there is a transition between every pair of states. Thus the system cannot be realized as a single-step-transition system with only two memory devices. The next question is whether the system can be realized with two memory units when multiple-step transitions are allowed. The answer to the above question for this particular example is yes. To show this, the *detailed transition diagram* must be defined.

The detailed transition diagram is obtained by representing each row of the reduced transition table by a point that is given the designation of the corresponding row. Two vertices, say, vertex a and vertex b, are joined by an edge marked k if the entry k appears in both rows a and b, one of which may or may not be circled. The detailed transition diagram of Example 8 is shown in Fig. 3–54.

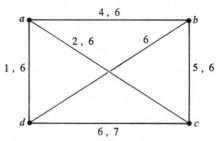

Figure 3–54.   Detailed transition diagram of Example 8.

Now, if the detailed transition diagram can be embedded in a p cube, so can the state diagram, because the detailed transition diagram includes all the required transitions. To embed the detailed transition diagram, some of its edges have to be removed. The removal of these edges has to be done in such a way that all the required transitions are permitted, that is, only an edge can be removed that represents a transition that can be rerouted via other edges. Thus in removing an edge the following rule is to be used:

> Any edge with labels $k_1 k_2 \cdots$ can be removed if it is in one loop with all the edges including the label k_1, and in another loop with all the edges including the label k_2, etc.

Checking the detailed transition diagram of Fig. 3–54 we see that only one edge satisfies the above condition. That is, the edge between the vertices b and d can be removed, because its transition if it is necessary can be accomplished via either vertex a or vertex c. Note also that the label 6 of the second diagonal edge can be removed, as it satisfies the above rule. This leaves us with a detailed transition diagram that has five edges, each of which includes a label that appears only once. And, as these five edges cannot be embedded in a 2-cube, the system in its present form cannot be realized with two memory units. But there is the undefined entry in row d, and if the uncircled 2 is entered here, two additional labels of 2 must be included in the detailed transition diagram, marking the edge between the vertices a and d and the edge between the vertices c and d. Thus the edge between the vertices a and c now can be completely removed, because its transition can be routed via vertex d. Thus by making the undefined entry in row d equal to 2, the system can now be realized as a multiple-step system using only two memory devices. The corresponding transition table and state diagram are shown in Fig. 3–55.

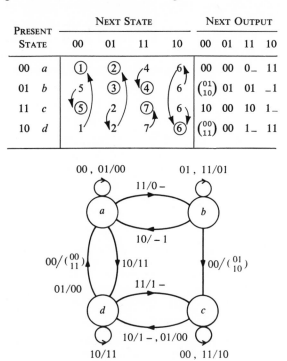

PRESENT STATE	NEXT STATE				NEXT OUTPUT			
	00	01	11	10	00	01	11	10
00 a	①	②	4	6	00	00	0_	11
01 b	5	③	④	6	$\binom{01}{10}$	01	01	_1
11 c	⑤	2	⑦	6	10	00	10	1_
10 d	1	2	7	⑥	$\binom{00}{11}$	00	1_	11

Figure 3–55. Embedded transition table and Mealy's state diagram of Example 8.

Note that in the above example the final transition table and state diagram are of Mealy's type. This was necessary in this example to avoid temporarily false outputs introduced by the multiple-step transitions. The arrows in the transition table have the same meaning as the arrows in a transition diagram, indicating the transition paths between the rows of the transition table. The double-output entries indicate that either one of these entries can be used without producing temporarily false outputs. A possible memory-state assignment for this example is presented in the present-state column of the transition table of Fig. 3–55.

EXAMPLE 9.   Obtain a memory-state assignment for the sequential system defined by the reduced transition table shown together with its detailed transition diagram in Fig. 3–56.

The transition table of Fig. 3–56 has four rows, thus requiring two

	NEXT STATE				
PRESENT STATE	00	01	11	10	OUTPUT
a	①	3	6	②	0
b	5	③	④	2	1
c	⑤	3	⑥	7	0
d	1	--	4	⑦	1

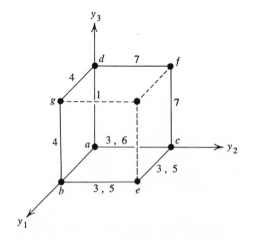

Figure 3–56. Reduced transition table and detailed transition diagram of Example 9.

		NEXT STATE				
PRESENT STATE		00	01	11	10	OUTPUT
a	000	①	3	6	②	0
d	001	1	--	4	⑦	1
f	011	--	--	--	7	--
c	010	⑤	3	⑥	7	0
e	110	5	3	--	--	--
–	111	--	--	--	--	--
g	101	--	--	4	--	1
b	100	5	③	④	2	1

Figure 3–57. Embedded transition table and detailed transition diagram of Example 9.

secondary variables to encode these rows. But checking the detailed transition diagram it can be seen that none of its edges can be eliminated; thus the number of required memory units is more than two. The next step is to use three secondary variables and try to embed the detailed transition diagram in a 3-cube. This embedding can be done in two different ways, either by adding additional vertices to the detailed transition diagram or by assigning more than one memory state for a given row of the transition table.

When more vertices are added to the detailed transition diagram, they are added in such form as to allow the resulting detailed transition diagram to be embedded in a p cube. For example, the detailed transition diagram of Fig. 3–56 can be embedded in a 3-cube by adding three vertices, for example, one in each of the edges not connected to vertex a. Assuming the 3-cube to be oriented as shown, the resulting transition diagram with the memory-state assignment is as given in Fig. 3–57. The arrows in this transition table represent the paths of transitions between the states of the system. Also note that only one of the additional vertices has a defined output, because only in this case does there exist the possibility of a temporarily false output.

When more than one memory state is assigned for a given row of the transition table, then in the detailed transition diagram such a row is represented by an edge or a surface, depending on how many memory states are assigned for that particular row. As an example, we shall assign two memory states for each row of the transition table of Fig. 3–56. The resulting transition table with a memory-state assignment and the detailed transition diagram are shown in Fig. 3–58. (*See page 150.*)

To obtain this transition table, the embedded detailed transition diagram and the condensed transition table are used. For example, if the first column is considered, there must be a transition between row d and row a, and as the edges d and a of the detailed transition table are adjacent at vertices d_1 and a_2, there is an arrow from row d_1 to row a_2, and to allow for a transition between row d_2 and the edge a there is an arrow from row d_2 to row d_1 under the influence of the input combination 00. The other transition paths of the above transition table are obtained in exactly the same manner.

From these examples it can be seen that with the help of the detailed transition diagram an exact fit can be obtained if one exists. Also, whenever an exact fit is impossible, the detailed transition diagram indicates the points where additional vertices are to be included and which rows of the transition table should be assigned multiple states. Generally this becomes a trial-and-error procedure that becomes quite complex in large problems.

In contrast to this procedure, one that results in a minimal number of memory units, the next assignment procedure is straightforward but uses a maximal number of memory units. It uses the same number of memory units as the number of rows in the reduced transition table. In presenting this procedure, the notations of the Y matrix are used, as this makes the presentation simpler. Given a P-row condensed transition table, the ith row has a P

		NEXT STATE				
PRESENT STATE		00	01	11	10	OUTPUT
a_1	000	①₁	3_2	6_2	②₁	0
a_2	001	①₂	3_1	6	②₂	0
b_1	011	5	③₁	④₁	2_2	1
b_2	010	5_1	③₂	④₂	2_1	1
c_1	110	⑤₁	3_2	⑥₁	7_2	0
c_2	100	⑤₂	3	⑥₂	7_1	0
d_1	101	1_2	--	4	⑦₁	1
d_2	111	1	--	4_1	⑦₂	1

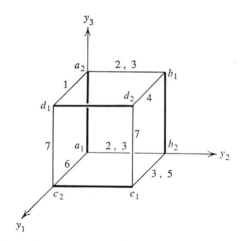

Figure 3–58. Embedded transition table and detailed transition diagram of Example 9.

tuple with an entry of 1 in the ith position and 0 elsewhere, assigned as its memory state. To execute the transition between a pair of rows of the condensed transition table, a new intermediate row is added. To see this, assume a required transition from, say, row i to row j in the lth column. This transition is then routed via a row marked ij that has as its memory-state assignment a P tuple with entries of 1 in the ith and jth positions and 0 elsewhere. Thus in row i and column l of the Y matrix, the P tuple of the ijth row is entered to provide the transition to row ij, and in row ij and column l the P tuple of the jth row is entered to complete the required transition from row i to row j. Thus all the transitions in this system are two-step transitions, and the output entries have to be defined accordingly. The partially defined Y matrix of Fig. 3–59 illustrates this procedure.

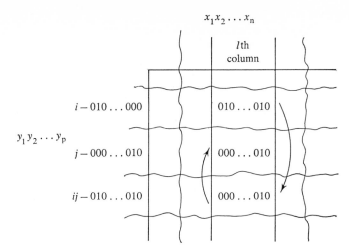

Figure 3–59. Partially defined Y matrix to illustrate a two-step memory-state assignment.

3–11.   SYNTHESIS PROCEDURE, STEP 4 (COMBINATIONAL DESIGN)

In this step the excitation and output matrices are obtained from the transition table with the help of the embedded state diagram or detailed transition diagram. The excitation and output functions are calculated from the Y and Z matrices. Synthesis is complete when these functions are realized in the specified hardware.

EXAMPLE 4 (*continued, IV*).   Checking the condensed transition table of this example as shown in Fig. 3–45, it has two rows, with the memory-state assignment I $= 0$ and II $= 1$, as defined in Section 3–10. To obtain the Y matrix, each circled entry in row I is replaced by a 0 and each uncircled entry by a 1, and in row II each circled entry is replaced by a 1 and each uncircled entry by a 0. The Z matrix is just the output part of the transition table. These matrices are shown in Fig. 3–60. They can now be used as a map

			$a\,b\,o$								$a\,b\,o$						
			Y								$L_A L_B$						
		000	001	011	010	110	111	101	100	000	001	011	010	110	111	101	100
y	0	0	0	__	0	1	__	__	0	00	00	__	01	00	__	__	10
	1	1	0	__	1	1	__	__	1	11	00	__	01	00	__	__	10

Figure 3–60. Y and Z matrices of simplified manual switchboard.

representation of the excitation and output functions. The corresponding minimal-sum-of-products representations are

$$Y = a \cdot b + y \cdot o',$$
$$L_A = a \cdot b' + y \cdot b' \cdot o',$$
$$L_B = a' \cdot b + y \cdot a' \cdot o'.$$

The corresponding minimal-contact-network realization of this system is shown in Fig. 3–61.

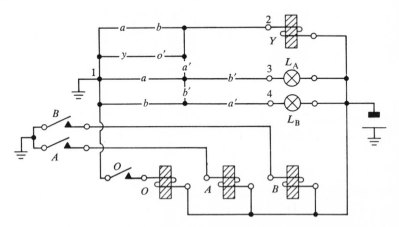

Figure 3–61.   Circuit diagram of simplified manual switchboard.

In this example a bridge contact network was used to obtain a realization that uses a minimal number of springs, as defined in Section 3–2. The reader should calculate the switching functions F_{12}, F_{13}, and F_{14} and check to see that they are equivalent to the excitation and output functions obtained above.

EXAMPLE 5 (*continued, IV*).   From the reduced transition table, Fig. 3-48, and the memory-state assignment, Fig. 3-50, a modified flow diagram can be obtained for this example by rearranging the rows of the transition table and indicating the transitions by arrows. Also, because this example can be realized as a Moore's system, an output vector is used instead of an output matrix. The flow diagram and the output vector of this example are shown in Fig. 3-62.

The transition matrix can now be obtained by finding which memory unit or units must change state at each transition. The ijth entry of the excitation matrix is then obtained using $(Y_1 Y_2 \cdots Y_p)_{ij} = (y_1 y_2 \cdots y_p)_i \oplus (\tau_1 \tau_2 \cdots \tau_p)_{ij}$. Actually, this step of obtaining the transition matrix is generally by-passed, and the excitation can be obtained straight from the modified flow diagram as follows. Every circled entry in a row is replaced by the assigned value of the row and every uncircled entry is replaced by the assigned value of the row to

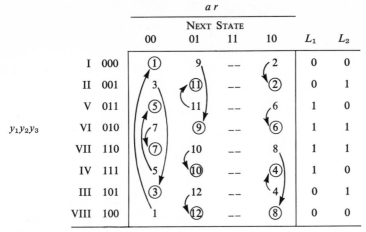

Figure 3–62. Modified flow diagram and output vector of modulo-four counter.

which its arrow is leading. The resulting Y matrix and Z vector are given in Fig. 3–63.

		$a\ r$					
			$Y_1 Y_2 Y_3$				
		00	01	11	10	L_1	L_2
	000	000	010	___	001	0	0
	001	101	001	___	001	0	1
	011	011	001	___	010	1	0
$y_1 y_2 y_3$	010	110	010	___	010	1	1
	110	110	111	___	100	1	1
	111	011	111	___	111	1	0
	101	101	100	___	111	0	1
	100	000	100	___	100	0	0

Figure 3–63. Y matrix and Z vector of modulo-four counter.

Again, considering the Y matrix and Z vector as map representations, the following excitation and output functions are obtained:

$$Y_1 = (a + r) \cdot y_1 + a' \cdot r' \cdot (y_2 \cdot y_3' + y_2' \cdot y_3),$$
$$Y_2 = [a' \cdot (y_1 + y_3') + r' \cdot y_1'] \cdot y_2 + a \cdot y_1 \cdot y_3 + r \cdot y_1' \cdot y_2' \cdot y_3',$$
$$Y_3 = (a' \cdot y_1' + r' \cdot y_1) \cdot y_3 + a \cdot y_1' \cdot y_2' + r \cdot y_1 \cdot y_2,$$
$$L_1 = y_2,$$
$$L_2 = y_2 \cdot y_3' + y_2' \cdot y_3.$$

A corresponding contact network realization is given in Fig. 3–64.

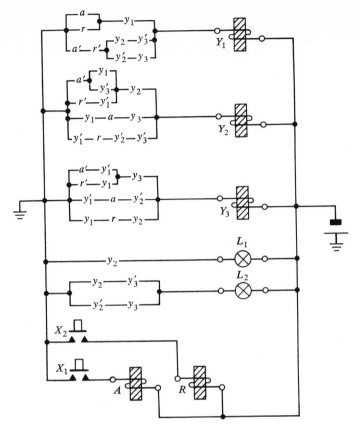

Figure 3–64.   Circuit diagram of modulo-four counter.

The above two examples were realized as contact networks; that is, using relays as the basic hardware. Although we assumed both in the analysis and synthesis that the systems are made up of relays, this is not a required assumption. To see this, we shall now obtain a gate realization of Example 7.

EXAMPLE 7 (*continued, I*).   The excitation matrix and output vector of this example as obtained from the transition table of Fig. 3–52(a) are given in Fig. 3–65. The corresponding excitation and output functions derived from the Y matrix and Z vector are as follows:

$$Y_1 = x_2' \cdot y_1 \cdot y_2 + x_1' \cdot x_2' \cdot y_2,$$
$$Y_2 = x_2 + y_1' \cdot y_2 + x_1' \cdot y_2,$$
$$z_1 = y_1,$$
$$z_2 = y_1' \cdot y_2.$$

The gate realization of these functions is given in Fig. 3–66. Note that delays

		$X_1 X_2$					
		$Y_1 Y_2$					
		00	01	11	10	z_1	z_2
$y_1 y_2$	a-00	00	01	--	00	0	0
	b-01	11	01	--	01	0	1
	c-11	11	01	--	10	1	0
	d-10	--	--	--	00	-	0

Figure 3–65. Y matrix and Z vector of Example 7.

δ are included in the feedback paths to differentiate between the present states and the next states of the systems. Also, these gates are assumed to be ideal gates that do not include delays; in other words, the total delay in these gates is assumed to be smaller than a delay δ in the feedback paths.

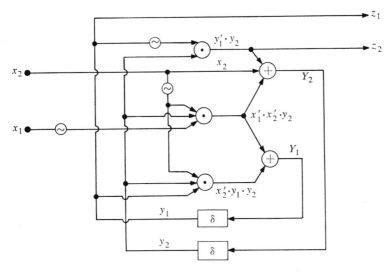

Figure 3–66. Gate realization of Example 7.

3–12. SYNTHESIS EXAMPLE

In this section an asynchronous sequential circuit is synthesized using the procedure developed in previous sections. The purpose of this example is not to introduce new ideas but to provide the over-all picture that could not be obtained previously, as the earlier examples were solved in parts.

EXAMPLE 10. A set-reset counter. The circuit to be designed has two inputs (x_1, x_2) and a single output (z). The inputs are restricted, so that only one input can change at any time and they cannot both have the value 1 at the same time. Physically this means that these inputs are either push-button switches that can only be activated singly, or pulses that cannot occur concurrently. The circuit to be designed has first to be SET by the input combination $x_1x_2 = 10$. The output is then to be 1 after the variable x_2 becomes 1 for the third time, without the occurrence of the input combination $x_1x_2 = 10$. The output remains 1 until the input combination $x_1x_2 = 10$ RESETS the system to the SET position. The occurrence of the input combination $x_1x_2 = 10$ at any time RESETS the system to its SET position.

Step 1. To obtain the Moore's state diagram of this problem it is assumed that the system is in state 1/0 when it is originally switched on. Under the influence of the input combination $x_1x_2 = 01$, state 2/0 is reached. The next input combination, $x_1x_2 = 00$, is forced and returns the system to state 1/0, because the counter was not SET before. If the input combination $x_1x_2 = 10$ is applied to the system in state 1/0, the counter is SET and the system is in state 3/0; the next input combination $x_1x_2 = 00$ takes the system to state 4/0. Three consecutive input combinations of $x_1x_2 = 01$ take the system through states 5/0, 6/0, 7/0, and 8/0 to state 9/1. The next input combination, $x_1x_2 = 00$, takes the system to state 10/1. From state 10/1 the system is taken to state 9/1 by the input combination $x_1x_2 = 01$ and is RESET, that is, is taken into state 3/0 by the input combination $x_1x_2 = 10$. Also from any of states 4/0, 6/0, and 8/0 the system is taken to state 3/1, that is, is RESET by the input combination $x_1x_2 = 10$. The corresponding Moore's state diagram and primitive transition table are shown in Figs. 3–67 and 3–68.

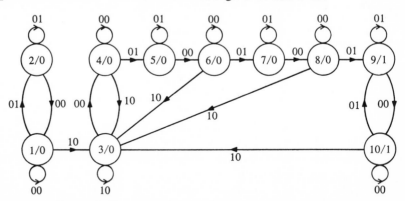

Figure 3–67. Moore's state diagram of set-reset counter.

Step 2. To check for equivalences the equivalence table of Fig. 3–69 is used. Checking the implied pairs of the equivalence table, the probably equivalent pairs (1, 8), (4, 8), and (6, 8) are eliminated, because their implied pairs are not included in the set of probably equivalent pairs. This is shown schematically in the column headed run 1. Similarly, in run 2, the probably equivalent pairs (2, 7) and (5, 7) are eliminated, in run 3 the probably equiva-

PRESENT STATE	NEXT STATE				PRESENT OUTPUT
	00	01	11	10	
1	①	2	––	3	0
2	1	②	––	––	0
3	4	––	––	③	0
4	④	5	––	3	0
5	6	⑤	––	––	0
6	⑥	7	––	3	0
7	8	⑦	––	––	0
8	⑧	9	––	3	0
9	10	⑨	––	––	1
10	⑩	9	––	3	1

Figure 3–68.   Primitive transition table of set-reset counter.

lent pairs (1, 6) and (4, 6) are eliminated, in run 4 the probably equivalent pair (2, 5) is eliminated, and in run 5 the last probably equivalent pair (1, 4) is eliminated. Thus the primitive transition table of Fig. 3–68 has no equivalent rows.

PROBABLY EQUIVALENT	IMPLIED PAIRS	RUN 1	RUN 2	RUN 3	RUN 4	RUN 5
1, 4	2, 5	✓	✓	✓	✓	X
1, 6	2, 7	✓	✓	X		
1, 8	2, 9	X				
2, 5	1, 6	✓	✓	✓	X	
2, 7	1, 8	✓	X			
4, 6	5, 7	✓	✓	X		
4, 8	5, 9	X				
5, 7	6, 8	✓	X			
6, 8	7, 9	X				

Figure 3–69.   Equivalence table of set-reset counter.

To check merging, in this particular case it is not necessary to use a merger diagram, because only pairs (1, 2), (3, 4), and (9, 10) of rows can be merged. The resulting state diagram is a Moore's state diagram. This state diagram and the reduced transition table are shown in Fig. 3–70.

PRESENT STATE		NEXT STATE				PRESENT OUTPUT
		00	01	11	10	
I	1, 2	①	②	--	3	0
II	3, 4	④	5	--	③	0
III	5	6	⑤	--	--	0
IV	6	⑥	7	--	3	0
V	7	8	⑦	--	--	0
VI	8	⑧	9	--	3	0
VII	9, 10	⑩	⑨	--	3	1

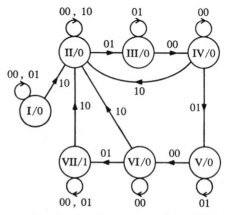

Figure 3–70. Reduced transition table and minimal Moore's state diagram of set-reset counter.

Step 3. In this example it can be seen that the embedding procedure becomes easy if the transitions caused by the input combination $x_1 x_2 = 10$ are omitted. And the necessary transitions under the influence of the input combination $x_1 x_2 = 10$ can always be executed, because all the transitions are to one row. The embedded detailed transition diagram, showing only the required transitions, and the corresponding modified flow diagram, are presented in Fig. 3–71.

Step 4. The Y matrix and the Z vector obtained from Fig. 3–71 are shown in Fig. 3–72. The minimal-sum-of-products representations of the excitation and output functions as obtained from Fig. 3–72 are as follows:

$$Y_1 = (x_2 + y_3') \cdot y_1 + x_1 \cdot y_2' \cdot y_3' + x_2 \cdot y_2 \cdot y_3',$$
$$Y_2 = x_1' \cdot y_2 + x_2 \cdot y_1' \cdot y_3,$$
$$Y_3 = (x_2 + x_1' \cdot y_1' \cdot y_2') \cdot y_3 + x_2 \cdot y_1 \cdot y_2',$$
$$z = y_1 \cdot y_2.$$

The corresponding gate realization is shown in Fig. 3-73.

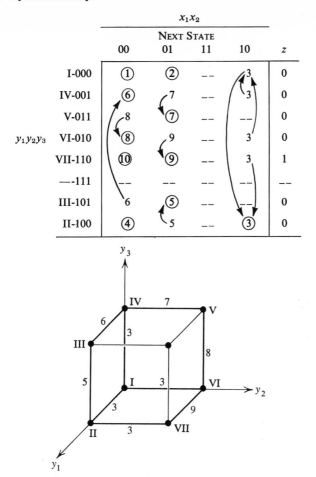

Figure 3–71.   Modified flow diagram and embedded detailed transition diagram of set-reset counter.

	x_1x_2				
	$Y_1Y_2Y_3$				
	00	01	11	10	z
000	000	000	— —	100	0
001	001	011	— —	000	0
011	010	011	— —	— —	0
$y_1y_2y_3$ 010	010	110	— —	000	0
110	110	110	— —	100	1
111	— —	— —	— —	— —	— —
101	001	101	— —	— —	0
100	100	101	— —	100	0

Figure 3–72. Y matrix and Z vector of set-reset counter.

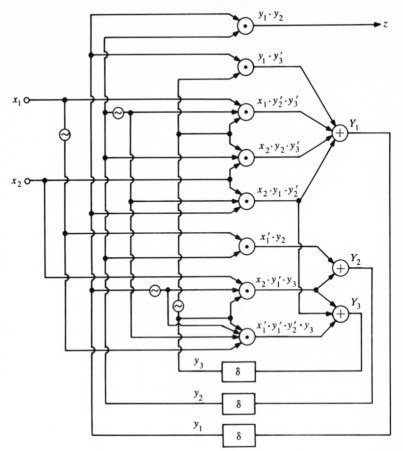

Figure 3–73.   Gate realization of set-reset counter.

3–13. OTHER TYPES OF MEMORY DEVICES

In this section we consider the required modifications in the synthesis procedure when flip-flop memory devices are used. The name *flip-flop memory device* is used because the first use of this type of memory device employed a specific vacuum-tube circuit called a *flip-flop*. An example of such a device is the set-reset memory unit defined in Definition 3 of this chapter. To see the changes that are to be introduced, an example will now be considered.

EXAMPLE 7 (*continued, II*).   Obtain a gate realization of Example 7, using set-reset memory units. The Y matrix and Z vector of this example are given in Fig. 3–74.

| | | $y_1 x_2$ | | | | | |
| | | $Y_1 Y_2 Y_3$ | | | | | |
		00	01	11	10	z_1	z_2
	00	00	01	--	00	0	0
$y_1 y_2$	01	11	01	--	01	0	1
	11	11	01	--	10	1	0
	10	--	--	--	00	-	0

Figure 3–74. Y matrix and Z vector of Example 7.

Before going further with the synthesis procedure, we shall redefine the behavior of a set-reset memory device by the table of Fig. 3–75, where $y_{+\delta}$

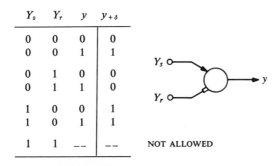

Y_s	Y_r	y	$y_{+\delta}$
0	0	0	0
0	0	1	1
0	1	0	0
0	1	1	0
1	0	0	1
1	0	1	1
1	1	--	--	NOT ALLOWED

Figure 3–75.   Tabular definition of set-reset memory.

denotes the next output. Thus from the Y matrix, the *set* and *reset functions* (Y_s, Y_r) are to be calculated. As a first trial in calculating these functions, Y_s is considered 1 whenever there is a "1" entry in the Y matrix, and Y_r is considered 1 whenever there is a "0" entry in the Y matrix. But checking Fig. 3–75 it can be seen that to obtain these functions only those entries are to be included that produce changes in the output. That is, in calculating Y_s only those 1's must be included where the row designation has the value 0 for this memory unit, and the remaining 1's are considered to be don't-care conditions and marked ɫ. Similarly, in calculating Y_r only those 0's must be included where the row designation has the value 1 for this memory unit, and the remaining 0's are considered to be don't-care conditions and marked Ø. Note that the ɫ's can be used only for simplifying Y_s and the Ø's can be used only for simplifying Y_r. Generally the entries at the coordinates representing the starting state are considered as required entries, to ensure that this is the starting state when the system is initially switched on. In our case this corresponds to the entries at the coordinates $x_1 x_2 / y_1 y_2 = 00/00$. The marked maps of the excitation functions of this example are given in Fig. 3–76. The corresponding gate realization is given in Fig. 3–77.

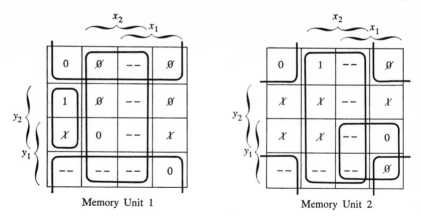

Memory Unit 1   Memory Unit 2

Figure 3–76. Set and reset maps of memory units of Example 7.

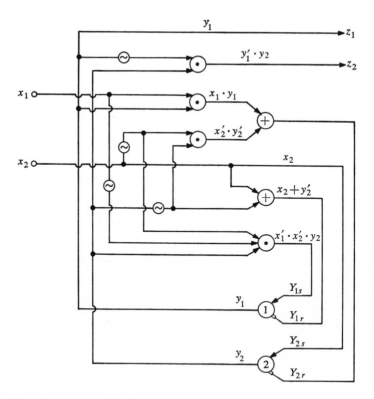

Figure 3–77. Gate realization of Example 7 with set-reset memory units.

The set and reset functions, from Fig. 3–76, and the output functions defined by the Z vector of Fig. 3–74 are as follows:

$$Y_{1s} = x_1' \cdot x_2' \cdot y_2, \qquad Y_{2s} = x_2, \qquad\qquad z_1 = y_1,$$
$$Y_{1r} = x_2 + y_2'. \qquad\quad Y_{2r} = x_1 \cdot y_1 + x_2' \cdot y_2'. \qquad z_2 = y_1' \cdot y_2.$$

Actually there are many other types of flip-flops in use, but most of them are more appropriate for use as memory devices for synchronous sequential circuits. We shall briefly define the behavior of two other types of flip-flops used in asynchronous sequential circuits. These two flip-flops are the *set-dominant* and the *J-K flip-flop*. Both these flip-flops have two inputs, and their behavior differs when both inputs are 1. The tabular definition of these flip-flops is given in Fig. 3–78.

Y_{sd}	Y_r	y	$y_{+\delta}$
0	0	0	0
0	0	1	1
0	1	0	0
0	1	1	0
1	0	0	1
1	0	1	1
1	1	0	1
1	1	1	1

Y_j	Y_k	y	$y_{+\delta}$
0	0	0	0
0	0	1	1
0	1	0	0
0	1	1	0
1	0	0	1
1	0	1	1
1	1	0	1
1	1	1	0

(a)   (b)

Figure 3–78. Tabular definition of the set-dominant and *J–K* flip-flops.

Whenever one of these flip-flops is to be used, the synthesis procedure has to be modified; that is, the maps of the excitation functions have to be modified according to the tabular definitions of the flip-flops as given in Fig. 3–78. The actual procedure for obtaining these modifications is left as a homework problem.

Note that these flip-flops can be designed using gates and delay units. This also is left as a homework problem. Actually in most hardware realizations the flip-flops are designed with two outputs, one as defined above and the other its complement. The block-diagrammatic representation of these two-output flip-flops is shown in Fig. 3–79.

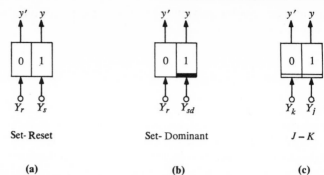

(a) (b) (c)

Figure 3–79. Block-diagrammatic representation of two-output flip-flops.

3–14. CONCLUDING REMARKS

In the first few sections of this chapter we considered the analysis of asynchronous sequential circuits in detail. The analysis procedure is divided into a set of steps. First, the Boolean functions of the excitations and outputs are calculated from the circuit diagram. These functions are then mapped to obtain the Y and Z matrices. The information included in the Y matrix can then be partially represented in the τ matrix and flow table, and the graphical representation of the Y matrix is obtained in the transition diagram. The transition diagram with the Z matrix is the final step of analysis. During the analysis two other graphical representations of a sequential circuit were introduced, the p cube and the state-diagram representations. These representations are seldom used in analysis; they are more appropriate to the synthesis procedure, although in the analysis of more complex circuits the state-diagram representation may be required. The above analysis procedure was introduced using transition memory elements, but it can be adapted quite easily for circuits that use flip-flop memory elements. Note that in the analysis procedure the input restrictions should be specified, as the input restrictions give rise to don't-care conditions in the Y matrix that can be used to simplify the circuit diagram. But when the circuit diagram is translated into a Y matrix all don't-care conditions are filled, and this can mask some of the black-box characteristics of the system.

The synthesis procedure, as described in this chapter, has two main stumbling blocks—the first and third steps of synthesis. That is, obtaining the state-diagram representation of a system from the word specification is basically a translation process that requires some intuition and experience. This is due to the fact that word specification is very seldom complete and exact, and in deriving the state diagram different interpretations can be made. The reduction of the transition table is discussed in detail in step 2 of the synthesis procedure. This step is obtained in two parts: finding all equivalences, then merging. Both parts are completely systematic and can be programed on a digital computer.

Note that the result of merging is not necessarily unique, and there can be a number of reduced transition tables that have a minimal number of rows or that require the same number of memory units for their realization. In general these will have different cost factors associated with their functions. Thus the proper choice can reduce the total cost factor of the circuit. There is no method other than trial and error to choose a particular reduced transition table. A rule of thumb is to choose the reduced transition table that has the largest number of undefined entries, as these correspond to don't-care conditions in the Y matrix; also, these undefined entries may simplify the embedding process. Actually the reduction procedure described in step 2 does not always lead to a minimal-row transition table. To ensure such a table, the procedure described in Chapter 4 must be used. Another synthesis step that involves experience or a bag of tricks is step 3, the assignment of secondary variables. In our discussion we only presented the more obvious assignment procedures, without considering some of the more detailed approaches reported in the literature, which are too specialized for the purpose of this presentation. Also, as seen from the examples, even after embedding the minimal state diagram, the memory assignment is not unique and can be used to reduce the cost of Boolean functions. Again, obtaining an assignment that leads to a minimal cost function is done by trial and error, because the requirement of avoiding races introduces too many restrictions on the assignment. Step 4 of the synthesis procedure again is completely formalized and both the procedure for obtaining the Y matrix from the modified flow diagram and the procedure of obtaining the Boolean functions from the Y matrix can be programed on a digital computer.

Another problem that was not considered is caused by the nonideal behavior of the circuit elements used in the realization. This can result in output signals different from the ones predicted, which are generally referred to as *hazards*. To check for hazards it is necessary to investigate the Boolean functions obtained from the Y and Z matrices[13, 14]. An example of such a hazard was discussed in Example 1. In most cases the potential trouble introduced by the hazards in combinational circuits is overcome by the smoothing effect of the delay in the action of the secondary variables.

One of the main drawbacks of Huffman's synthesis procedure is the fact that it leads to totally sequential machines by eliminating all race conditions. By inserting noncritical races at the level of the detailed transition diagram, the speed of operation of the final circuit will usually be increased. It may also result in further reduction in the number of required memory units.

[13] D. A. Huffman, "The Design and Use of Hazard-Free Switching Networks," *J. Assoc. Computing Machinery*, **4**, (1957).

[14] M. Yoeli and S. Rinon, "Applications of Ternary Algebra to the Study of Static Hazards," *J. Assoc. Computing Machinery*, **11**, (1964).

Another drawback of the procedure described in this chapter is that it does not lend itself to simple programing. That is, even very large problems must be handled by paper-and-pencil methods. A partial solution to this is obtained by breaking up the design specifications into a set of simpler problems at the following levels: (1) by breaking up the actual design requirements into smaller parts (the drawback here is that it requires a great deal of intuition to avoid complicating the over-all circuit); (2) by breaking up the primitive or partially condensed transition diagram. The second method is the most commonly discussed in the literature, but, in turn, requires that a flow table be obtained first, which in itself is a major project for larger problems.

Actually, the procedure presented above is applicable to relatively simple problems. Whenever a really large problem is to be solved, such as the control unit of a digital computer, it is in general impossible to find a minimal realization in a reasonable amount of time. On the other hand, the synthesis procedure described above is the basis of all programable algorithms that lead to engineering solutions, that is, solutions that are not minimal but acceptable.[15]

The most complete coverage of asynchronous sequential circuits is found in:

S. H. Caldwell. *Switching Circuits and Logical Design*. New York: Wiley, 1958, pp. 453–578. The coverage of this book is based on Huffman's work, but does not cover the state-diagram representation of sequential circuits. This book provides an excellent and most complete coverage of the problem of secondary assignment.

---

[15] J. Elsey, "An Algorithm for the Synthesis of Large Sequential Switching Circuits," *Univ. Ill. Rep. R-169*, May 1964; also available from Defense Documentation Center as *AD418163*. A good example of an algorithm for which a compromise between minimality and ease of solution is considered.

PROBLEMS

1. Analyze the following asynchronous sequential circuits. That is, derive the Y, Z, and τ matrices, flow table, transition diagram, Moore's and Mealy's state diagrams, and the p cube.

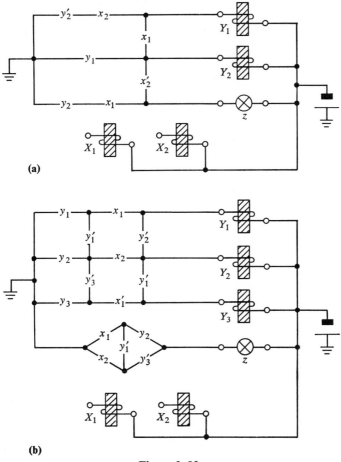

(a)

(b)

Figure 3–80.

(c) $Y_1 = y_2 \cdot y_3' \cdot x_1' \cdot x_2' + y_2' \cdot x_2 + y_1 \cdot (x_1 + x_2)$,
$Y_2 = y_1' \cdot y_3' \cdot x_1 \cdot x_2 + y_2 \cdot x_1' \cdot (x_2 + y_1)$,
$Y_3 = y_1' \cdot y_3' \cdot x_1 \cdot x_2 + y_3 \cdot x_2' \cdot (y_1' + x_1')$,
$z = x_1' \cdot (y_1' \cdot y_2 + y_3) + x_2 \cdot y_2'$.

(d) $Y_1 = x_1 \cdot x_2' + x_2 \cdot y_2' \cdot y_3 + y_1 \cdot y_2' \cdot y_3$,
$Y_2 = x_2' \cdot y_3 + y_2 \cdot x_1$,
$Y_3 = x_1 \cdot x_2 + y_3 \cdot (y_1 + x_2')$,
$z = x_2$.

2. Analyze the following asynchronous sequential circuits with set-reset memory devices. That is, obtain all the representations specified in Problem 1.

Note: When set-reset memory units are used, an input must be applied to a memory unit only when its output has to change.

(a)

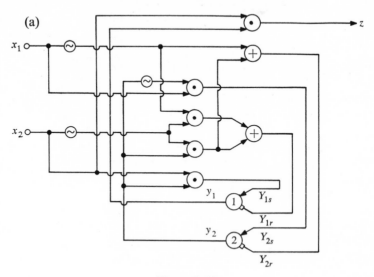

Figure 3–81.

(b) Assume that the input combination $x_1 x_2 = 11$ cannot occur:

$$Y_{1s} = x_2 \cdot y_2 \cdot y_3',$$
$$Y_{1r} = x_1' \cdot x_2' \cdot y_2',$$
$$Y_{2s} = x_2 \cdot y_2' \cdot y_3' + y_1 \cdot (x_1 + x_2),$$
$$Y_{2r} = x_1' \cdot x_2' \cdot y_2' + x_1 \cdot y_1' \cdot y_2,$$
$$Y_{3s} = x_2 \cdot y_2' + y_2 \cdot (x_1 \cdot y_1' \cdot y_3' + x_1' \cdot x_2' \cdot y_1),$$
$$Y_{3r} = x_1' \cdot x_2' \cdot y_1' + x_1 \cdot (y_1 + y_2 \cdot y_3),$$
$$z = x_2 \cdot y_2.$$

Note: Each of the following problems should be solved in four steps, corresponding to the synthesis procedure defined in the text. That is:

(a) Obtain the primitive transition table and Moore's state diagram;
(b) Derive the condensed transition table and the minimal state diagram;
(c) Obtain a secondary state assignment; and
(d) Derive the Boolean functions assuming transition memory devices.

Also assume, if it is not stated otherwise, that in each problem specification only one input variable can change at any given time.

3. Design the following two-input (x_1, x_2) and single-output (z) circuit. The output $z = x_1$ if $x_2 = 1$, but if $x_2 = 0$ the output is to remain fixed at its last value before x_2 became 0.

4. Design each of the following two-input and single-output memory devices:

(a) SET-RESET;
(b) SET-DOMINANT;
(c) J-K.

The operations of these memory devices are defined in Figs. 3–75 and 3–78. Assume that the input signals are completely synchronized and that more than one input can change at a time.

5. Design the two-input (x_1, x_2) and single-output (z) circuit whose output $z = x_1$ if $x_2 = 1$, and z takes on the previous value of x_1 if $x_2 = 0$.

6. Given the two-input (x_1, x_2) circuit whose output is a lamp z. The lamp z is to be turned on whenever x_1 changes from 0 to 1, and is turned off whenever x_2 changes from 1 to 0. Design each of the following two circuits that have the above-defined behavior:

(a) x_1 is a push-button switch that must be released before the other switch can be changed. x_2 is an ON-OFF switch;
(b) both x_1 and x_2 are ON-OFF switches.

7. *Delay line.* Design a circuit that has two outputs (z_1, z_2) and two inputs (x_1, x_2) such that the output combination at any time is equal to the previous input combination.

8. The two inputs (x_1, x_2) of the circuit to be designed represent, in binary form, the numbers 0, 1, 2, and 3. The single output $z = 1$ if the input change produces an increase over the number represented by the previous inputs, $z = 0$ if the input change produces a decrease, and the output should not change when $x_1 x_2 = 00$.

9. *Pulse counter.* Given the single-input (x) circuit whose output is a lamp (z). The input x is a push-button switch. Design a circuit in which

(a) the lamp will light whenever the push-button switch is pressed the third time;
(b) the lamp will light whenever the push-button switch is pressed the third time and stays on until the push-button switch is pressed again;
(c) the lamp will light when the push-button switch is pressed the third time and remain on independent of what is done afterward.

10. *Combination lock.* Given a circuit having two inputs (x_1, x_2) and a single output (z), where the output $z = 1$ means that the lock is opened, and once the output becomes 1 it remains so independent of what happens afterward. Design each of the following circuits:

(a) The output z becomes 1 whenever any one of the following input sequences is applied to the circuit:

$$\begin{array}{ll} \text{(I)} & 00, 01, 11; \\ \text{(II)} & 10, 11, 01, 00; \\ \text{(III)} & 10, 00. \end{array}$$

(b) The output z becomes 1 whenever there is a sequence of four consecutive input changes with $x_2 = 1$.

(c) The output z becomes 1 if there is a sequence of four consecutive input changes with $x_2 = 1$, but if after two or three consecutive input changes with $x_2 = 1$, the input x_2 becomes 0, the output z will remain 0 independent of what happens afterward.

11. *Combination lock.* The circuit has two inputs (x_1, x_2) and two outputs (z_1, z_2). Suppose the output $z_1 = 1$ opens the lock and the output $z_2 = 1$ sounds an alarm. If one of the following input sequences is fed to the lock, the output z_1 becomes 1 and remains so independent of what happens afterward.

(a) 00, 01, 00, 10, 00;

(b) 00, 10, 11, 01, 00.

Any departure from one of the specified input sequences should make $z_2 = 1$, and z_2 remains 1 independent of what happens afterward.

12. Assume that Problems 5, 7, 8, and 10 are to be designed using set-reset memory elements. Calculate the memory SET and RESET functions for these problems and obtain the corresponding gate realizations.

13. Derive the procedure for obtaining the controlling functions for the following memory devices:

(a) SET-DOMINANT;

(b) *J-K*.

14. Use the procedures derived in Problem 13 and obtain the gate realizations of the pulse-counter circuits defined in Problem 9, using

(a) SET-DOMINANT memory devices;

(b) *J-K* memory devices.

Assume the input x is a set of pulses.

Note: The next problems are basically synchronous in nature, but here asynchronous sequential circuits are to be designed. To do this the information has to be transformed and/or additional control signals added. The inputs 1 and 0 are represented by the presence and absence of pulses at equally spaced instances of time. Assume that clock pulses, that is, a string of 1's, are available whenever required and that all input signals are completely synchronized.

15. *Binary comparator.* The circuit to be designed compares two input sequences of 1's and 0's, denoted $\bar{X}_1$ and $\bar{X}_2$, with the least significant digit arriving first. The circuit has two outputs (z_1, z_2). If $\bar{X}_1 > \bar{X}_2$, $z_1 z_2 = 10$; if $\bar{X}_1 = \bar{X}_2$, $z_1 z_2 = 00$; and if $\bar{X}_1 < \bar{X}_2$, $z_1 z_2 = 01$. The circuit has a third input (r), the reset signal, that can be applied only in the interval between pulses to reset the circuit output to $z_1 z_2 = 00$.

16. The circuit to be designed has only two inputs $\bar{X}_1$ and $\bar{X}_2$. Its output behavior with respect to these inputs is the same as the binary comparator defined above. The circuit is to reset itself automatically after every set of three inputs.

17. *Serial Binary adder.* The circuit to be designed adds two input sequences of 1's and 0's, denoted $\bar{X}_1$ and $\bar{X}_2$, with the least significant digits arriving first. The output is to be a sequence of 1's and 0's, denoted $\bar{Z} = \bar{X}_1 + \bar{X}_2$, where + represents binary addition. The circuit has a third input (r), the reset signal, that can be applied only in the interval between pulses to reset the circuit.

18. The circuit to be designed has only two inputs, $\bar{X}_1$ and $\bar{X}_2$. Its output behavior with respect to these inputs is the same as the serial binary adder defined above. The circuit is to reset itself automatically after every set of three inputs.

CHAPTER

4

Synchronous Sequential Circuits

4–1. INTRODUCTION

In this chapter we shall consider synchronous sequential circuits as defined by Definition 1 of Chapter 3. Many logical designers consider synchronous sequential circuits to be a special case of asynchronous sequential circuits with an additional synchronizing or clock input. At the same time there are others who hold exactly the opposite point of view. From a theoretical point of view there are enough differences between these two kinds of sequential circuits to warrant separate coverage in this text.

From practical design considerations the differentiation between synchronous and asynchronous sequential circuits seems arbitrary, as most large switching systems include both kinds of circuits. Generally, synchronous design techniques are advisable when exact timing is necessary. Also as a general rule, when a given system can be synthesized either as an asynchronous or as a synchronous system, the synchronous circuit uses fewer logical elements but is slower in operation.

Another reason the study of synchronous sequential circuits is introduced as a separate chapter is the fact that this theory forms the bridge between switching-circuit theory and automata theory, the theory of abstract mathematical machines. The interested reader is referred to McNaughton[1] for a survey of the early work on automata theory.

In the first part of this chapter the synchronous sequential circuit is redefined and some of its specific properties are investigated. This is done by using the terminology introduced in Chapter 3, and in this part both the similarities and the differences between the synchronous and asynchronous systems are considered in detail. Later in the chapter a second state-reduction procedure is introduced. This procedure was developed to produce more reductions than those obtainable by row merging when the transition diagram includes undefined entries. This reduction procedure is based on the work of Paull and Unger[2] and Ginsburg.[3] The procedure described is equally effective in asynchronous circuit design, but it is introduced here because it is quite abstract and fits better with the contents of the chapter. In the last part of the chapter the differences between synchronous and asynchronous systems in the secondary assignment and realizations are introduced.

4–2. BASIC CONCEPTS

In Chapter 3 we saw that the synthesis of an n-input, m-output sequential circuit is based on the addition of p secondary variables; that is, the above problem is transformed into an $(n + p)$-input and $(m + p)$-output combinational circuit with p memory devices. The output values of the p memory devices define the state of the sequential circuit. Using this terminology a more precise definition of a sequential circuit is as follows.

Definition 1. A *sequential circuit* is a system whose behavior can be completely defined in terms of functional relationships among its input vector $\bar{X}$, output vector $\bar{Z}$, and state vector $\bar{S}$.

The distinguishing characteristic of the synchronous sequential circuit is that these vectors, generally referred to as *system variables*, $\bar{V}$, are sampled at discrete moments of time. In the study of asynchronous sequential circuits, the system variables $\bar{V}$ had to be considered as explicit functions of time $V(t)$. That is to say, the system behavior can be understood only in terms of the continuity of time. Owing to the assumption of time discreteness in synchronous sequential systems, the system variables can be defined only at

[1] R. McNaughton, "The Theory of Automata: A Survey," in *Advances in Computers,* Vol. 2, edited by F. L. Alt (New York: Academic, 1961), pp. 379–421.

[2] M. C. Paull and S. H. Unger, "Minimizing the Number of States in Incompletely Specified Sequential Switching Functions," *IRE Trans. Electron. Computers,* **8,** 356–367 (1959).

[3] S. Ginsburg, "A Technique for the Reduction of a Given Machine to a Minimal-State Machine," *IRE Trans. Electron. Computers,* **8,** 346–355 (1959).

sampling times. The general notation used is V_k, which designates the value of the system variable $\bar{V}$ at the kth sampling time. Using this notation, a synchronous sequential system is defined as follows.

Definition 2. A *synchronous sequential system* is a system with a finite input vector $\bar{X}$, a finite output vector $\bar{Z}$, a finite state vector $\bar{S}$, and a pair of characterizing functions F and G given by

$$Z_k = F(X_k, S_k),$$
$$S_{k+1} = G(X_k, S_k),$$

where X_k, the input symbol, is an n-dimensional vector representing the value of the n inputs at the kth sampling time;

Z_k, the output symbol, is an m-dimensional vector representing the value of the m outputs at the kth sampling time;

S_k, the state symbol, is a p-dimensional vector representing the value of the p state variables, the internal state, at the kth sampling time; and

F and G are the characterizing functions that define uniquely the kth output symbol and the $(k + 1)$th internal state of the system in terms of the kth input symbol and kth internal state.

In this definition an additional implied assumption is that the system behavior is completely defined by the events during the kth sampling time and is independent of the length of the interval between sampling times. Note that this does not mean that the circuit is necessarily quiescent between sampling times, only that it reaches a specific value before the next sampling time. This definition of synchronous sequential systems is quite general, as no assumptions were made regarding the values the components of the system variables V_k can take on or the uniformity of the sampling times.

Our purpose is to study the behavior of switching circuits, which are a subclass of mathematical machines, so the generality of Definition 2 has to be reduced. As a first assumption, the system variables will be restricted to binary variables. A second assumption is that there exists a synchronizing signal that governs the sampling process. Considering these assumptions applied to Definition 2, a corresponding switching-circuit model is shown in Fig. 4–1.

In Fig. 4–1 the boxes marked C_1, C_2, and C_3 represent sampling or clamping circuits. The word-statement definition of such a sampling circuit is as follows:

The input vector can change at any time, but the output vector has the value of the input vector at the instant of sampling and remains constant until the next sampling pulse is applied.

Such clamping circuits have to be designed as asynchronous sequential circuits using the procedure described in Chapter 3. In fact, this is not a

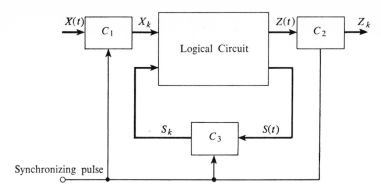

Figure 4–1.   Circuit model of synchronous sequential circuit with synchronizing input.

practical system model; in reality we forced the word statement of a system into a synchronous mode of operation. As we shall see later, the logical circuit of a synchronous sequential circuit is generally simpler than the logical circuit of the corresponding asynchronous sequential circuit, but in this model this is more than counteracted by the added complexity of the three clamping circuits. It would be simpler to design such a circuit as an asynchronous sequential circuit with an additional input, the synchronizing pulse.

These considerations lead us to further restrictions on the switching circuits that are to be considered as synchronous sequential circuits. That is, only those systems that satisfy all the required assumptions will be designed according to the synthesis procedure of synchronous sequential circuits. In this chapter we shall refer to synchronous systems as those systems that include synchronizing signals that have a specified repetition rate. Such synchronizing signals are called *clock pulses*. Also, the signals that are to be used are restricted. We shall consider two basic kinds. One is referred to as a

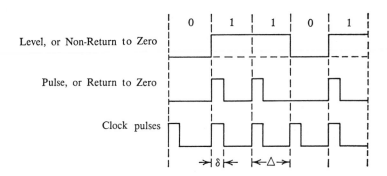

Figure 4–2.   Signals used in synchronous sequential circuits.

level or *non-return to zero*; such a signal can change only at the start of each clock pulse. The second type of signal is represented by the presence or absence of pulses that are coincident with the clock pulses. This signal is called *pulsed* or *return to zero*. These signals are shown in Fig. 4–2.

The actual system model that is used for a given synchronous sequential switching circuit depends on the signal used. Two system models corresponding to level and pulsed signals that use transition memory devices are shown in Fig. 4–3. Figure 4–3(a) represents the system model of a synchronous

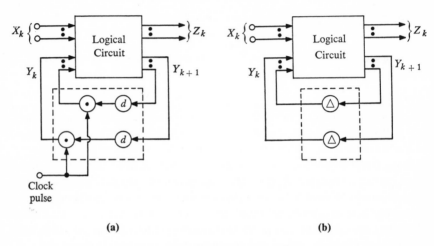

(a)   **(b)**

Figure 4–3. System models of sequential systems with level and pulsed signals.

sequential circuit when level signals are used. The delays d in the feedback path are just slightly larger than the clock-pulse duration δ. These delays have to be included, so that the values of Y_{k+1}, representing the next internal state of the system, should be applied as input signals to the logical circuit only when the next clock pulse arrives. In most practical realizations of such a system these delays are not necessarily included as separate physical units; the elements of the logical circuit are not ideal and provide the necessary delay.

Figure 4–3(b) represents the system model of a synchronous sequential circuit when pulsed signals are used. The delays Δ in the feedback path correspond to the time between the start of two clock pulses as shown in Fig. 4–2. This delay is introduced to ensure that all the signals to the logical circuit are applied at exactly the same time. Again, if the elements of the logical circuit are not ideal, these delays have to be adjusted so that all the signals to the input of the logical circuit are synchronized.

Actually, in both these system models it was assumed that the elements of the logical circuit were ideal, that is, delay-free, or that their delays were much smaller than Δ. Hohn[4] discusses the case when the logical elements include delays comparable to Δ or a multiple of Δ.

Another implied assumption concerns the signal shapes shown in Fig. 4–2, because all practical signals have finite rise and decay times. Also, the choice of pulse width and the time interval between successive pulses present a complicated engineering problem. Here we shall assume that these are chosen to be compatible with the physical characteristics of the components used in the specified hardware realization.

Note that in both these system models we assumed transition-type memory devices. In practice, these are in general circuits that simulate the delay action and not actual physical delays. Also, all the flip-flop memory devices defined in Chapter 3 can be used in the realization of synchronous systems, as is indicated later.

4–3. FURTHER PROPERTIES OF SYNCHRONOUS SYSTEMS

In Chapter 3 we saw that in the design of asynchronous systems the changes in both the input and memory variables had to be restricted drastically to avoid races. In a synchronous system, all the changes can only occur concurrently with the clock pulses, providing simultaneous changes in all the input variables to the logical circuit and thus avoiding race conditions. Also, owing to the behavior of the system variables described above, in a synchronous sequential system each memory state lasts at least until the next clock pulse is applied; thus every state is stable during this interval. These properties of the synchronous systems are easily detected, both in the state diagram and the flow diagram of a system. These characteristics of the synchronous sequential circuits can best be observed by way of an example.

EXAMPLE 1.   Design the single-input (x) and single-output (z) pulsed synchronous sequential circuit whose output $z = 1$ if both the number of 0's and the number of 1's applied to the input from time 0 are odd; otherwise the output $z = 0$.

The first step in the design is to obtain a state diagram of the circuit. From the word specification of this problem it can be seen that we have to distinguish among four different conditions according to past history. These conditions can be listed as follows:

(1)   The numbers of both 0's and 1's applied to the input are even.
(2)   The number of 0's applied to the input is even and the number of 1's is odd.

[4] F. E. Hohn, "States of Sequential Machines Whose Logical Elements Involve Delays," *Proc. Third Ann. Symp. Switching Circuit Theory and Logical Design*, 1962, pp. 82–89.

(3) The number of 0's applied to the input is odd and the number of 1's is
     even.
(4) The numbers of both 0's and 1's applied to the input are odd.

To obtain a state diagram of this system, these conditions are considered
as the states of the state diagram. And to obtain the transitions between these
states the effect of the input changes must be considered. At this point it would
seem appropriate to associate the outputs with the transitions, as this is
always possible, but checking the above conditions it can be seen that in this
case the outputs can be associated with the states, 0 with states 1, 2, and 3, and
1 with state 4. Thus, a Moore's state diagram is used here. To start, suppose
the system is in state 1; that is, the numbers of 0's and 1's applied to the
circuit are both even. If the next input is 0, the number of 0's becomes odd and
the system reaches state 3, this being indicated by an arrow marked 0 connecting state 1 with state 3. Similarly, if the system is in state 1 and the next input
is 1, a transition to state 2 is obtained; this is indicated by an arrow marked 1
connecting state 1 with state 2. The rest of the transitions between the states
of the system are obtained exactly in the same manner. The resulting Moore's
state diagram and transition table of this example are shown in Fig. 4–4.

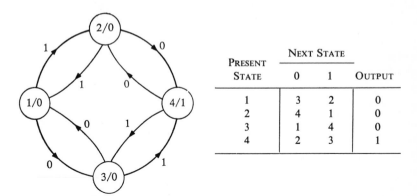

Figure 4–4. Moore's state diagram and transition table of Example 1.

Checking this transition table it can be seen that there are no stable states in
the asynchronous sense, since each input produces a transition between the
rows of the transition table.

The last step of synthesis is to obtain a memory-state assignment and to
calculate the corresponding Boolean functions. To obtain the secondary
assignment, we have first to decide on the initial state. If we consider 0 an even
number, state 1 is assigned the value 00. By letting state 2 be 01, state 3 be 10,
and state 4 be 11, the Y matrix of Fig. 4–5(a) is obtained. But by letting state
2 be 01, state 3 be 11, and state 4 be 10, the Y matrix of Fig. 4–5(b) is obtained.

y_1y_2		x		
		Y_1Y_2		
		0	1	z
	1-00	10	01	0
	2-01	11	00	0
	4-11	01	10	1
	3-10	00	11	0

(a)

y_1y_2		x		
		Y_1Y_2		
		0	1	z
	1-00	11	01	0
	2-01	10	00	0
	3-11	00	10	0
	4-10	01	11	1

(b)

Figure 4-5. The Y matrices of Example 1 for two secondary assignments.

The corresponding Boolean functions are as follows:

Assignment (a):
$$Y_1 = x_1' \cdot y_1' + x_1 \cdot y_1,$$
$$Y_2 = x_1' \cdot y_2 + x_1 \cdot y_2',$$
$$z = y_1 \cdot y_2.$$

Assignment (b):
$$Y_1 = x_1' \cdot y_1' + x_1 \cdot y_1,$$
$$Y_2 = y_2'$$
$$z = y_1 \cdot y_2'.$$

Note that we used Y to denote a state variable at the $(k + 1)$th instant of sampling and a lower-case letter to denote a state variable at the kth instant of observation. That is, the notation of Chapter 3 is used so as not to carry all the subscripts. In checking assignment (a) it can be seen that all race conditions are avoided. But this is not a necessary requirement in synchronous systems, and the assignment is generally made so as to simplify the logical circuit. This can be seen from assignment (b), which includes race conditions but leads to a set of Boolean functions having a total cost factor of 8; assignment (a) leads to a set of Boolean functions having a total cost factor of 14. This assignment procedure will be discussed briefly later.

In the above example we saw some of the differences between a synchronous and an asynchronous system. These properties can also be seen in the state diagrams of the two types of systems. Before considering how these differences show up in the state diagrams, we should distinguish among the different types of state diagrams used in the study of asynchronous systems. The differentiation we are interested in here is between a proper state diagram and the embedded state diagram. These can be either Mealy's or Moore's type. In a proper state diagram an arrow between two circles represents a transition between two stable states, whereas in the embedded state diagram some of the transitions have to be routed via circles that do not represent stable states for the particular input combination in order to avoid races.

Actually an embedded state diagram should be referred to as a p cube. Thus, in comparing the state diagrams of an asynchronous sequential circuit with those of a synchronous sequential circuit, only the proper state diagram of an asynchronous sequential circuit is considered.

In the state-diagram representation of an asynchronous sequential system, if there is a transition into a state q_j under the influence of a specific input combination $\bar{x}^i$, there cannot be a transition from this state into another state under the influence of the same input combination. This is due to the fact that in asynchronous sequential circuits there is no way to measure time; that is, two successive identical input combinations are not distinguishable. This is shown by the fact that for every arrow that represents a transition into a specified state, there must be a self-loop, and a transition between states can occur only when there is a change in the input signal. In the state-diagram representation of a synchronous sequential system there can be transitions both entering and leaving the same specified state q_j under the influence of the same input combination $\bar{x}^i$. This is due to the fact that successive identical input combinations are distinguishable by the time of their occurrence, since either the clock pulses or the repetition rate of the pulsed inputs enables the system to measure time. This can be easily seen in the state diagram of Example 1, as shown in Fig. 4-4. In this state diagram there are no self-loops, thus no stable states in the asynchronous sense. Another observable difference in the state-diagram representations of these two types of systems is in the number of arrows that can leave a specified state q_j. In synchronous systems, there can be transitions from a specified state q_j under the influence of all possible input combinations. In asynchronous systems, given a specified state q_j that has self-loops under the influence of the input combinations $\bar{x}^i, \bar{x}^l, \ldots,$ there can be transitions from this state only under the influence of the input combinations that differ only in one variable from the input combination $\bar{x}^i, \bar{x}^l, \ldots,$ because no race conditions are allowed in asynchronous systems.

Note that the synchronous system of Example 1 was chosen especially to accentuate the differences between synchronous and asynchronous sequential systems. Generally the differences between these two systems are not as clear-cut. This can best be seen by the examples introduced in Section 4-4.

4-4. EXAMPLES OF SYNCHRONOUS SYSTEMS

In this section we present a few examples of synchronous sequential circuits. This is done for the following reasons: (1) to provide examples of problems that are solved as synchronous systems, (2) to provide examples for the reduction procedure introduced later, and (3) to provide exercise in translating the verbal specification of a problem into its state-diagram representation. As this is the least well-defined part of the synthesis procedure, we cannot have too many examples.

EXAMPLE 2.   Obtain the state diagram and transition table of the following two-input (x_1, x_2) and single-output (z) synchronous sequential circuit.

The two inputs represent the digits 0, 1, 2, and 3 in binary notation. The output z is to be 0 if the sum of all inputs that have occurred from time zero is divisible by 2 but not by 3. The output z is to be 1 if the sum of all inputs that have occurred from time zero is divisible by 3 but not by 2. The output z may be either 0 or 1 in all other cases, that is, a don't-care condition.

To obtain the state-diagram representation, consider the sums of all possible inputs and the corresponding outputs. A don't-care output condition is denoted by a dash (–).

Sum of inputs:	0	1	2	3	4	5
Outputs:	–	–	0	1	0	–
Sum of inputs:	6	7	8	9	10	11
Outputs:	–	–	0	1	0	–
Sum of inputs:	$6i + 0$	$6i + 1$	$6i + 2$	$6i + 3$	$6i + 4$	$6i + 5$
Outputs:	–	–	0	1	0	–

From this we can see that the sum of inputs can be grouped in sets of six that have the same associated outputs. Thus for the state diagram we need six states corresponding to the sums of inputs in a general set. Also since the

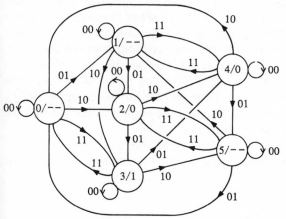

PRESENT	NEXT STATE				
STATE	00	01	11	10	OUTPUT
0	0	1	3	2	– –
1	1	2	4	3	– –
2	2	3	5	4	0
3	3	4	0	5	1
4	4	5	1	0	0
5	5	0	2	1	– –

Figure 4-6.   Moore's state diagram and transition table for Example 2.

outputs depend on the sum of inputs, they can be associated with the states of the state diagram, and a Moore's state diagram is used to represent this problem. The transitions of the state diagram are obtained by observing the effect of input changes. To see this, let us suppose the system is in the state $6i + 0$, denoted $0/--$, and let us observe the transitions caused by the different input combinations. If the next input combination is 00, 0 is added to the sum, and the system remains in the state denoted $0/--$. If the next input combination is 01, 1 is added to the sum and the system reaches the state $6i + 1$, denoted $1/--$. If the next input combination is 10, 2 is added to the sum and the system reaches the state $6i + 2$, denoted $2/0$. And if the next input combination is 11, 3 is added to the sum and the system reaches the state $6i + 3$, denoted $3/1$. The other transitions are obtained in exactly the same manner, assuming the system to be in the different possible states. The resulting state diagram and transition table are shown in Fig. 4–6.

EXAMPLE 3.   Obtain the state diagram and transition table of the following single-input, single-output synchronous sequential circuit. The circuit scans sets of three input signals. The output is defined only at every third interval and is 1 if and only if there was an odd number of 1's during the interval of the set of three inputs.

To obtain the state diagram we shall assume that the system is in its initial state, to which it must return at the end of each set of three inputs. Suppose this is state 1. After the first input we must distinguish between two cases: whether the first input was a 0 or a 1. These two conditions are represented by states 2 and 3, respectively. After the second input we must distinguish again between two cases: if the first two inputs were both 1's or both 0's, or if the first two inputs only included one 1. These two conditions are represented by states 4 and 5, respectively. Up to this point the outputs associated with the transitions are undefined and are denoted by dashes.

If the system is in state 4 this means that the number of 1's in the first two inputs is even; thus the transitions back to state 1 are marked 0/0 and 1/1. If

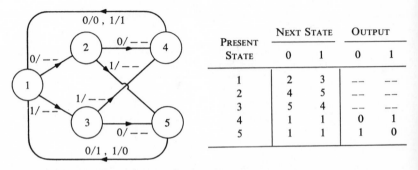

Figure 4–7.   Mealy's state diagram and transition table for Example 3.

the system is in state 5, this means that there was only one 1 in the first two inputs, and the transitions back to state 1 must be marked 0/1 and 1/0. The corresponding state diagram and transition table are shown in Fig. 4–7.

EXAMPLE 4.   Obtain the state diagram and transition table of the two-input (x_1, x_2), two-output (z_1, z_2) synchronous sequential circuit that acts as a *senary* (base 6) *comparator*. The circuit scans a set of three consecutive inputs that represent two senary numbers X_1 and X_2. Each of these senary numbers is in 321 code (as shown in Fig. 4–8), with the least significant digit applied first to the circuit, that is, $X_i = x_{i,k} x_{i,k-1} x_{i,k-2} = 321$. The outputs are only defined at the third input of a set of inputs, and are $z_1 z_2 = 00$ if $X_1 = X_2$, $z_1 z_2 = 01$ if $X_1 < X_2$, and $z_1 z_2 = 10$ if $X_1 > X_2$.

To obtain the state diagram we assume that the initial state of the system is state 1. Before considering the other states we should observe first the characteristics of the code chosen. As three binary numbers are used to encode a senary number, there are two input combinations that are not used. From

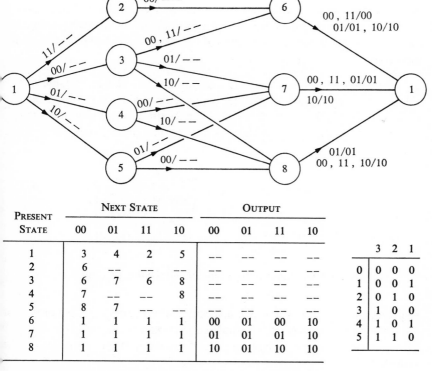

PRESENT STATE	NEXT STATE				OUTPUT			
	00	01	11	10	00	01	11	10
1	3	4	2	5	--	--	--	--
2	6	--	--	--	--	--	--	--
3	6	7	6	8	--	--	--	--
4	7	--	--	8	--	--	--	--
5	8	7	--	--	--	--	--	--
6	1	1	1	1	00	01	00	10
7	1	1	1	1	01	01	01	10
8	1	1	1	1	10	01	10	10

	3	2	1
0	0	0	0
1	0	0	1
2	0	1	0
3	1	0	0
4	1	0	1
5	1	1	0

Figure 4–8.   Mealy's state diagram and transition table of Example 4 and the 321 senary code.

the definition of the code these input combinations are 011 and 111. That is, if the least significant digit is 1, it can be followed only by a 0. Thus after the first input we need to distinguish among four cases, because the conditions $x_1x_2 = 00$ and $x_1x_2 = 11$ cannot be considered the same conditions, as the input combination 11 must be followed by 00 and there is no such restriction if the first input combination is 00. Note that the input combination 01 can only be followed by either 00 or 10, and the input combination 10 can only be followed by either 00 or 01. After the second input all possible input combinations can occur; thus we require only three states to distinguish whether up to this point one of the senary numbers was greater than, equal to, or smaller than the other senary number. Since the outputs are defined only at every third input combination, all transitions corresponding to the first two input combinations have dashes associated with them. From the three states representing the past history of the system after the first two input combinations, all transitions under the influence of the third input combination take the system to state 1, reinitiating the operation. The corresponding state diagram and transition table of this example are shown in Fig. 4–8.

Note that in the state diagram of Fig. 4–8 there are two states marked 1. They represent the same state and were separated only to simplify the drawing. Also note that binary-coded senary numbers are used instead of binary-coded decimal numbers to reduce the complexity of the circuits, and note that the 321 code shown corresponds to the 5421 code of the binary-coded decimal numbers.

EXAMPLE 5. Obtain the state diagram and the transition table of the single-input and single-output synchronous sequential circuit whose behavior is defined by the finite set of specified input-output sequences presented in Fig. 4–9. In this type of synchronous sequential circuit, only those input

I.P.	O.P.		I.P.	O.P.		I.P.	O.P.
0	0		0	0 ⎫		1	0
0	1		1	1 ⎭ REPEAT		0	1
1	0 ⎫					1	0
1	0 ⎬ REPEAT					1	1
0	1 ⎭						

Figure 4–9. Input-output sequences specifying Example 5.

sequences are specified for which a specific output response is required. For all other input sequences the output sequence can be anything. In Fig. 4–9 REPEAT means that the designated part of the input-output sequence can be repeated.

The simplest way to obtain the state diagram of such a system is to translate each input-output sequence into a separate state diagram. To obtain such a separate state diagram is straightforward. To obtain the state diagram of the first sequence, let us assume that the system is in state 1_1 and that the input 0 provides a transition to state 2_1. This transition is marked 0/0 because the associated output is 0. For each transition a new state is defined, until state 5_1 is reached by the transition marked 1/0. As the last three elements of the sequence can be repeated, there is a transition 0/1 from state 5_1 back to state 3_1. The resulting state diagrams for all three sequences and the combined transition table are shown in Fig. 4-10. Note that in the state diagram of the

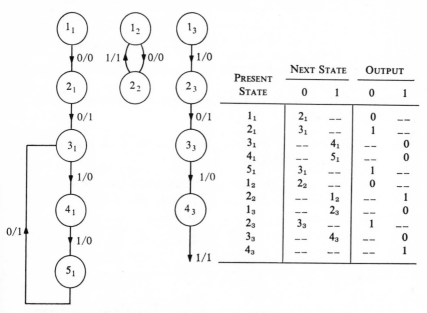

Present State	Next State		Output	
	0	1	0	1
1_1	2_1	--	0	--
2_1	3_1	--	1	--
3_1	--	4_1	--	0
4_1	--	5_1	--	0
5_1	3_1	--	1	--
1_2	2_2	--	0	--
2_2	--	1_2	--	1
1_3	--	2_3	--	0
2_3	3_3	--	1	--
3_3	--	4_3	--	0
4_3	--	--	--	1

Figure 4-10.   Mealy's state diagram and transition table of Example 5.

third sequence in Fig. 4-10 there is a transition that leads nowhere. This is due to the fact that this transition represents the last input-output pair in the sequence and all further behavior of the system is undefined.

Generally in such a system further restrictions are placed on the circuit—such as which input-output sequences, if any, have to be started from the same initial state. In the above example we can require that all defined input-output sequences start from the same initial state. To obtain this, states 1_1, 1_2, and 1_3 are replaced by a single initial state 1. But this in turn implies that states 2_1 and 2_2 must be replaced by a single state 2, as both these states have to be reached from state 1 by the transition marked 0/0. No further combination of states is made, because no other combinations are required, and unnecessary combinations may block some possible reductions, as will be shown later. The resulting state diagram and transition table are

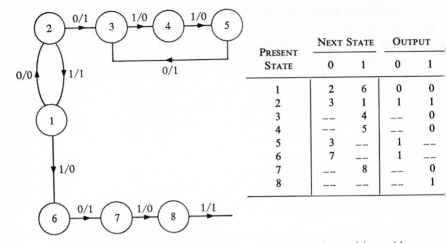

Figure 4–11. Combined Mealy's state diagram and transition table of Example 5.

shown in Fig. 4–11. To avoid subscripts the states of the state diagram in Fig. 4–10 are renamed as follows:

Combined	Original
1	$1_1, 1_2, 1_3$
2	$2_1, 2_2$
3	3_1
4	4_1
5	5_1
6	2_3
7	3_3
8	4_3

Note that in many cases not all sequences can be started in the same starting state, because there can be conflicts in the sequences defined. In such cases arrangements have to be made to start the operation of the system at the different required starting states.

4-5. STATE REDUCTION FOR INCOMPLETELY SPECIFIED SEQUENTIAL SYSTEMS. Part I: Preliminary Definitions

The state-reduction procedure described in this chapter treats the problem of reducing the number of states of a sequential system without changing its *required* behavior. The word "required" is used here because this procedure was developed to reduce the states of an incompletely specified sequential system, that is, a system where not all the input-output sequences are specified.

Before considering the outline of the reduction procedure, the exact meaning of a don't-care entry in the transition table needs to be clarified. If the system enters an unspecified state under the influence of a given input combination, it is obvious that all further output combinations from the circuit can be ignored, as they correspond to an unspecified input-output sequence. On the other hand, if the output is unspecified this can be quite ambiguous and we must define further what is meant by such an unspecified output entry in the transition table. The actual meaning of such an entry is exactly the meaning of the word unspecified; that is, it can be 1 or 0 and it need not be the same every time it occurs. To see some of the ambiguities, consider the following two examples.

EXAMPLE 6. Obtain the minimal state diagram and transition table of the following single-input (x), single-output (z) synchronous sequential circuit.

The circuit compares the present input x_k with the previous input x_{k-1}. The output $z = 1$ if the present input is greater than the previous one, and $z = 0$ if the previous input is greater than the present one. The output is unspecified whenever the present and previous inputs are equal. To obtain a state diagram we have to distinguish between two conditions: whether the previous input was 0 or 1. These two conditions are represented respectively by the states marked 0 and 1. The corresponding state diagram and transition table are shown in Fig. 4–12.

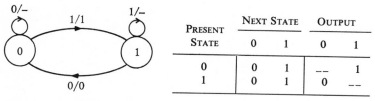

	NEXT STATE		OUTPUT	
PRESENT STATE	0	1	0	1
0	0	1	--	1
1	0	1	0	--

Figure 4–12. Mealy's state diagram and transition table of Example 6.

The question now is how to interpret the unspecified entries in the above transition table. One way would be to redefine the problem in either one of the following two ways:

(a) $z = 1$ if $x_k \geq x_{k-1}$ and $z = 0$ if $x_k < x_{k-1}$,
(b) $z = 1$ if $x_k > x_{k-1}$ and $z = 0$ if $x_k \leq x_{k-1}$.

For both these cases the unspecified outputs of the transition table of Fig. 4–12 are defined. For case (a), both of the unspecified outputs are changed to 1's and for case (b) both of the unspecified outputs are changed to 0's. The corresponding transition tables are shown in Fig. 4–13(a) and (b), respectively.

In both cases the resulting systems are minimal, as there cannot be a reduction in the number of states of these systems. Actually, these assignments of output values are forced, as they are not indicated by the original specification of the problem. For example, another assignment that satisfies

PRESENT STATE	NEXT STATE		OUTPUT	
	0	1	0	1
0	0	1	1	1
1	0	1	0	1

(a)

PRESENT STATE	NEXT STATE		OUTPUT	
	0	1	0	1
0	0	1	0	1
1	0	1	0	0

(b)

Figure 4–13. Transition-table representation of the redefined Example 6.

the original specification of the problem is obtained by changing the unspecified entry of the first row into a 0 and that of the second row into a 1. By this assignment the two rows of the transition table of Fig. 4–12 are made equal. Thus the two states are equal and can be replaced by one state; that is, the problem is no longer a sequential problem but a combinational problem with the output $z = x$.

EXAMPLE 7.   Obtain the minimal state diagram and transition table of the synchronous sequential circuit defined by the state diagram and transition table given in Fig. 4–14.

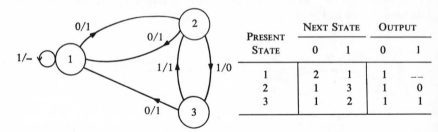

PRESENT STATE	NEXT STATE		OUTPUT	
	0	1	0	1
1	2	1	1	--
2	1	3	1	0
3	1	2	1	1

Figure 4–14. Mealy's state diagram and transition-table representation of Example 7.

Suppose we want to simplify this circuit by assigning a specific value to the unspecified output entry. Suppose this entry is changed to 1; then rows 1 and 3 are probably equivalent pairs. But for states 1 and 3 to be equivalent it is necessary that states 1 and 2 be equivalent. Thus if the unspecified output is changed to a 1, the circuit cannot be reduced. Now if the unspecified entry is changed to 0, rows 1 and 2 are probably equivalent pairs. But for states 1 and 2 to be equivalent requires that states 1 and 3 be equivalent. Thus if the unspecified output is changed to a 0, the circuit cannot be reduced. On the other hand, if row 1 is split into two rows 1_1 and 1_2, the circuit behavior remains unchanged. If the unspecified entry of row 1_1 is changed to 0 and the unspecified entry of row 1_2 is changed to 1, rows 1_1 and 2 and rows 1_2 and 3 become probably equivalent pairs, and these states become equivalent if the subscripts are added in the transition table of Fig. 4–15(a). By combining rows

PRESENT STATE	NEXT STATE		OUTPUT		PRESENT STATE	NEXT STATE		OUTPUT	
	0	1	0	1		0	1	0	1
1_1	2	1_2	1	0̶	A	A	B	1	0
1_2	2	1_1	1	+̶	B	A	A	1	1
2	1_1	3	1	0					
3	1_1	2	1	1			(b)		

(a)

Figure 4–15.   Expanded and minimal transition tables of Example 7.

1_1 and 2 and rows 1_2 and 3 and denoting the resulting states by A and B, respectively, we obtain the transition table of Fig. 4–15(b).

Note that this reduction was obtained by splitting the row with the un-specified entry and assigning different values to the two resulting unspecified entries. That is, the unspecified output entry of the transition table in Fig. 4–14 was not defined uniquely. To see this, consider applying the same input sequence (00110) to both the original (Fig. 4–14) and the minimal [Fig. 4–15(b)] systems assuming corresponding starting states. When the above input sequence is applied to the original system, starting in state 1, the result-ing output sequence is (11_ _1). Applying the same input sequence to the minimal system, starting in state A, the resulting output sequence is (11011). That is, the first unspecified output was replaced by a 0 and the second by a 1. Note that in this example both states A and B of the minimal system can be considered as corresponding states of state 1 of the original system, because both include this state.

Thus the meaning of an unspecified output is that the output at this point is ignored, and an unspecified next state is interpreted to mean that all sub-sequent behavior of the system is of no consequence. Note that here we only mentioned unspecified next states that are not results of prohibited input combinations. This is done because the meaning of the unspecified next-state and output entries, owing to input restrictions, is unambiguous, as the system cannot reach any of these states.

The next step is to define exactly what is meant by obtaining a sequential system having the same required behavior. This can be done with the aid of the following definitions.

Definition 3.   *Applicable input sequence to s. I_s* is an applicable input sequence to the system S with s as its starting state if and only if I_s leads to a specified next state after each input of the sequence, except possibly the last.

Definition 4.   *t covers s, t > s.* State t of system T is said to cover state s of system S if and only if for all I_s applied to system S starting in state s, and to system T starting in state t, the outputs of T are the same as the outputs of S whenever the latter are specified.

Note that this definition includes an implied requirement on the system T. This requirement is that all the applicable input sequences I_s be included in the set of the applicable input sequences I_t. Also note that the covering relation is a binary relation, and if we allow the system T to represent system S also, it has the following properties:

(1) $s > s$ for all s; thus it is *reflexive*.
(2) If $t > s$ and $r > t$ then $r > s$; thus it is *transitive*.
(3) If $t > s$ it does not mean that $s > t$, because I_t is not necessarily included in I_s; thus it is *nonsymmetric*.

Definition 5.   *T covers S, $T > S$.* System T is said to cover system S if and only if for every state s in S there exists a state t in T such that $t > s$.

Note that the coverage relationship between two systems is also a binary relation, just as is the covering relation between two states of the system. Also note that this relation is reflexive, transitive, and nonsymmetric. Using these definitions, the problem statement of the state-reduction procedure can be stated as follows:

Given a sequential system S, it is required to obtain another sequential system T such that $T > S$ and has a minimal number of states.

At this point we digress and consider completely specified sequential systems. These are systems in which all the entries of the transition table are defined; a complete column may be unspecified, as this shows only invalid input combinations. If the sequential system is completely specified, all input sequences are applicable and the coverage relation between two states becomes the equivalence relation as defined by Definition 11 of Chapter 3. In this case the reduction process becomes one of finding an equivalent system T that has a minimal number of states. This can be stated in the format of a theorem, which was originally stated by Ginsburg[5]:

Theorem 1.   *Given a completely specified sequential system, the recognition of all the equivalences leads to a minimal state system.*

To return to sequential systems with unspecified entries, the state-reduction procedure presented here follows essentially the outline of Paull and Unger[6] and has to satisfy the above statement. This procedure is a generalization of the one presented in Chapter 3, and it also indicates which of the states should be split to provide more efficient row merging. Another difference between this procedure and the reduction procedure of Chapter 3 is that here it is not required to find all the equivalences first, because they are automatic-

---

[5] S. Ginsburg, *IRE Trans. Electron. Computers*, **8**, 346–355 (1959).

[6] M. C. Paull and S. H. Unger, *IRE Trans. Electron. Computers*, **8**, 356–367 (1959).

ally obtained during the process. Although this is not necessary, generally all the equivalences are found first and only then is the reduction procedure applied. This is done because the two-step process generally requires less work.

The actual procedure is executed in two steps. In the first step, the states of system S are used to obtain a set of maximal compatible states referred to as M.C.'s. The second step of the procedure is an enumeration process that uses the set of maximal compatible states to obtain the states of the minimal system T. These two steps of the reduction procedure are considered in Sections 4–6 and 4–7.

4–6. STATE REDUCTION FOR INCOMPLETELY SPECIFIED SEQUENTIAL SYSTEMS. Part II: Computation of the Sets of Maximal Compatible States

The basic idea of this section is to obtain maximal subsets of the states of the system S that do not have contradictory output sequences. To clarify this statement the following definitions are used.

Definition 6. *Compatible output sequences.* Two output sequences are said to be *compatible* if the corresponding outputs of the two sequences are equal whenever they are both specified.

To simplify our discussion, we shall denote by Z_s^r an output sequence of length r, the outputs obtained when an applicable input sequence I_s of length r is applied to system S with s as its starting state.

Definition 7. *Compatible states icj.* Two states, i and j, of system S are said to be compatible if and only if the output sequences Z_i^r and Z_j^r are compatible for all input sequences I_{ij}^r.

In this definition I_{ij}^r represents the input sequences of length r that are applicable to S with i or j as its starting state. Note that this is a binary relation between two states of the system and is reflexive, nontransitive, and symmetric. When the sequential system is completely specified, this relation becomes the equivalence relation. The binary relation of compatibility can be extended to include n states of a system S by the following definitions.

Definition 8. *n mutually compatible states.* A set of n states of system S is said to be *mutually compatible* if and only if every pair of states of the set is compatible.

Definition 9. *Maximal compatible states.* A set of n mutually compatible states is said to be a *set of maximal compatible states* if and only if it does not form a proper subset of another set of states that is mutually compatible.

From these definitions it can be seen that computing the sets of maximal compatible states of a system corresponds to obtaining a partition, generally not exclusive, of the states of a sequential system by observing its input-output behavior. A subset of the partition includes those states of the system that do not lead to contradictory output sequences when the system is started in any one of these states. At this point we have an exactly defined objective, and the above definitions also suggest a procedure for obtaining this objective. To see this, a simple example is now introduced.

EXAMPLE 8.   Obtain the sets of maximal compatible states of system S, which is represented by the state diagram and transition table of Fig. 4–16.

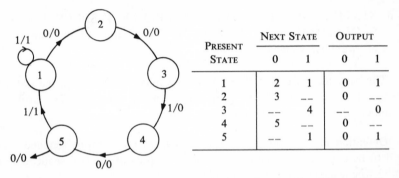

Figure 4–16.   Mealy's state diagram and transition table of Example 8.

To obtain the sets of maximal compatible states, input sequences of different lengths are applied, with each of the states of the system as starting states, and the resulting output sequences are observed. If no input is applied, that is, an experiment of 0 length is executed, there is no way to distinguish among the different states that the system may be in, as this is a Mealy's system. If an experiment of length 1 is executed, some of the starting states can be distinguished. There is no contradiction if input 0 is applied, because under the influence of this input all the outputs, if defined, are 0. But if input 1 is applied, there is a contradiction in the outputs, and states 1 and 3 and states 3 and 5 have to be distinguished. That is, state 3 cannot be included in a set with states 1 and 5. Thus, as a result of executing experiments of length 1, the states of the system are partitioned into two subsets: $\sigma_1, \sigma_2 = (1, 2, 4, 5)$, $(2, 3, 4)$.

Now, if experiments of length 2 are executed, states 2 and 4 are differentiated, because the next states that are reached from these states under the influence of input 0 are states 3 and 5. Thus the above-obtained subsets have to be partitioned again so that states 2 and 4 are not included in one subset. That is, the following four subsets are obtained: $\sigma_1, \sigma_2, \sigma_3, \sigma_4 = (1, 2, 5)$, $(1, 4, 5), (2, 3), (3, 4)$. By seeking contradictions among the output sequences resulting from all the experiments of length 2, we can distinguish whether the system was started in a state included in a specified subset σ_i. For this particular example experiments of greater length will not provide further contradictions, and thus the above subsets are the sets of mutually compatible states. Also, since none of the sets of mutually compatible states forms a proper subset of another set, they are the sets of maximal compatible states. These are generally denoted as follows:

$$\text{M.C.'s} = (1, 2, 5), (1, 4, 5), (2, 3), (3, 4) = C_1, C_2, C_3, C_4.$$

Actually, these sets of maximal compatible states could also have been obtained by first calculating all the pairs of compatible states. Then the sets of maximal compatible states are obtained by combining the pairs of compatible states according to Definitions 8 and 9. To check compatibility, the rows of the transition table are compared pairwise, exactly in the same manner as checking for equivalence in Chapter 3 (see Example 6, Chapter 3), the only difference being that the outputs must be identical only whenever both are specified. To see this we shall consider the states of this example; that is, we shall compare the rows of the transition table of Fig. 4–16.

Comparing rows 1 and 2, it can be seen that there is no contradiction in the output entries. But in order that these rows represent compatible states it is necessary that states 2 and 3 be compatible, as they are the next-state entries under the influence of input 0. States 2 and 3 are referred to as *implied states*, and to denote the above relationship between the two pairs of states the following notation is used: $(1, 2) \rightarrow (2, 3)$. Note that there is no such requirement for the next states under the influence of input 1, because the next-state entry under the influence of this input is unspecified. Comparing rows 1 and 3, it can be seen that there is a contradiction in the output entries; that is, states 1 and 3 are incompatible. This is denoted by placing an X against this pair. Comparing rows 1 and 5 it can be seen that there is no contradiction in the output entries, and also that these states do not imply any other pair of states. This is denoted by placing a check mark ($\checkmark$) against this pair. The remaining pairs of rows of the transition table are checked in exactly the same manner, and, as the compatible relationship is a symmetric relationship, only the following pairs need be listed:

$$
\begin{aligned}
&(1, 2) \rightarrow (2, 3) \\
&(1, 3) \qquad \text{X} \\
&(1, 4) \rightarrow (2, 5) \\
&(1, 5) \qquad \checkmark \\
&(2, 3) \qquad \checkmark \\
&(2, 4) \rightarrow (3, 5) \qquad \text{X} \\
&(2, 5) \qquad \checkmark \\
&(3, 4) \qquad \checkmark \\
&(3, 5) \qquad \text{X} \\
&(4, 5) \qquad \checkmark.
\end{aligned}
$$

The pairs of states that imply another pair or pairs of states have to be checked to see whether the implied pairs are compatible. If the implied pairs are incompatible, these pairs are also incompatible and are marked X. In our case, only the pair (2, 4) is so eliminated. It may be necessary to execute more than one such run, to eliminate all the incompatible pairs. Thus in our example the pairs of compatible states are (1, 2), (1, 4), (1, 5), (2, 3), (2, 5), (3, 4), and (4, 5). By applying Definitions 8 and 9 the sets of maximal compatible states are obtained as follows:

$$(1, 2), (1, 5), (2, 5) \Rightarrow (1, 2, 5)$$
$$(1, 4), (1, 5), (4, 5) \Rightarrow (1, 4, 5)$$
$$(2, 3) \Rightarrow (2, 3)$$
$$(3, 4) \Rightarrow (3, 4).$$

From this example it can be seen that the sets of maximal compatible states can be computed in two ways. In the first procedure, input sequences of different lengths are applied to the system, with each one of its states as a starting state. The states of the system are then partitioned according to the contradictions in the resulting output sequences. The length of the input sequences is increased until no further contradiction is obtained. The resulting sets of states are mutually compatible sets but not necessarily maximal. To obtain the sets of maximal compatible states, all the sets of states in the partition that are proper subsets of another set are excluded. This procedure, as seen from the above example is straightforward, and with a little experience one can become efficient in its use. A good presentation of the procedure is given by Miller.[7] The disadvantage of the procedure is that it is quite hard to program on a computer. In the second procedure, the pairs of compatible states are computed by comparing the rows of the transition table pairwise, and then the pairs are combined to form sets of maximal compatible states. This procedure lends itself to simple programing and is the one generally used in automatic design procedures. This is also the procedure used in this chapter to obtain the sets of maximal compatible states, because the steps of this procedure can be defined more precisely than the steps of the first procedure. The actual procedure for obtaining the pairs of compatible states is slightly modified to make it more convenient for paper-and-pencil computations. In this step of the procedure a tabular format is used, as suggested by Paull and Unger.[8] This step is introduced by way of an example.

EXAMPLE 2 (*continued, I*).   Obtain the sets of maximal compatible states of Example 2. The transition table of Fig. 4–6 is reproduced here as part of Fig. 4–17.

The implication table of Fig. 4–17, used to obtain the pairs of compatible states, is organized so that all the required pairs of states can be compared. In computing the implication table the notation of the previous example is used.

[7] R. E. Miller, "State Reduction for Sequential Machines," *IBM Res. Rept. RC-121*, June 15, 1959.

[8] M. C. Paull and S. H. Unger, *IRE Trans. Electron. Computers*, **8**, 356–357 (1959).

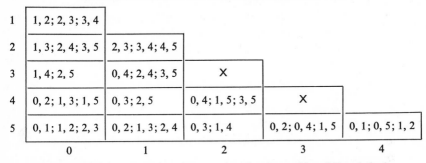

PRESENT STATE	NEXT STATE				OUTPUT
	00	01	11	10	
0	0	1	3	2	––
1	1	2	4	3	––
2	2	3	5	4	0
3	3	4	0	5	1
4	4	5	1	0	0
5	5	0	2	1	––

	0	1	2	3	4
1	1, 2; 2, 3; 3, 4				
2	1, 3; 2, 4; 3, 5	2, 3; 3, 4; 4, 5			
3	1, 4; 2, 5	0, 4; 2, 4; 3, 5	X		
4	0, 2; 1, 3; 1, 5	0, 3; 2, 5	0, 4; 1, 5; 3, 5	X	
5	0, 1; 1, 2; 2, 3	0, 2; 1, 3; 2, 4	0, 3; 1, 4	0, 2; 0, 4; 1, 5	0, 1; 0, 5; 1, 2

Figure 4–17. Transition table and implication table of Example 2.

That is, in each of the squares of the implication table, the implied pairs of states or an X or a check mark (√) is entered, depending on the next states and the outputs associated with the pair of states designated by the corresponding row and column of the implication table. The pairs of states marked X in the implication table are not compatible, and are referred to as incompatible pairs. The pairs of states marked √ are compatible pairs. The rest have to be checked to see whether they are compatible. To obtain pairs of compatible states, those pairs whose compatibility implies a pair of incompatible states must be excluded. This is done by starting from one of the X entries and entering an X in each square where this pair of incompatible states is listed. To indicate that the effect of such a pair of incompatible states was already considered, a second X is entered in such a square. By repeated application of the above step an implication table with each square containing either two X's or no X's is obtained. Such a table is shown in Fig. 4–18.

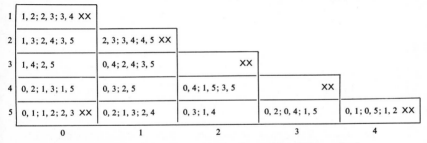

	0	1	2	3	4
1	1, 2; 2, 3; 3, 4 XX				
2	1, 3; 2, 4; 3, 5	2, 3; 3, 4; 4, 5 XX			
3	1, 4; 2, 5	0, 4; 2, 4; 3, 5	XX		
4	0, 2; 1, 3; 1, 5	0, 3; 2, 5	0, 4; 1, 5; 3, 5	XX	
5	0, 1; 1, 2; 2, 3 XX	0, 2; 1, 3; 2, 4	0, 3; 1, 4	0, 2; 0, 4; 1, 5	0, 1; 0, 5; 1, 2 XX

Figure 4–18. Completed implication table of Example 2.

In the table of Fig. 4–18 the squares that do not include X's represent pairs of compatible states. To obtain the sets of maximal compatible states another table is used. This table, referred to as the *table of mutual compatibles*, has rows corresponding to the columns of the implication table. If the last column of the implication table indicates a compatible pair of states, this is entered in the first row of this table; otherwise a dash (−−) is entered. In the consecutive rows, both the compatibles of the previous rows and the new pairs of compatibles of the corresponding column of the implication table are entered. In each row, whenever possible, the sets of mutually compatible states are combined to form larger sets of mutually compatible states. In each row only the largest sets of mutually compatible states are left. The table of mutually compatible states of this example is presented in Fig. 4–19. Thus

```
4 |  --
3 |  (3, 5)
2 |  (3, 5)  (2, 5)  (2, 4)
1 |  (3, 5)  (2, 5)  (2, 4)  (1, 5)  (1, 4)  (1, 5)  (1, 3, 5)
0 |  (1, 3, 5)  (2, 5)  (2, 4)  (1, 4)  (0, 4)  (0, 3)  (0, 2)  (0, 2, 4)
```

Fig. 4–19. Table of mutually compatible states of Example 2.

the sets of maximal compatible states are listed in the last row of the figure; that is,

$$\text{M.C.'s} = (0, 2, 4), (1, 3, 5), (2, 5), (1, 4), (0, 3) = C_1, C_2, C_3, C_4, C_5.$$

EXAMPLE 3 (*continued, I*). Obtain the sets of maximal compatible states of the states of Example 3, as represented by the transition table of Fig. 4–7.

The required steps for obtaining the sets of maximal compatibles of this example are presented in Fig. 4–20.

2	2, 4; 3, 5			
3	2, 5; 3, 4	4, 5 XX		
4	1, 2; 1, 3	1, 4; 1, 5	1, 4; 1, 5	
5	1, 2; 1, 3	1, 4; 1, 5	1, 4; 1, 5	XX
	1	2	3	4

PRESENT STATE	NEXT STATE 0	NEXT STATE 1	OUTPUT 0	OUTPUT 1
1	2	3	−−	−−
2	4	5	−−	−−
3	5	4	−−	−−
4	1	1	0	1
5	1	1	1	0

```
4 |  --
3 |  (3, 5) (3, 4)
2 |  (3, 5) (3, 4) (2, 5) (2, 4)
1 |  (3, 5) (3, 4) (2, 5) (2, 4) (1, 5) (1, 4) (1, 3) (1, 2) (1, 2, 4) (1, 2, 5) (1, 3, 4) (1, 3, 5)
```

$$\text{M.C.'s} = (1, 2, 4), (1, 2, 5), (1, 3, 4), (1, 3, 5) = C_1, C_2, C_3, C_4$$

Figure 4–20. Tables used in the computation of the sets of maximal compatible states of Example 3.

EXAMPLE 4 (*continued, I*).   Obtain the sets of maximal compatible states of the states of Example 4 as represented by the transition table of Fig. 4–8.

The required steps for obtaining the sets of maximal compatibles of this example are presented in Fig. 4–21.

PRESENT STATE	NEXT STATE				OUTPUT			
	00	01	11	10	00	01	11	10
1	3	4	2	5	--	--	--	--
2	6	--	--	--	--	--	--	--
3	6	7	6	8	--	--	--	--
4	7	--	--	8	--	--	--	--
5	8	7	--	--	--	--	--	--
6	1	1	1	1	00	01	00	10
7	1	1	1	1	01	01	01	10
8	1	1	1	1	10	01	10	10

	1	2	3	4	5	6	7
2	3, 6						
3	2, 6; 3, 6; 4, 7; 5, 8	√					
4	3, 7; 5, 8	6, 7 XX	6, 7 XX				
5	3, 8; 4, 7	6, 8 XX	6, 8 XX	7, 8 XX			
6	1, 2; 1, 3; 1, 4; 1, 5	1, 6	1, 6; 1, 7; 1, 8	1, 7; 1, 8	1, 7; 1, 8		
7	1, 2; 1, 3; 1, 4; 1, 5	1, 6	1, 6; 1, 7; 1, 8	1, 7; 1, 8	1, 7; 1, 8	XX	
8	1, 2; 1, 3; 1, 4; 1, 5	1, 6	1, 6; 1, 7; 1, 8	1, 7; 1, 8	1, 7; 1, 8	XX	XX

7 | --
6 | --
5 | (5, 8) (5, 7) (5, 6)
4 | (5, 8) (5, 7) (5, 6) (4, 8) (4, 7) (4, 6)
3 | (5, 8) (5, 7) (5, 6) (4, 8) (4, 7) (4, 6) (3, 8) (3, 7) (3, 6)
2 | (5, 8) (5, 7) (5, 6) (4, 8) (4, 7) (4, 6) ~~(3, 8)~~ ~~(3, 7)~~ ~~(3, 6)~~ ~~(2, 8)~~ ~~(2, 7)~~ ~~(2, 6)~~ ~~(2, 3)~~
   (2, 3, 6) (2, 3, 7) (2, 3, 8)
1 | ~~(2, 3, 6)~~ ~~(2, 3, 7)~~ ~~(2, 3, 8)~~ ~~(5, 8)~~ ~~(5, 7)~~ ~~(5, 6)~~ ~~(4, 8)~~ ~~(4, 7)~~ ~~(4, 6)~~ ~~(1, 8)~~ ~~(1, 7)~~ ~~(1, 6)~~
   ~~(1, 5)~~ ~~(1, 4)~~ ~~(1, 3)~~ ~~(1, 2)~~ (1, 2, 3, 6) (1, 2, 3, 7) (1, 2, 3, 8) (1, 4, 6) (1, 4, 7) (1, 4, 8)
   (1, 5, 6) (1, 5, 7) (1, 5, 8)

M.C.'s = (1, 2, 3, 6), (1, 2, 3, 7), (1, 2, 3, 8), (1, 4, 6), (1, 4, 7), (1, 4, 8), (1, 5, 6),
   (1, 5, 7), (1, 5, 8) = C_1, C_2, C_3, C_4, C_5, C_6, C_7, C_8, C_9

Figure 4–21.   Tables used in the computation of the sets of maximal compatible states of Example 4.

EXAMPLE 5 (*continued, I*).   Obtain the sets of maximal compatible states of the states of Example 5 as represented by the transition table of Fig. 4–11.

The required steps for obtaining the sets of maximal compatibles of this example are shown in Fig. 4–22.

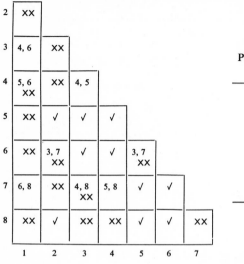

Present State	Next State 0	1	Output 0	1
1	2	6	0	0
2	3	1	1	1
3	--	4	--	0
4	--	5	--	0
5	3	--	1	--
6	7	--	1	--
7	--	8	--	0
8	--	--	--	1

```
7 | --
6 | (6, 8)  (6, 7)
5 | (6, 8)  (6, 7)  (5, 8)  (5, 7)
4 | (6, 8)  (6, 7)  (5, 8)  (5, 7)  (4, 7)  (4, 6)  (4, 5)  (4, 5, 7)  (4, 6, 7)
3 | (4, 5, 7)  (4, 6, 7)  (6, 8)  (5, 8)  (3, 6)  (3, 5)  (3, 4)  (3, 4, 5)  (3, 4, 6)
2 | (3, 4, 5)  (3, 4, 6)  (4, 5, 7)  (4, 6, 7)  (6, 8)  (5, 8)  (2, 8)  (2, 5)  (2, 5, 8)
1 | (2, 5, 8)  (3, 4, 5)  (3, 4, 6)  (4, 5, 7)  (4, 6, 7)  (6, 8)  (1, 7)  (1, 3)
```

M.C.'s = (2, 5, 8), (3, 4, 5), (3, 4, 6), (4, 5, 7), (4, 6, 7), (1, 3), (1, 7), (6, 8)
= $C_1, C_2, C_3, C_4, C_5, C_6, C_7, C_8$

Figure 4–22.   Tables used in the computation of the sets of maximal compatible states of Example 5.

As seen from the above examples the computation of the sets of maximal compatible states is straightforward. Also, it can be seen that there is no relation between the number of sets of maximal compatible states (h) and the number of original states in the system representation (h'). In Example 2, $h = h'$; in Example 3, $h < h'$; and in Examples 4 and 5, $h > h'$. Another point is obtained by definition; that is, the union of all sets of maximal compatible states includes all states of the original system. But, given a system that has a state which is not compatible with any other state of the system, the last row of the table of mutually compatible states does not include this state. And to obtain all the sets of maximal compatible states, the above states must be added as additional sets that include only one state. To see this, consider the following example.

EXAMPLE 9.   Obtain the sets of maximal compatible states of the system represented by the transition table of Fig. 4–23.

PRESENT STATE	NEXT STATE 0	NEXT STATE 1	OUTPUT 0	OUTPUT 1
1	2	1	0	1
2	3	--	1	--
3	4	6	0	0
4	--	5	--	0
5	--	1	--	0
6	--	1	--	0

	1	2	3	4	5
2	XX				
3	XX	XX			
4	XX	√	5, 6		
5	XX	√	1, 6 XX	1, 5 XX	
6	XX	√	1, 6 XX	1, 5 XX	√

5 | (5, 6)
4 | (5, 6)
3 | (5, 6) (3, 4)
2 | (5, 6) (3, 4) (2, 6) (2, 4) (2, 5) (2, 5, 6)
1 | (2, 5, 6) (2, 4) (3, 4)

Figure 4–23. Tables used in the computation of the sets of maximal compatible states of Example 9.

Note that state 1 is not included in any one of the sets of states in the last row of the table of mutually compatible states. Thus state 1 must be included as an additional set, and the sets of maximal compatible states of this example are

$$\text{M.C.'s} = (2, 5, 6), (2, 4), (3, 4), (1) = C_1, C_2, C_3, C_4.$$

4–7. STATE REDUCTION FOR INCOMPLETELY SPECIFIED SEQUENTIAL SYSTEMS. Part III: Computation of the Minimal-State System

In this section we derive a minimal-state sequential system T that covers the system S whose sets of maximal compatibles were obtained as outlined in Section 4–6. As a first trial, consider sequential system τ. This system has as its states $\theta_1, \theta_2, \ldots, \theta_h$, each θ_i corresponding to the set C_i from the sets of maximal compatible states. Note that this represents a sequential system, because the next states of the states included in a specific set C_i must all be included in at least one set C_j; otherwise the states of C_i would not be mutually compatible. Also, there can be no contradiction in the outputs associated either with these states or with the transitions from these states. That is, it is always possible to define such a system τ, although it is not necessarily unique, as will be seen later. This sequential system τ covers the original system S, because every state of S is included in at least one of the C_i's and thus satisfies the conditions of Definition 5. It is obvious that, in general, this system τ is not minimal, because it can have more states than the original system S, as was shown in Section 4–6. From this discussion it can be seen that at best system τ can serve only as an upper bound on the number of states that must be used in the minimal representation. This upper bound is denoted by H and $H = \min(h, h')$, where h and h' represent the number of states of τ and S, respectively.

To obtain the minimal-state system T, we start from the system τ and omit as many sets of maximal compatible states as possible while maintaining the coverage property. Actually, to retain the coverage property during this reduction procedure, it may be necessary to exclude some of the states from sets included in τ. That is, the minimal system T is a system whose states $p_1, p_2, \ldots, p_k$ correspond to a selection of sets or subsets of maximal compatibles that satisfy the following characteristics:

    I. *Completeness.* The union of the states in all p sets contains all the states of the original system S.

    II. *Consistency.* Any set of next states $\bar{p}$, produced by an input combination applied to the system S with any one of the states of a p set as a starting state, is either a p set or a subset of a p set of T.

    III. *Minimality.* The system T contains a minimum number of p sets satisfying I and II.

Thus obtaining a minimal-state system T is equivalent to selecting a p set from the sets of maximal compatible states that satisfy the above three characteristics. As will be shown later, this selection is done by trial and error; thus it is helpful first to obtain bounds on the number of states k required in the realization of the minimal-state system. As shown above, an upper bound on k is $H = \min(h, h')$, and the next step is to obtain a lower bound. The lower bound, denoted by L, is determined by the sets of maximal incompatible states of the original system S. To see this, the following possibilities are considered:

(1) Suppose there are no crossed entries in the implication table. This means that all pairs of states are compatible, and there is no need to distinguish among the states of system S. In this case, the lower bound on the number of states of T is 1.

(2) Suppose there is only *one* crossed entry in the implication table. This represents one pair of incompatible states of system S, and these two

states must be distinguishable in T. Thus in this case the lower bound on the number of states of T is 2.

(3) Suppose the number of crossed entries in the implication table exceeds one. Thus it is required to distinguish among two or more pairs of states of S. The question now arises whether or not two states of T are enough to distinguish among all pairs of incompatible states. To obtain a partial answer the following three pairs of incompatible states are considered: (i, j), (i, k), and (j, k). Since every pair of the states i, j, k is an incompatible pair, they form a set of three mutually incompatible states. That is, they must all be distinguishable from one another, and thus to achieve this T must include at least three states. We see that to obtain a lower bound on the number of states of T it is necessary to compute the sets of mutually incompatible states of S.

Using the above arguments and defining the sets of maximal incompatible states analogously to Definition 9 of the sets of maximal compatible states, the following statement about the lower bound L can be made:

A lower bound on the number of required states of a minimal-state system T is the number $L = \max(l_1, l_2, \ldots, l_j)$, where l_i is the number of states in set i of the sets of maximal incompatible states of the original system S.

Note that the number L is only a lower bound. Generally the number of states k of a minimal system T is larger than L, and is bounded by $L \leq k \leq H$. To see some of the problems that arise in the selection of p sets within these bounds, the following examples are introduced.

EXAMPLE 2 (*continued, II*).   Obtain a minimal-state representation of Example 2.

The sets of maximal compatible states with the corresponding sets of next states obtained from the tables of Fig. 4–17 are given in Fig. 4–24.

M.C.'s	(0, 2, 4)	(1, 3, 5)	(2, 5)	(1, 4)	(0, 3)	C_1	C_2	C_3	C_4	C_5
NEXT STATE SETS	(0, 2, 4)	(1, 3, 5)	(2, 5)	(1, 4)	(0, 3)	C_1	C_2	C_3	C_4	C_5
	(1, 3, 5)	(2, 4, 0)	(3, 0)	(2, 5)	(1, 4)	C_2	C_1	C_5	C_3	C_4
	(3, 5, 1)	(4, 0, 2)	(5, 2)	(4, 1)	(3, 0)	C_2	C_1	C_3	C_4	C_5
	(2, 4, 0)	(3, 5, 1)	(4, 1)	(3, 0)	(2, 5)	C_1	C_2	C_4	C_5	C_3

Figure 4–24.   Table of next-state sets of Example 2.

As a first step, the upper and lower bounds on the number of required states is obtained. The number of states of the original system is six and the number of sets of maximal compatible states is five. Thus the upper bound $H = \min(5, 6) = 5$. Also from the implication table of Fig. 4–17, the sets of maximal incompatible states are M.I.$_c$'s $= (4, 5), (3, 4), (2, 3), (1, 2), (0, 5),$

(0, 1). Thus the lower bound $L = \max(2, 2, 2, 2, 2, 2) = 2$. That is, the number of required states of the minimal state system $2 \leq k \leq 5$.

We see that as a first trial it is required to find two sets of states that satisfy all three characteristics of p sets postulated earlier. In this example the only two sets that satisfy the characteristic of completeness are the sets (0, 2, 4) and (1, 3, 5). To check for the required characteristics the following steps are executed.

I. *Completeness*
$$(0, 2, 4) \cup (1, 3, 5) = (0, 1, 2, 3, 4, 5).$$

II. *Consistency*

To check for consistency the table of Fig. 4–24 is used.

(a) The set of states (0, 2, 4) leads either to states (0, 2, 4) or to states (1, 3, 5) as next states under the influence of the different input conditions.

(b) The set of states (1, 3, 5) leads either to states (1, 3, 5) or to states (0, 2, 4) as next states under the influence of the different input conditions. Since in both cases the sets of next states are included in the p sets, consistency is satisfied.

III. *Minimality*
$$k = L = 2.$$

Thus all three required characteristics are satisfied and the p sets of this example are $p_1, p_2 = (0, 2, 4), (1, 3, 5)$. By letting these sets correspond to states A and B, respectively, the minimal state system of this example is obtained. The state diagram and the transition table of the minimal-state system are shown in Fig. 4–25.

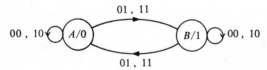

PRESENT	NEXT STATE				
STATE	00	01	11	10	OUTPUT
A-0, 2, 4	A	B	B	A	0
B-1, 3, 5	B	A	A	B	1

Figure 4–25.   Minimal-state diagram and transition table of Example 2.

EXAMPLE 3 (*continued, II*).   Obtain a minimal-state representation of Example 3.

The sets of maximal incompatible states and the sets of maximal compatible states with the corresponding sets of next states obtained from the tables of Fig. 4–20 are given in Fig. 4–26.

M.I.$_c$'s $= (4, 5), (2, 3)$

M.C.'s	$(1, 2, 4)$	$(1, 2, 5)$	$(1, 3, 4)$	$(1, 3, 5)$	C_1	C_2	C_3	C_4
NEXT STATE SETS	$(2, 4, 1)$	$(2, 4, 1)$	$(2, 5, 1)$	$(2, 5, 1)$	C_1	C_1	C_2	C_2
	$(3, 5, 1)$	$(3, 5, 1)$	$(3, 4, 1)$	$(3, 4, 1)$	C_4	C_4	C_3	C_3

Figure 4–26. Sets of maximal incompatible states and table of next-state sets of Example 3.

In this example $H = \min(4, 5) = 4$ and $L = \max(2, 2) = 2$; thus $2 \le k \le 4$. Checking for combinations of two sets that satisfy the completeness requirement, there are two such combinations, $(1, 2, 4)$ with $(1, 3, 5)$ and $(1, 2, 5)$ with $(1, 3, 4)$. But from the table of Fig. 4–26 it can be seen that neither of these combinations satisfies the consistency requirement. Thus there cannot be a two-state representation for this system. The next question is whether or not it is possible to obtain a three-state representation of the system. To check this, all possible combinations of three sets or subsets of maximal compatible states must be considered. Actually, in this example it is simpler to start from the sets of incompatible states.

For a three-state realization to be possible it is required that at least two states from the maximal sets of incompatible states be included in one p set. Suppose that states $(2, 4)$ are considered a p set; this implies pairs $(1, 4)$ and $(1, 5)$. These pairs in turn imply pairs $(1, 2)$ and $(1, 3)$. Pair $(1, 2)$ implies pairs $(2, 4)$ and $(3, 5)$, and pair $(1, 3)$ implies pairs $(2, 5)$ and $(3, 4)$. But these pairs of states cannot be combined into three sets. And since each of the pairs $(3, 4)$,

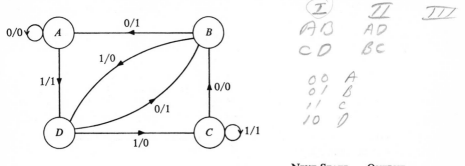

		NEXT STATE		OUTPUT	
PRESENT STATE		0	1	0	1
A-1, 2, 4		A	D	0	1
B-1, 2, 5		A	D	1	0
C-1, 3, 4		B	C	0	1
D-1, 3, 5		B	C	1	0

Figure 4–27. Minimal-state diagram and transition table of Example 3.

(2, 5), and (3, 5) implies the same two pairs (1, 4) and (1, 5), there cannot be a three-state realization for this system.

The next step is to try for a four-state realization. In this case this corresponds to the number of sets of maximal compatible states. Thus the sets of maximal compatible states can be considered as the p set, and thus the completeness and consistency requirements are automatically satisfied. The minimality is also satisfied, because we could not obtain a system with fewer states. By letting the sets (1, 2, 4), (1, 2, 5), (1, 3, 4), and (1, 3, 5) correspond to states A, B, C, and D, the minimal-state system is obtained. The state diagram and the transition table of the minimal-state system are shown in Fig. 4–27.

EXAMPLE 4 (*continued, II*).   Obtain a minimal-state representation of Example 4.

The sets of maximal incompatible states and the sets of maximal compatible states with the corresponding sets of next states obtained from the tables of Fig. 4–21 are as shown in Fig. 4–28.

M.I.$_c$'s = (2, 4, 5), (3, 4, 5), (6, 7, 8)

	C_1 (1, 2, 3, 6)	C_2 (1, 2, 3, 7)	C_3 (1, 2, 3, 8)	C_4 (1, 4, 6)
M.C.'s				
NEXT STATE SETS	(3, 6, 6, 1) (4, –, 7, 1) (2, –, 6, 1) (5, –, 8, 1)	(3, 6, 6, 1) (4, –, 7, 1) (2, –, 6, 1) (5, –, 8, 1)	(3, 6, 6, 1) (4, –, 7, 1) (2, –, 6, 1) (5, –, 8, 1)	(3, 7, 1) (4, –, 1) (2, –, 1) (5, 8, 1)

C_5 (1, 4, 7)	C_6 (1, 4, 8)	C_7 (1, 5, 6)	C_8 (1, 5, 7)	C_9 (1, 5, 8)
(3, 7, 1) (4, –, 1) (2, –, 1) (5, 8, 1)	(3, 7, 1) (4, –, 1) (2, –, 1) (5, 8, 1)	(3, 8, 1) (4, 7, 1) (2, –, 1) (5, –, 1)	(3, 8, 1) (4, 7, 1) (2, –, 1) (5, –, 1)	(3, 8, 1) (4, 7, 1) (2, –, 1) (5, –, 1)

Figure 4–28.   Sets of maximal incompatible states and table of next-state sets of Example 4.

In this example $H = \min(9, 8) = 8$ and $L = \max(3, 3, 3) = 3$; thus, $3 \leq k \leq 8$. The combinations of three sets that satisfy the completeness characteristics are six. These are $\{C_1, C_5, C_9\}$, $\{C_1, C_6, C_8\}$, $\{C_2, C_4, C_9\}$, $\{C_2, C_6, C_7\}$, $\{C_3, C_4, C_8\}$, and $\{C_3, C_5, C_7\}$. From the table of Fig. 4–28 it can be seen that none of these combinations satisfies the consistency requirement. The next step is to try all combinations of four sets, but this becomes quite cumbersome, because the number of combinations becomes quite large. It is simpler in this case to start by first observing the characteristics of the table of Fig. 4–28.

To include the pair of states (2, 3) in a p set, any one of the sets C_1, C_2, and C_3 can be used. Checking the next-state sets of these sets it can be seen that each requires C_1, C_5, and C_9 to be included in the p sets. Thus as a first trial, C_1, C_5, and C_9 are included in the p sets; these satisfy the completeness requirement but not the consistency requirement. To satisfy the consistency requirement the two subsets (1, 3, 7) and (1, 3, 8) must be included. Thus a five-state system is required to satisfy the consistency requirement. This leads to the p sets

$$p_1, p_2, p_3, p_4, p_5 = (1, 2, 3, 6), (1, 4, 7), (1, 5, 8), (1, 3, 7), (1, 3, 8).$$

These p sets satisfy all the required characteristics and can be used to define a minimal-state system. Now by adding the state 2 in p_4 and p_5 no additional states are implied, and this forms a new combination of p sets:

$$p_1, p_2, p_3, p_4, p_5 = (1, 2, 3, 6), (1, 4, 7), (1, 5, 8), (1, 2, 3, 7), (1, 2, 3, 8).$$

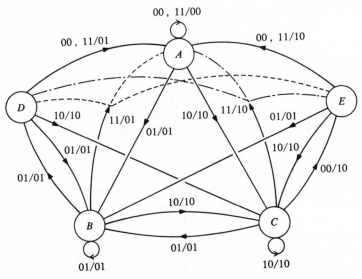

PRESENT STATE	NEXT STATE				OUTPUT			
	00	01	11	10	00	01	11	10
A-1, 2, 3, 6	A	B	A	C	00	01	00	10
B-1, 4, 7	D	B	A, D, E	C	01	01	01	10
C-1, 5, 8	E	B	A, D, E	C	10	01	10	10
D-1, 2, 3, 7	A	B	A	C	01	01	01	10
E-1, 2, 3, 8	A	B	A	C	10	01	10	10

Figure 4–29. Minimal-state state diagram and transition table of Example 4.

At this point the question arises which of these two p sets should be used to define a minimal-state system. For this particular example the choice is obvious. The second combination is the more advisable, because the next-state sets of p_2 and p_3 include the pair of states (1, 2), which can be considered proper subsets of p_1, p_4, or p_5. Thus any one of these can be considered as the next state and this freedom of choice can be used to simplify the logical circuit. In the first combination the same next-state set is only a proper subset of p_1, providing less freedom for the later design steps. By letting the sets of the second combination correspond to states A, B, C, D, and E, respectively, the minimal-state system of this example is obtained. The state diagram and transition table are shown in Fig. 4–29.

EXAMPLE 5 (*continued, II*). Obtain a minimal-state representation of Example 5.

The sets of maximal incompatible states and the sets of maximal compatible states with the corresponding sets of next states obtained from the tables of Fig. 4–22 are given in Fig. 4–30.

M.I.$_c$'s = (1, 2, 4), (1, 2, 6), (1, 4, 8), (1, 5, 6), (2, 3, 7), (3, 7, 8)

M.C.'s	C_1 (2, 5, 8)	C_2 (3, 4, 5)	C_3 (3, 4, 6)	C_4 (4, 5, 7)	C_5 (4, 6, 7)	C_6 (1, 3)	C_7 (1, 7)	C_8 (6, 8)
NEXT STATE SETS	(3, 3, _)	(_, _, 3)	(_, _, 7)	(_, 3, _)	(_, 7, _)	(2, _)	(2, _)	(7, _)
	(1, _, _)	(4, 5, _)	(4, 5, _)	(5, _, 8)	(5, _, 8)	(6, 4)	(6, 8)	(_, _)

Figure 4–30. Sets of maximal incompatible states and table of next-state sets of Example 5.

In this example $H = \min(8, 8) = 8$ and $L = \max(3, 3, 3, 3, 3, 3) = 3$; thus $3 \le k \le 8$. In this example the set C_1, or a subset of C_1, must be included in the p sets because it is the only set that includes state 2. Also, one of the sets C_6 or C_7 must be included because only these sets include state 1. There are thus two combinations of three sets that satisfy completeness: $\{C_1, C_3, C_7\}$ and $\{C_1, C_5, C_6\}$. From the table of Fig. 4–30 it can be seen that only the combination $\{C_1, C_5, C_6\}$ satisfies all the requirements. By letting these sets

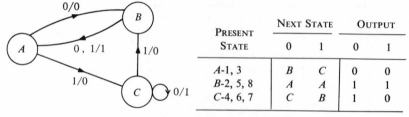

PRESENT STATE	NEXT STATE		OUTPUT	
	0	1	0	1
A-1, 3	B	C	0	0
B-2, 5, 8	A	A	1	1
C-4, 6, 7	C	B	1	0

Figure 4–31. Minimal-state state diagram and transition table of Example 5.

correspond to states B, C, and A, the minimal-state system shown in Fig. 4-31 is obtained.

EXAMPLE 8 (*continued, I*).   Obtain a minimal-state representation of Example 8, as defined by the state diagram and transition table of Fig. 4-16. The sets of maximal incompatible states and the sets of maximal compatible states with the corresponding next-state sets are represented in Fig. 4-32.

M.I.$_c$'s = (1, 3), (2, 4), (3, 5)

M.C.'s	(1, 2, 5)	(1, 4, 5)	(2, 3)	(3, 4)	C_1	C_2	C_3	C_4
NEXT STATE SETS	(2, 3, -)	(2, 5, -)	(3, -)	(-, 5)	C_3	C_1	C_3, C_4	C_1, C_2
	(1, -, 1)	(1, -, 1)	(-, 4)	(4, -)	C_1, C_2	C_1, C_2	C_2, C_4	C_2, C_4

Figure 4-32.   Sets of maximal incompatible states and table of next-state sets of Example 8.

In this example $H = \min(4, 5) = 4$ and $L = \max(2, 2, 2) = 2$; thus $2 \le k \le 4$. Checking the sets of maximal compatible states it can be seen that there are two combinations of two sets that satisfy the completeness requirement. These are $\{C_1, C_4\}$ and $\{C_2, C_3\}$, but neither of these satisfies the consistency requirement, as seen from the table of Fig. 4-32. Thus there is no two-state system that covers the original system.

To obtain a three-state system we can start from the combination $\{C_1, C_4\}$, and to satisfy the consistency requirement the set C_3 is added. The corresponding p sets that satisfy all the requirements are as follows: $p_1, p_2, p_3 = (1, 2, 5)$, (3, 4), (2, 3). The corresponding minimal-state system is shown in Fig. 4-33(a). Another possibility is to split the set C_1 into two parts to avoid the implied pair (2, 3). The resulting p sets that satisfy all the requirements are $p_1, p_2, p_3 = (1), (2, 5), (3, 4)$. The corresponding minimal-state system is shown in Fig. 4-33(b). In exactly the same manner two other p sets can be obtained, starting from the combinations $\{C_2, C_3\}$. These p sets are $p_1, p_2, p_3 = (1, 4, 5), (2, 3), (1, 2, 5)$ and $p_1, p_2, p_3 = (1), (4, 5), (2, 3)$. The corresponding minimal-state systems are shown in Fig. 4-33(c) and (d). (*See page 208.*)

From the above examples it can be seen that the actual selection of p sets is a trial-and-error procedure that uses the upper and lower bounds, H and L, as a guideline. In the actual selection of p sets, any and all aids are used. Some of these aids as shown in the examples are:

(1)   The distribution of the states in the sets of maximal compatible states.
(2)   The completeness characteristic of p sets, as this is the easiest to check.
(3)   The table of next-state sets.
(4)   The sets of maximal incompatible states.

Another point that appears from the above example is the fact that the minimal-state system that covers the original system is not necessarily unique,

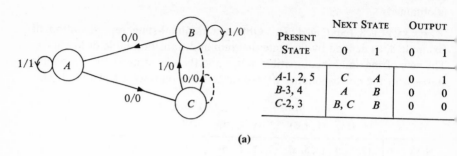

PRESENT STATE	NEXT STATE 0	NEXT STATE 1	OUTPUT 0	OUTPUT 1
A-1, 2, 5	C	A	0	1
B-3, 4	A	B	0	0
C-2, 3	B, C	B	0	0

(a)

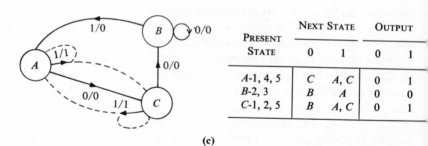

PRESENT STATE	NEXT STATE 0	NEXT STATE 1	OUTPUT 0	OUTPUT 1
A-1	B	A	0	1
B-2, 5	C	A	0	1
C-3, 4	B	C	0	0

(b)

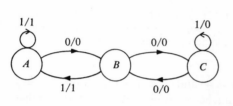

PRESENT STATE	NEXT STATE 0	NEXT STATE 1	OUTPUT 0	OUTPUT 1
A-1, 4, 5	C	A, C	0	1
B-2, 3	B	A	0	0
C-1, 2, 5	B	A, C	0	1

(c)

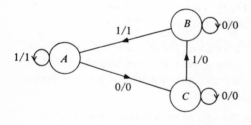

PRESENT STATE	NEXT STATE 0	NEXT STATE 1	OUTPUT 0	OUTPUT 1
A-1	C	A	0	1
B-4, 5	B	A	0	1
C-2, 3	C	B	0	0

(d)

Figure 4–33.   Four minimal-state diagrams and transition tables of Example 8.

because not all the input-output sequences are defined. If there is a choice of different minimal-state systems, the one with most undefined or multiple entries is chosen, because it will generally lead to a simpler combinational circuit.

Considering the procedure described here and in Section 4-6, it can be seen that the amount of required computation generally increases very rapidly with the number of states of the original system. Thus it is advisable to reduce the number of states of the original system before applying the above-described reduction procedure. This partial reduction of the original system is obtained by first computing all the equivalent states. The definition of equivalent states (Def. 11, Chapter 3) must be changed to allow unspecified entries that are not only due to unallowable input combinations.

Definition 10.   *Equivalent states.* Two states i and j of system S are said to be equivalent if and only if the applicable input sequences I_i^r and I_j^r are equal and the corresponding output sequences Z_i^r and Z_j^r are equal.

In this definition, $Z_i^r = Z_j^r$ means that the output sequences are equal whenever both are specified, and in addition the unspecified entries must coincide. The actual computation of the equivalent states is performed using the table of equivalences as defined in Section 3-9. The rows of the transition table are compared pairwise, considering an undefined next-state entry as an additional state and an undefined output entry as an additional output combination. No example will be presented here, because the procedure is the same as shown in Chapter 3 for asynchronous systems.

Note that the reduction procedures introduced in these sections apply to all sequential systems. If the system does not include unspecified entries, the sets of maximal compatible states are the sets of equivalent states, and the system cannot be further reduced, as stated in Theorem 1. Another subset of the general sequential system is the set of input-restricted systems, denoted S^* and defined as follows.

Definition 11.   *Input-restricted systems S^*.* A sequential system is said to be *input-restricted* if and only if its unspecified entries are due only to input constraints of the following form: The input combination I_i can never immediately follow the input combination I_j.

Note that in an input-restricted system, both the unspecified next-state entries and the unspecified output entries must occur concurrently. Also, in such a system there can be a complete column in which the next-state and the output entries are all unspecified, because this only represents an input combination that can never occur. For such a system, the selection of the p sets representing a minimal-state system is greatly simplified. This is due to a theorem originated by Unger,[9] presented here without proof.

[9] S. H. Unger, "Flow Table Simplification—Some Useful Aids," *IRE Trans. Electron. Computers*, **14**, 472–475 (1965).

Theorem 2. *Given an input-restricted system S*, every combination of sets of maximal compatible states of S* that satisfies the completeness requirement also satisfies the consistency requirement.*

Thus in the selection of p sets in an input-restricted system, a minimal-state system is obtained by choosing a minimal combination of sets of maximal compatible states that satisfies the consistency requirement.

4–8. ASSIGNMENT OF SECONDARY STATES AND COMBINATIONAL DESIGN

In this section we consider the problem of encoding the states of a minimal system in such a way as to reduce the cost functions associated with the resulting combinational circuits. In the first part, we do this by trial and error, considering the examples introduced in previous sections. In the latter part of this section we introduce some of the basic ideas used in obtaining an encoding that reduces the interdependence among the secondary variables of the system.

EXAMPLE 2 (*continued, III*).   Derive the combinational circuits associated with Example 2.

The minimal-state transition table of this example, presented in Fig. 4–25, has two rows. Thus this system requires only one secondary variable Y, and since the starting state of this example, represented in Fig. 4–6, is state 0, the value 0 is assigned to row a of Fig. 4–25. The corresponding Y matrix and Z vector are shown in Fig. 4–34.

		$x_1 x_2$				
		Y				
		00	01	11	10	z
y	A-0	0	1	1	0	0
	B-1	1	0	0	1	1

Fig. 4–34.   The Y matrix and Z vector of Example 2.

The corresponding excitation and output functions are

$$Y = x_2 \cdot y' + x_2' \cdot y,$$
$$z = y.$$

EXAMPLE 3 (*continued, III*).   Derive the combinational circuits associated with Example 3.

The minimal-state transition table of this example, presented in Fig. 4–27, has four rows. Thus this system requires two secondary variables to encode the four rows. From the original state-diagram representation, presented in Fig. 4–7, it can be seen that state 1 is the starting state, and thus row A of

Fig. 4–27 is assigned the value 00. After assigning this value to row A, the other three rows can be encoded in six different ways, as shown in Fig. 4–35(a). Actually these six encodings result only in three different cost functions, because the encodings II, IV, and VI can be obtained from the encodings I, III, and V by interchanging the secondary variables y_1 and y_2. The Y and Z matrices corresponding to assignments I, III, and V are shown in Fig. 4–35(b), (c), and (d).

	I	II	III	IV	V	VI
A	00	00	00	00	00	00
B	01	10	01	10	11	11
C	10	01	11	11	10	01
D	11	11	10	01	01	10

(a)

		x Y_1Y_2 0	1	x z 0	1
	A-00	00	11	0	1
	B-01	00	11	1	0
y_1y_2	D-11	01	10	1	0
	C-10	01	10	0	1

(b)

		x Y_1Y_2 0	1	x z 0	1
	A-00	00	10	0	1
	B-01	00	10	1	0
y_1y_2	C-11	01	11	0	1
	D-10	01	11	1	0

(c)

		x Y_1Y_2 0	1	x z 0	1
	A-00	00	01	0	1
	D-01	11	10	1	0
y_1y_2	B-11	00	01	1	0
	C-10	11	10	0	1

(d)

Figure 4–35. Different assignments and the resulting Y and Z matrices of Example 3.

The corresponding excitation and output functions with the associated cost factors for the above three assignments are as follows:

Assignment I, with cost of $0 + 6 + 6 = 12$:

$$Y_1 = x,$$
$$Y_2 = x \cdot y_1' + x' \cdot y_1,$$
$$z = x \cdot y_2' + x' \cdot y_2.$$

Assignment III, with cost of $0 + 0 + 16 = 16$:

$$Y_1 = x,$$
$$Y_2 = y_1,$$
$$z = x' \cdot y_1' \cdot y_2 + x' \cdot y_1 \cdot y_2' + x \cdot y_1' \cdot y_2' + x \cdot y_1 \cdot y_2.$$

Assignment V, with cost of $6 + 16 + 6 = 28$:

$$Y_1 = y_1' \cdot y_2 + y_1 \cdot y_2',$$
$$Y_2 = x' \cdot y_1' \cdot y_2 + x' \cdot y_1 \cdot y_2' + x \cdot y_1' \cdot y_2' + x \cdot y_1 \cdot y_2,$$
$$z = x' \cdot y_2 + x \cdot y_2'.$$

Note that the above cost factors were calculated using two-level single-output functions. Actually these cost factors can be reduced by allowing more than two-level realizations and considering multiple-output functions. Note also that these cost factors are applicable only when unit-delay memory devices are used; the cost factors must be rechecked if other types of memory devices are used. For example, if T (trigger) flip-flops are used as memory devices to realize the above example, the resulting cost factors are for assignment I, $6 + 16 + 6 = 28$; for assignment III, $6 + 6 + 16 = 28$; and for assignment V, $0 + 6 + 6 = 12$. The actual design of the required circuits for this example with trigger flip-flops as memory devices will be shown later (see Fig. 4–52).

EXAMPLE 4 (*continued, III*).   Derive the combinational circuits associated with Example 4.

The minimal-state transition table of this example, presented in Fig. 4–29, has five rows. Thus this system requires three secondary variables to encode the five rows. Note that the transition table of Fig. 4–29 is not unique, since there are some multiple entries. Here these entries are chosen as A, as this choice leads to a column in the transition table with equivalent next states. In checking the original state diagram of this example, it can be seen that state 1 is the starting state, and as state 1 is included in each of the states of the reduced state diagram, any one of these states can be considered the starting state. But it is convenient to assign the value 000 to row A, because the output will remain 00 if the two senary numbers are equal. Thus there remain seven codes to encode the other four rows; that is, $7!/(7 - 4)! = 840$ different encodings. Although some of these encodings will have the same cost factor (because they result by interchanging the secondary variables), there remain $840/6 = 140$ encodings that must be checked. The next step would be to choose an encoding that reduces the output functions, as these are easier to check. An example of such an encoding is given in Fig. 4–36. The correspond-

		$x_1 x_2$				$x_1 x_2$		
		$Y_1 Y_2 Y_3$				$z_1 z_2$		
		00	01	11	10	00	01	11	10
	A-000	000	101	000	110	00	01	00	10
	D-001	000	101	000	110	01	01	01	10
	_-011	---	---	---	---	--	--	--	--
	E-010	000	101	000	110	10	01	10	10
$y_1 y_2 y_3$	C-110	010	101	000	110	10	01	10	10
	_-111	---	---	---	---	--	--	--	--
	B-101	001	101	000	110	01	01	01	10
	_-100	---	---	---	---	--	--	--	--

Figure 4–36.   The Y and Z matrices of Example 4.

ing excitation and output functions are

$$Y_1 = x_1' \cdot x_2 + x_1 \cdot x_2',$$
$$Y_2 = x_1 \cdot x_2' + x_2' \cdot y_1 \cdot y_2,$$
$$Y_3 = x_1' \cdot x_2 + x_1' \cdot y_1 \cdot y_3,$$
$$z_1 = x_1 \cdot x_2' + (x_1 + x_2') \cdot y_2,$$
$$z_2 = x_1' \cdot x_2 + (x_1' + x_2) \cdot y_3.$$

Assuming two-level single-output functions, the associated cost factor is $6 + 7 + 7 + 9 + 9 = 38$. Allowing multilevel multiple-output circuits, the cost factor becomes $6 + 5 + 5 + 4 + 4 = 24$.

EXAMPLE 5 (continued, III).   Derive the combinational circuits associated with Example 5.

The minimal-state transition table of this example, Fig. 4–31, has three rows. Thus this system requires two secondary variables to encode the three rows. From the original state diagram of this problem, Fig. 4–10, it can be seen that state 1 is the starting state, and, as this state is included in state A of the reduced state diagram, row A is assigned the value 00. Just as in Example 3, there can be three encodings with different cost factors. These are given in Fig. 4–37. The corresponding excitation and output functions with the

		x		x
		$Y_1 Y_2$		z
		0 1		0 1
$y_1 y_2$	A-00	01 10		0 0
	B-01	00 00		1 1
	_-11	-- --		- -
	C-10	10 01		1 0

(a)

		x		x
		$Y_1 Y_2$		z
		0 1		0 1
$y_1 y_2$	A-00	10 11		0 0
	_-01	-- --		- -
	C-11	11 10		1 0
	B-10	00 00		1 1

(b)

		x		x
		$Y_1 Y_2$		z
		0 1		0 1
$y_1 y_2$	A-00	11 10		0 0
	_-01	-- --		- -
	B-11	00 00		1 1
	C-10	10 11		1 0

(c)

Figure 4–37.   The Y and Z matrices of Example 5 for different assignments.

associated cost factors for the above three assignments are as follows:
Assignment (a), with cost factor $7 + 7 + (4 - 2) = 16$:

$$Y_1 = x' \cdot y_1 + x \cdot y_1' \cdot y_2',$$
$$Y_2 = x \cdot y_1 + x' \cdot y_1' \cdot y_2',$$
$$z = y_2 + x' \cdot y_1.$$

Assignment (b), with cost factor $2 + 6 + (6 - 2) = 12$:

$$Y_1 = y_1' + y_2,$$
$$Y_2 = x' \cdot y_2 + x \cdot y_1',$$
$$z = y_1 \cdot y_2' + x' \cdot y_2.$$

Assignment (c), with cost factor $0 + 7 + 4 = 11$:

$$Y_1 = y_2',$$
$$Y_2 = x' \cdot y_1' + x \cdot y_1 \cdot y_2',$$
$$z = y_2 + x' \cdot y_1.$$

As will be shown later, the cost factors associated with the different assignments when trigger flip-flops are used as memory devices are: for assignment (a), $2 + 7 + 4 = 13$; for assignment (b), $0 + 4 + 4 = 8$; and for assignment (c), $2 + 7 + 4 = 13$ (see Fig. 4–53).

From the above examples of state assignments, it can be seen that the cost factors associated with the excitation and the output functions are reduced whenever their dependence on the input and state variables is reduced. This is quite simple to prove for the output functions by assigning adjacent codes to rows with equivalent output combinations. That is, equivalent output combinations are grouped together so that they can be covered by larger subcubes. To obtain simplified excitation functions, the basic idea is to obtain an encoding that reduces the interdependence among the state variables. That is, we must find subsets of state variables that can be computed from the knowledge of the input variables and the same or another subset of state variables. The actual computation of such subsets of state variables is equivalent to finding partitions on the states of the sequential system.[10, 11] To introduce the basic ideas required for finding partitions, the following definitions are used.

Definition 12. *Partition π.* A partition π on the set of states $\sigma = (q_1, q_2 \ldots, q_l)$ of the sequential system S is a collection of disjoint subsets of σ such that their set union is σ.

There are two specific partitions, denoted $\pi = 0$ and $\pi = I$. The first partition, $\pi = 0$, has l blocks; that is, each block includes only one state of S. The second partition, $\pi = I$, is a trivial partition, having only one block that includes all the states of S. In general, the k blocks of a partition π are denoted $\pi = (p_1, p_2, \ldots, p_k)$, where a specific block $p_i = \overline{q_a q_b q_c}$, if this block is the subset that includes the states q_a, q_b, and q_c. Considering two partitions π_1 and π_2 on the states of system S, the following relationships are defined.

[10] J. Hartmanis, "On the State Assignment Problem for Sequential Machines I," *IRE Trans. Electron. Computers*, **10**, 157–165 (1961).

[11] R. E. Stearns and J. Hartmanis, "On the State Assignment Problem for Sequential Machines II," *IRE Trans. Electron. Computers*, **10**, 593–603 (1961).

Definition 13. $\pi_1 \leq \pi_2$. Partition π_1 is said to be smaller than partition π_2 if and only if every block p_{1j} of π_1 is included in a block p_{2j} of π_2, that is, if and only if each $p_{1j} \leq p_{2j}$.

Definition 14.   *Greatest lower bound (g.l.b.)* $\pi_1 \cdot \pi_2 = \pi_3$. The partition π_3 is the g.l.b. of partitions π_1 and π_2 if and only if every block of π_3 is an intersection of the blocks of π_1 with the blocks of π_2, that is, if and only if each $p_{3i} = p_{1n} \cap p_{2m}$.

Definition 15.   *Least upper bound (l.u.b.)* $\pi_1 + \pi_2 = \pi_4$. The partition π_4 is the l.u.b. of partitions π_1 and π_2 if and only if every block p_{4n} of π_4 is a minimal subset of σ that includes each block of π_1 or π_2, p_{ij}, for which the intersection of p_{4n} and p_{ij} is nonempty.

In other words, the greatest lower bound $\pi_3 = \pi_1 \cdot \pi_2$ is the partition with largest blocks that satisfies the conditions $\pi_3 \leq \pi_1$ and $\pi_3 \leq \pi_2$. The least upper bound $\pi_4 = \pi_1 + \pi_2$ is the partition with smallest blocks that satisfies the conditions $\pi_4 \geq \pi_1$ and $\pi_4 \geq \pi_2$. These are only the basic relationships between two partitions on the states of system S. Actually, these partitions form a finite lattice and satisfy all the algebraic properties of lattices. This is discussed in detail by Hartmanis and Stearns.[12] To obtain better understanding of these relationships, consider the two partitions $\pi_1 = (\overline{1; 2, 3, 4};$ $\overline{5, 6, 7}; \overline{8})$ and $\pi_2 = (\overline{1, 2}; \overline{3, 4}; \overline{5, 7}; \overline{6}; \overline{8})$ on the set of states $\sigma = (1, 2, 3, 4,$ $5, 6, 7, 8)$ of system S. The greatest lower bound and the least upper bound of these partitions are the partitions

$$\pi_3 = \pi_1 \cdot \pi_2 = (\overline{1}; \overline{2}; \overline{3, 4}; \overline{5, 7}; \overline{6}; \overline{8}),$$
$$\pi_4 = \pi_1 + \pi_2 = (\overline{1, 2, 3, 4}; \overline{5, 6, 7}; \overline{8}).$$

Definition 16.   *Partition pair* (π, τ). An ordered pair of partitions (π, τ) on the set of states $\sigma = (q_1, q_2, \ldots, q_l)$ of a sequential system S is a partition pair (P.P.) if and only if, for any two states q_i and q_j in the same block of π, the next states Iq_i and Iq_j, reached under the influence of any input combination I, are in the same block of τ.

Definition 17.   *Substitution property.* A partition π is said to have the substitution property (S.P.) if and only if the partition π forms a partition pair with itself. That is, π has S.P. if and only if (π, π) is a P.P.

Note that the pairs (π, I) and $(0, \tau)$ for any π and τ are partition pairs. Note also that there are two trivial partitions with the substitution property, the partitions $\pi = 0$ and $\pi = I$. For a given sequential system S, the computation

[12] J. Hartmanis and R. E. Stearns, "Pair Algebra and Its Application to Automata Theory," *Information and Control*, 7, 485–507 (1964).

of the partitions with substitution property and partition pairs is based on the following theorem, presented here without proof.[13]

Theorem 3.   *Given the two partition pairs (π_1, τ_1) and (π_2, τ_2), on the states of a completely defined system S,*

(a) $(\pi_1 \cdot \pi_2, \tau_1 \cdot \tau_2)$ *is a partition pair,*
(b) $(\pi_1 + \pi_2, \tau_1 + \tau_2)$ *is a partition pair,*

where $\cdot$ and $+$ stand for g.l.b. and l.u.b., respectively.

From this theorem it can be seen that, given two partitions π_1 and π_2 on the states of a completely specified system S that have the substitution property, the partitions $\pi_1 \cdot \pi_2$ and $\pi_1 + \pi_2$ also have the substitution property.

At this point we have the required background to derive whenever possible a secondary state assignment that leads to minimal-cost excitation functions. The actual procedure is shown by the following example.

EXAMPLE 10.   Given the completely specified sequential system, as defined by the transition table of Fig. 4–38, obtain a secondary state assignment that leads to minimal-cost excitation functions. Assume that state 1 is the initial state; that is, assign the value 000 to row 1.

| | NEXT STATE | | |
PRESENT STATE	0	1	OUTPUT
1	1	2	0
2	2	1	1
3	3	5	0
4	4	4	0
5	5	3	1

Figure 4–38.   Transition table of Example 10.

One way to solve this problem is to check all possible encodings, and, as shown earlier in this section, this requires $7!/(7 - 4)!6 = 140$ trials. The method used here is to compute the different partition pairs on the states of the system and see what can be learned from these. To compute all the partition pairs, the basic partition pairs (π_{ij}, τ_{ij}) are first obtained. A basic partition pair is obtained by letting π_{ij} be a partition that has only two states blocked, and τ_{ij} is the smallest partition that will make (π_{ij}, τ_{ij}) be a partition pair. The basic partition pairs of this example are given in Fig. 4–39(a).

Starting from the τ_{ij}'s, the maximal π's that satisfy the partition-pair requirements are calculated. The resulting partition pairs are shown in Fig.

[13] R. E. Stearns and J. Hartmanis, *IRE Trans. Electron. Computers*, **10**, 593–603 (1961).

π_{ij}	τ_{ij}
$\overline{1,2};\overline{3};\overline{4};\overline{5}$	$\overline{1,2};\overline{3};\overline{4};\overline{5}$
$\overline{1,3};\overline{2};\overline{4};\overline{5}$	$\overline{1,3};\overline{2,5};\overline{4}$
$\overline{1,4};\overline{2};\overline{3};\overline{5}$	$\overline{1,2,4};\overline{3};\overline{5}$
$\overline{1,5};\overline{2};\overline{3};\overline{4}$	$\overline{1,5};\overline{2,3};\overline{4}$
$\overline{2,3};\overline{1};\overline{4};\overline{5}$	$\overline{1,5};\overline{2,3};\overline{4}$
$\overline{2,4};\overline{1};\overline{3};\overline{5}$	$\overline{1,2,4};\overline{3};\overline{5}$
$\overline{2,5};\overline{1};\overline{3};\overline{4}$	$\overline{1,3};\overline{2,5};\overline{4}$
$\overline{3,4};\overline{1};\overline{2};\overline{5}$	$\overline{3,4,5};\overline{1};\overline{2}$
$\overline{3,5};\overline{1};\overline{2};\overline{4}$	$\overline{3,5};\overline{1};\overline{2};\overline{4}$
$\overline{4,5};\overline{1};\overline{2};\overline{3}$	$\overline{3,4,5};\overline{1};\overline{2}$

(a)

	π	τ_{ij}
(1)	$\overline{1,2};\overline{3};\overline{4};\overline{5}$	$\overline{1,2};\overline{3};\overline{4};\overline{5}$
(2)	$\overline{3,5};\overline{1};\overline{2};\overline{4}$	$\overline{3,5};\overline{1};\overline{2};\overline{4}$
(3)	$\overline{1,3};\overline{2,5};\overline{4}$	$\overline{1,3};\overline{2,5};\overline{4}$
(4)	$\overline{1,5};\overline{2,3};\overline{4}$	$\overline{1,5};\overline{2,3};\overline{4}$
(5)	$\overline{1,2,4};\overline{3};\overline{5}$	$\overline{1,2,4};\overline{3};\overline{5}$
(6)	$\overline{3,4,5};\overline{1};\overline{2}$	$\overline{3,4,5};\overline{1};\overline{2}$

(b)

Figure 4-39. Basic partition pairs of Example 10.

4-39(b). Note that the partition pairs in Fig. 4-39(b) represent partitions with the substitution property; thus these partitions and all the least upper bound combinations have S.P. and need not be listed as pairs. To obtain all the partitions that have S.P., the six partitions π_i are combined pairwise; then all the combinations of three, four, etc., are considered until no new partitions are obtained. The least upper bounds of every pair of π_i's are computed as shown by the table of Fig. 4-40(a). The new partitions thus obtained are listed in Fig. 4-40(b).

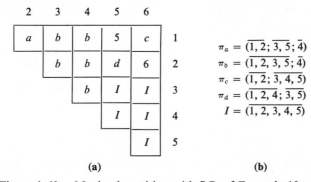

(a) (b)

Figure 4-40. Maximal partition with S.P. of Example 10.

Checking the partitions of Fig. 4-40(b) it can be seen that they cannot be combined either with the original six partitions or among themselves to provide new partitions. Now observing partition π_c it can be seen that with its help we can distinguish between two subsets of states. If the secondary variable y_1 is associated with this partition, then from its value we know in which subset the state of the system is located. Also the excitation function Y_1 depends on the input variable and y_1 only. This is shown in Fig. 4-41(a). In the same manner, if the secondary variable y_2 is associated with the blocks of

π_d, the excitation function $Y_2 = f(x, y_2)$. This is shown in Fig. 4–41(b). Now since $\pi_c \cdot \pi_d = (\overline{1, 2}; \overline{3, 5}; \overline{4})$, we still need to distinguish between states 1 and 2, and 3 and 5. But as neither partitions $(\overline{1, 3, 4}; \overline{2, 5})$ or $(\overline{1, 3}; \overline{2, 4, 5})$ have the substitution property, we cannot obtain the excitation function Y_3 as a function of x and y_3 only; thus $Y_3 = f(x, y_1, y_2, y_3)$. Since state 1 is the initial state and has to be assigned the value 000, there can be four different encodings that satisfy the above requirements. These assignments are shown in Fig. 4–41(c). The Y matrix, Z vector, and the resulting combinational functions for the first assignment are shown in Fig. 4–41(d) and (e).

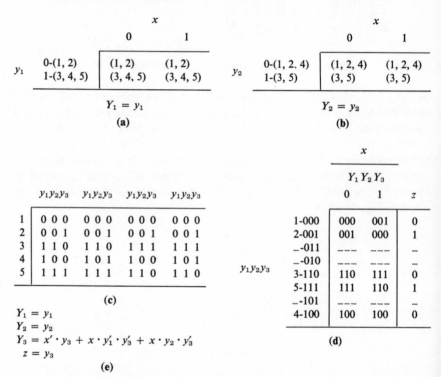

$$Y_1 = y_1$$

(a)

$$Y_2 = y_2$$

(b)

(c)

$$Y_1 = y_1$$
$$Y_2 = y_2$$
$$Y_3 = x' \cdot y_3 + x \cdot y_1' \cdot y_3' + x \cdot y_2 \cdot y_3'$$
$$z = y_3$$

(e)

(d)

Figure 4–41. Secondary assignments and combinational functions of Example 10.

EXAMPLE 11.   Given the completely specified sequential system defined by the transition table of Fig. 4–42, obtain a secondary state assignment that leads to minimal-cost excitation functions. Assume that state 1 is the initial state.

The computation of the partition pairs on the states of this example is shown in Fig. 4–43. Checking the partition pairs of the third column, it can be seen that there is only one partition with the substitution property. Thus one of the excitation functions can be obtained as a function of the input and its

PRESENT STATE	NEXT STATE		OUTPUT
	0	1	
1	1	2	0
2	3	4	1
3	2	1	0
4	4	3	0

Figure 4-42.   Transition table of Example 11.

π_{ij}	τ_{ij}		π	τ_{ij}		π	τ
$\overline{1,2};\overline{3};\overline{4}$	$\overline{1,3};\overline{2,4}$	(1)	$\overline{1,4};\overline{2,3}$	$\overline{1,4};\overline{2,3}$	(a)	$\overline{1,4};\overline{2,3}$	$\overline{1,4};\overline{2,3}$
$\overline{1,3};\overline{2};\overline{4}$	$\overline{1,2};\overline{3};\overline{4}$	(2)	$\overline{1,2};\overline{3,4}$	$\overline{1,3};\overline{2,4}$	(b)	$\overline{1,2};\overline{3,4}$	$\overline{1,3};\overline{2,4}$
$\overline{1,4};\overline{2};\overline{3}$	$\overline{1,4};\overline{2,3}$	(3)	$\overline{1,3};\overline{2};\overline{4}$	$\overline{1,2};\overline{3};\overline{4}$	(c)	$\overline{1,3};\overline{2,4}$	$\overline{1,2};\overline{3,4}$
$\overline{2,3};\overline{1};\overline{4}$	$\overline{1,4};\overline{2,3}$	(4)	$\overline{2,4};\overline{1};\overline{3}$	$\overline{3,4};\overline{1};\overline{2}$			
$\overline{2,4};\overline{1};\overline{3}$	$\overline{3,4};\overline{1};\overline{2}$						
$\overline{3,4};\overline{1};\overline{2}$	$\overline{1,3};\overline{2,4}$						

Figure 4-43.   Partition pairs of Example 11.

own variables. Let us choose $Y_1 = f_1(x, y_1)$ and $Y_2 = f_2(x, y_1, y_2)$. The corresponding minimal assignment and combinational functions are presented in Fig. 4-44(a). Consider now another type of assignment, say, an

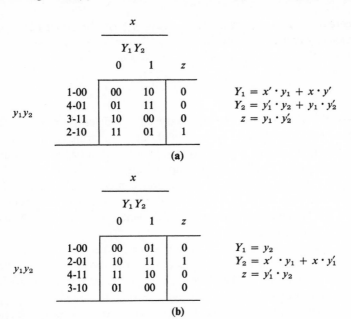

Figure 4-44.   Two assignments and corresponding combinational functions of Example 11.

association of the secondary variable y_1 with the blocks of π_b and of the secondary variable y_2 with the blocks of π_c. In this case, since $\tau_b = \tau_c$, the next value of y_2 (Y_2) depends only on the input and the present blocks of π_b; that is, $Y_2 = f_2(x, y_1)$. In exactly the same manner, since $\tau_c = \pi_b$, $Y_1 = f_1(x, y_2)$. The corresponding secondary state assignment and combinational functions are presented in Fig. 4–44(b). Note that this second assignment resulted in simple excitation functions. This is due to the fact that each of the resulting excitation functions depends on fewer variables.

From these two examples it can be seen that from knowledge of the partitions with substitution property and of the partition pairs on the states of a system, one can derive a secondary state assignment that leads to simpler excitation functions. Although in these examples we only considered a completely specified system, with slight modification the same procedure can be used to obtain the partitions on the states of an incompletely specified system.

Actually the role of partitions that have the substitution property is more important than just the one indicated. This can be seen from the following two theorems, given without proof.

Theorem 4. *The state behavior of a system S can be realized by a serial connection of two simpler systems S_1 and S_2 if and only if there exists a partition $0 \neq \pi \neq 1$ with S.P. on the states of S.*

Theorem 5. *The state behavior of a system S can be realized by a parallel connection of j simpler systems $S_1, S_2, \ldots, S_i, \ldots, S_j$ if and only if there exist j distinct partitions $0 \neq \pi_i \neq I$ with S.P. on the states of S such that*

$$\pi_1 \cdot \pi_2 \cdot \ldots \cdot \pi_i \cdot \ldots \cdot \pi_j = 0.$$

These theorems define the necessary and sufficient conditions for the decomposition of sequential systems, without considering the outputs. That is, the outputs of system S generally will be a function of the inputs and the secondary variables of each of the simpler subsystems.

One of the main drawbacks of the above procedure is that it is quite laborious and will not necessarily lead to a solution. This process was extended by Kohavi[14] to obtain an equivalent system for which such an encoding is always possible.

In this presentation we shall not consider further the problem of state assignment, because for larger systems both of the above procedures become impractical as a result of the large amount of computation required. This procedure was introduced only to indicate that there exists a theoretical solution for this problem and also to serve as an introduction to the study of

[14] Z. Kohavi, "Secondary State Assignment for Sequential Machines," *IRE Trans. Electron. Computers*, **13**, 193–203 (1964).

machine decomposition. To obtain simpler excitation functions, we present three suggestions, which usually lead to acceptable realizations:

(1) Use a minimal number p of secondary variables, where p satisfies the condition $2^{p-1} < l \leq 2^p$ and l is the number of rows of the minimal-row transition table.
(2) Assign adjacent codes to states that lead to the same next states.
(3) Assign adjacent codes to the states that are the next states of a given state.

Note that these suggestions will generally lead to contradictory requirements; when they do, the order of precedence to be followed is the order of presentation. The advantage of these suggestions lies in the fact that they are easily programed. This becomes the most important consideration in large systems, because they must be designed using digital computers. An example of an algorithm that uses similar guidelines and leads to programed solution of this problem is presented by Armstrong.[15, 16]

Another point that should be made is that all the above procedures and discussion apply only to sequential systems that use delay units as memory elements. That is, the excitation functions are the Boolean functions corresponding to coverage of the 1's or 0's in the Y matrix. Whenever other types of memory devices are used, there may not be any correlation. This can be seen from the cost factors calculated in Examples 3 and 5 (parts III and IV), for sequential systems that use trigger flip-flops as memory devices.

4–9. SYNTHESIS EXAMPLE

In this section a synchronous sequential circuit is synthesized using the procedure developed in previous sections. This example is introduced here to provide a unified picture of the different steps used in the synthesis procedure.

EXAMPLE 12.   5421 *binary-coated-decimal serial to parallel complementer*. The circuit to be designed has a single input (x) and four outputs (z_5, z_4, z_2, z_1). The inputs are considered in sets of four, and represent a decimal digit N, (0–9) in 5421 code, with the least significant digit applied first. This code is shown in Fig. 4–45(c). The outputs are specified only at the occurrence of every fourth input and $Z = 9 - N$ in 5421 code, where Z stands for the decimal number represented by $z_5z_4z_2z_1$.

---

[15] D. B. Armstrong, "A Programed Algorithm for Assigning Internal Codes to Sequential Machines," *IRE Trans. Electron. Computers*, **11**, 446–472 (1962).

[16] D. B. Armstrong, "On the Efficient Assignment of Internal Codes to Sequential Machines," *IRE Trans. Electron. Computers*, **11**, 611–622 (1962). This paper presents a more complicated procedure, which may require a large amount of computation.

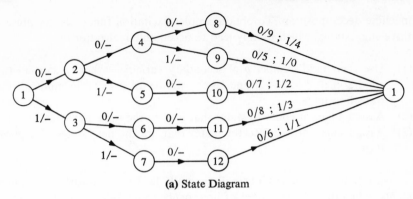

(a) State Diagram

PRESENT STATE	NEXT STATE		OUTPUT	
	0	1	0	1
1	2	3	–	–
2	4	5	–	–
3	6	7	–	–
4	8	9	–	–
5	10	–	–	–
6	11	–	–	–
7	12	–	–	–
8	1	1	9	4
9	1	1	5	0
10	1	1	7	2
11	1	1	8	3
12	1	1	6	1

(b) Transition Table

	y_5	y_4	y_2	y_1
0	0	0	0	0
1	0	0	0	1
2	0	0	1	0
3	0	0	1	1
4	0	1	0	0
5	1	0	0	0
6	1	0	0	1
7	1	0	1	0
8	1	0	1	1
9	1	1	0	0

(c) 5421 Code

Figure 4–45. State diagram, transition table, 5421 code, and implication table of Example 12.

To obtain the state diagram the characteristics of the given code are observed. From Fig. 4–45(c) it can be seen that the combinations 0101, 0110, 0111, 1101, 1110, and 1111 do not occur. That is, if either y_1 or y_2 or both are equal to 1, then $y_3 = 0$. This is reflected in the state diagram by having only one arrow leaving each of states 5, 6, and 7. To simplify the drawing of the state diagram, state 1 is drawn twice, and the outputs whenever specified are represented as decimal numbers in 5421 code. The resulting state diagram and the corresponding transition table are shown in Fig. 4–45(a) and (b). Because this table does not include equivalent rows (the reader should check this), the next step is to derive the implication table. The implication table of this example is shown in Fig. 4–45(d).

From the implication table the sets of maximal incompatible states are

$$\text{M.I.}_{c}\text{'s} = (2, 3), (4, 5, 6, 7), (8, 9, 10, 11, 12).$$

Figure 4-45 (*Continued*).

	1	2	3	4	5	6	7	8	9	10	11
2	2, 4; 3, 5										
3	2, 6; 3, 7	4, 6; 5, 7 XX									
4	2, 8; 3, 9	4, 8; 5, 9	6, 8; 7, 9								
5	2, 10	4, 10	6, 10	8, 10 XX							
6	2, 11	4, 11	6, 11	8, 11 XX	10, 11 XX						
7	2, 12	4, 12	6, 12	8, 12 XX	10, 12 XX	11, 12 XX					
8	1, 2; 1, 3	1, 4; 1, 5	1, 6; 1, 7	1, 8; 1, 9	1, 10	1, 11	1, 12				
9	1, 2; 1, 3	1, 4; 1, 5	1, 6; 1, 7	1, 8; 1, 9	1, 10	1, 11	1, 12	XX			
10	1, 2; 1, 3	1, 4; 1, 5	1, 6; 1, 7	1, 8; 1, 9	1, 10	1, 11	1, 12	XX	XX		
11	1, 2; 1, 3	1, 4; 1, 5	1, 6; 1, 7	1, 8; 1, 9	1, 10	1, 11	1, 12	XX	XX	XX	
12	1, 2; 1, 3	1, 4; 1, 5	1, 6; 1, 7	1, 8; 1, 9	1, 10	1, 11	1, 12	XX	XX	XX	XX

(**d**) Implication Table

Listing the sets of maximal compatible states becomes quite cumbersome, as there are forty such sets. From the implication table it can be seen that each one of states 4, 5, 6, and 7 is compatible with each of states 8, 9, 10, 11, and 12. These will form twenty pairs of compatible states. And since each of these pairs is compatible with states 2 and 3, and since states 2 and 3 are incompatible, this results in forty sets of three compatible states. And as state 1 is compatible with each state, there are forty sets of maximal compatible states, each of four states. These are listed in a shorthand notation in Fig. 4–46(a), where each group includes eight sets. For example, the eight sets of the first group are (1, 2, 4, 8), (1, 2, 5, 8), (1, 2, 6, 8), (1, 2, 7, 8), (1, 3, 4, 8), (1, 3, 5, 8), (1, 3, 6, 8), and (1, 3, 7, 8). Also, in checking the next-state sets only one such group needs to be considered, because the next states of states 8, 9, 10, 11, and 12 are all equal. This partial table of next-state sets is shown in Fig. 4–46(b).

The choice of a minimal set of compatible states is not as hopeless as might be expected from the large number of sets of maximal compatible

$$1, \frac{2}{3}, \frac{5}{6}, \frac{4}{8} \qquad 1, \frac{2}{3}, \frac{5}{6}, \frac{4}{9} \qquad 1, \frac{2}{3}, \frac{5}{6}, \frac{4}{10} \qquad 1, \frac{2}{3}, \frac{5}{6}, \frac{4}{11} \qquad 1, \frac{2}{3}, \frac{5}{6}, \frac{4}{12}$$

(a)

PARTIAL M.C.'s	$(1, 2, 4, x)$	$(1, 2, 5, x)$	$(1, 2, 6, x)$	$(1, 2, 7, x)$
NEXT STATE SETS	$(2, 4, 8, 1)$	$(2, 4, 10, 1)$	$(2, 4, 11, 1)$	$(2, 4, 12, 1)$
	$(3, 5, 9, 1)$	$(3, 5, \text{--}, 1)$	$(3, 5, \text{--}, 1)$	$(3, 5, \text{--}, 1)$

	$(1, 3, 4, x)$	$(1, 3, 5, x)$	$(1, 3, 6, x)$	$(1, 3, 7, x)$
	$(2, 6, 8, 1)$	$(2, 6, 10, 1)$	$(2, 6, 11, 1)$	$(2, 6, 12, 1)$
	$(3, 7, 9, 1)$	$(3, 7, \text{--}, 1)$	$(3, 7, \text{--}, 1)$	$(3, 7, \text{--}, 1)$

(b)

Figure 4–46. Sets of maximal compatible states and partial table of next-state sets of Example 12.

states, because only ten of these are included as next-state sets. The simplest way to choose is to start from either set $(1, 3, 5, 9)$ or set $(1, 3, 7, 9)$ and see which of the other sets must be included. Suppose we start from the set $(1, 3, 5, 9)$, and, as its next-state sets are $(1, 2, 6, 10)$ and $(1, 3, 7)$, these sets must also be included. In exactly the same manner the sets $(1, 2, 4, 11)$, $(1, 2, 6, 12)$, and $(1, 2, 4, 8)$ must also be included. Note that this combination of sets of compatible states satisfies the completeness and consistency requirements, and, because there is no combination of five sets $L = 5$ that satisfies the consistency requirement, the minimality requirement is also satisfied. The corresponding minimal-row transition table is shown in Fig. 4–47(a).

PRESENT STATE	NEXT STATE		OUTPUT			PRESENT STATES LEADING TO	NEXT STATE
	0	1	0	1			
A-1, 2, 4, 8	A	E	9	4		A, B	A
B-1, 2, 4, 11	A	E	8	3		C, D	B
C-1, 2, 6, 10	B	E	7	2		E	C
D-1, 2, 6, 12	B	E	6	1		F	D
E-1, 3, 5, 9	C	F	5	0		A, B, C, D	E
F-1, 3, 7	D	F	–	–		E, F	F

(a)	(b)

Figure 4–47. Minimal-row transition table and table of adjacencies of Example 12.

To obtain a secondary state assignment, the three suggestions of Section 4–8 are used.

(1) As the minimal transition table has five rows, $2^2 < 5 \leq 2^3$, three memory devices are used.
(2) To check for states that lead to the same next state, the table of Fig. 4–47(b) is constructed. This indicates adjacent assignment to the sets (A, B), (C, D), (A, B, C, D), and (E, F).
(3) Checking the states that are next states to a given present state, the adjacencies indicated are (A, E), (B, E), (C, F), and (D, F).

An encoding that satisfies most of these indications is as follows: $A = 000$, $B = 001$, $C = 010$, $D = 011$, $E = 100$, and $F = 110$. The corresponding Y matrix, Z matrix, and combinational functions are shown in Fig. 4–48(a) and (b). Note that the choice of state A as the initial state was quite arbitrary, as the initial state (1) of the original state diagram is included in every one of the states of the minimal state diagram.

$y_1y_2y_3$	$Y_1Y_2Y_3$, x = 0	$Y_1Y_2Y_3$, x = 1	$z_5z_4z_2z_1$, x = 0	$z_5z_4z_2z_1$, x = 1
A-000	000	100	1100	0100
B-001	000	100	1011	0011
D-011	001	100	1001	0001
C-010	001	100	1010	0010
F-110	011	110	----	----
_-111	---	---	----	----
_-101	---	---	----	----
E-100	010	110	1000	0000

(a)

$$Y_1 = x$$
$$Y_2 = y_1$$
$$Y_3 = x' \cdot y_2$$

$$z_5 = x'$$
$$z_4 = y_1' \cdot y_2' \cdot y_3'$$
$$z_2 = y_2' \cdot y_3 + y_2 \cdot y_3'$$
$$z_1 = y_3$$

(b)

Figure 4–48. Y and Z matrices and combinational functions of Example 12.

The circuit diagram of this example, with unit-delay elements as memory devices, is shown in Fig. 4–49. In Fig. 4–49(a) the circuit diagram is drawn in the format of Fig. 4–3(b) of Section 4–2. In Fig. 4–49(b) the same circuit is redrawn in a format whose action is simpler to check. Checking Fig. 4–49(b) it becomes apparent that the solution to this example could have been obtained quite simply empirically. Because the input number, N, can be stored by interconnecting three unit delays in series, the combinational circuit shown is used to obtain $Z = 9 - N$. The additional AND gate used in this solution ensures that the output combination Z is a proper decimal digit in 5421 code even when an improper input set is applied to the system.

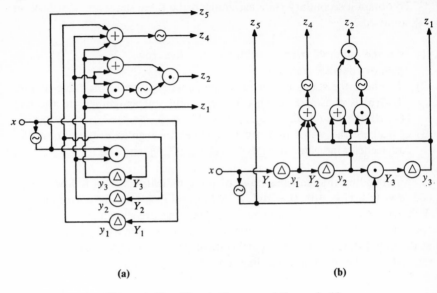

(a)   (b)

Figure 4–49. Circuit diagram of Example 12.

4–10. OTHER TYPES OF MEMORY DEVICES

In Sections 4–8 and 4–9 the excitation functions were calculated assuming unit-delay elements as memory devices. But any one of the flip-flop memory devices defined in Section 3–13 could have been used equally well. The only difference is that the outputs of these devices are voltage levels instead of pulses. To transform these signals into pulses they are fed into a two-input AND gate whose other input is the clock pulses. The actual procedure for calculating the SET and RESET functions is exactly the same as presented in Chapter 3. The only difference occurs in the circuit realization, where the SET and RESET inputs must be 0 between the clock pulses. Another possibility is to use specially designed set-reset flip-flops whose inputs can be activated only concurrently with the clock pulses. To show this, the SET and RESET functions of Example 12 are calculated next. This is done in Fig. 4–50, where the Y matrix of this example is reproduced with the notation introduced in Section 3–13.

In Fig. 4–50 the output functions are listed only for convenience; also, the circuit diagram of Fig. 4–50(c) is drawn in a form that is easy to check. Note that all the inputs to the flip-flops can appear only concurrently with the clock pulses.

Another type of flip-flop memory device that is used in pulsed synchronous sequential circuits is the *trigger flip-flop*. The basic circuit of this flip-flop has a single input Y_t and two outputs y and y'. Whenever an input

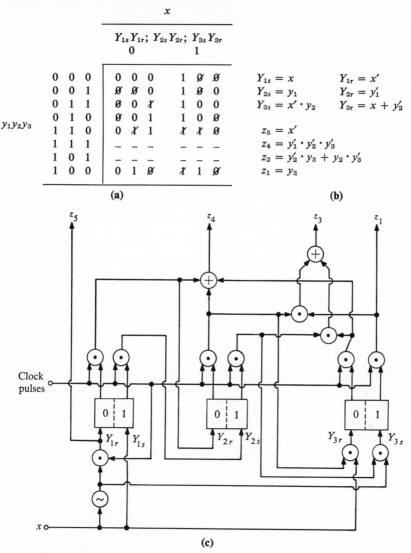

$$x$$

| | $Y_{1s}Y_{1r};\ Y_{2s}Y_{2r};\ Y_{3s}Y_{3r}$ | |
	0	1
0 0 0	0 0 0	1 ∅ ∅
0 0 1	∅ ∅ 0	1 ∅ 0
0 1 1	∅ 0 ✗	1 0 0
0 1 0	∅ 0 1	1 0 ∅
1 1 0	0 ✗ 1	✗ ✗ ∅
1 1 1	– – –	– – –
1 0 1	– – –	– – –
1 0 0	0 1 ∅	✗ 1 ∅

$y_1y_2y_3$ (row label for the left column)

(a)

$$Y_{1s} = x \qquad\qquad Y_{1r} = x'$$
$$Y_{2s} = y_1 \qquad\qquad Y_{2r} = y_1'$$
$$Y_{3s} = x' \cdot y_2 \qquad Y_{3r} = x + y_2'$$

$$z_5 = x'$$
$$z_4 = y_1' \cdot y_2' \cdot y_3'$$
$$z_2 = y_2' \cdot y_3 + y_2 \cdot y_3'$$
$$z_1 = y_3$$

(b)

(c)

Figure 4–50. SET–RESET functions and circuit diagram of Example 12, with $S\text{-}R$ flip-flops.

pulse is applied to Y_t, the value of the output terminals changes and remains so until the next input pulse is applied to Y_t. When such a flip-flop is used, it is generally assumed that its output $y = 0$ when it is switched on originally. Another method is to include additional SET and/or RESET inputs that are used to assure the required initial state. In this presentation we shall always indicate the initial setting by indicating the additional inputs. A block diagram of the T flip-flop is shown in Fig. 4–51(a).

Figure 4–51(b) is a block diagram of the *set-trigger-reset (S-T-R) flip-flop*. This flip-flop has the combined operating characteristics of the *S-R* and *T* flip-flop. Whenever an input pulse is applied to Y_s, the output $y = 1$; when an input pulse is applied to Y_r, the output $y = 0$; and when an input pulse is applied to Y_t, the output changes. The output remains constant between input pulses. Also the inputs to this flip-flop are restricted, so that only one input pulse can be applied at any given time.

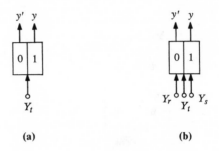

                      (a)   **(b)**

Figure 4–51.   Block-diagrammatic representation of T and S-T-R flip-flops.

Both the above flip-flops are generally used with pulsed signals, but they can also be used with level signals if the input to Y_t is applied via a two-input AND gate whose other input is the clock pulses. In this presentation we shall restrict our discussions to trigger flip-flops, since the actual choice of input combinations that provides the required behavior of an S-T-R flip-flop is largely done by trial and error.

To obtain the trigger (excitation) functions for a sequential circuit with T flip-flops, the first step is to obtain a translation of the Y matrix. This translation is required because an input must be applied to the memory device whenever its output has to change. The new mapping is called the T matrix and is obtained from the Y matrix by entering a 1 wherever $y_i \neq Y_i$. Note that the T matrix has equivalent entries to the τ matrix of Chapter 3. The final step of synthesis is then obtained by computing the combinational functions that cover the 1's of the T matrix. To see this we now consider two examples.

EXAMPLE 3 (*continued, IV*).   Obtain the trigger functions for each of the three assignments used in Example 3.

The Y matrices of Example 3, given in Fig. 4–35(b), (c), and (d), with the corresponding T matrices and trigger functions, are as shown in Fig. 4–52. The output functions are included so that the total cost factors can be calculated. These output functions are the functions represented in the Z matrices of Fig. 4–35.

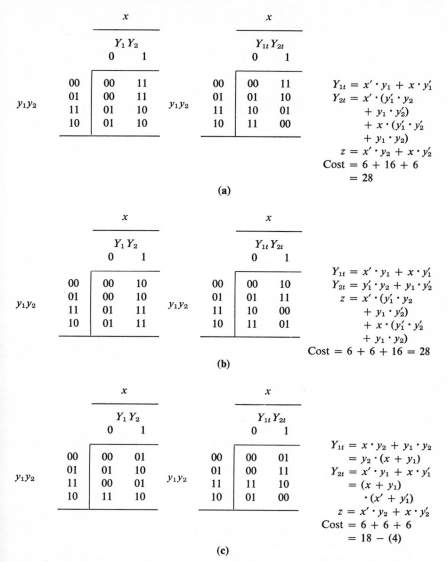

$$Y_{1t} = x' \cdot y_1 + x \cdot y_1'$$
$$Y_{2t} = x' \cdot (y_1' \cdot y_2$$
$$+ y_1 \cdot y_2')$$
$$+ x \cdot (y_1' \cdot y_2'$$
$$+ y_1 \cdot y_2)$$
$$z = x' \cdot y_2 + x \cdot y_2'$$
$$\text{Cost} = 6 + 16 + 6$$
$$= 28$$

(a)

$$Y_{1t} = x' \cdot y_1 + x \cdot y_1'$$
$$Y_{2t} = y_1' \cdot y_2 + y_1 \cdot y_2'$$
$$z = x' \cdot (y_1' \cdot y_2$$
$$+ y_1 \cdot y_2')$$
$$+ x \cdot (y_1' \cdot y_2'$$
$$+ y_1 \cdot y_2)$$
$$\text{Cost} = 6 + 6 + 16 = 28$$

(b)

$$Y_{1t} = x \cdot y_2 + y_1 \cdot y_2$$
$$= y_2 \cdot (x + y_1)$$
$$Y_{2t} = x' \cdot y_1 + x \cdot y_1'$$
$$= (x + y_1)$$
$$\cdot (x' + y_1')$$
$$z = x' \cdot y_2 + x \cdot y_2'$$
$$\text{Cost} = 6 + 6 + 6$$
$$= 18 - (4)$$

(c)

Figure 4–52. Y and T matrices and trigger functions of Example 3.

EXAMPLE 5 (*continued, IV*).   Obtain the trigger functions for each of the three assignments used in Example 3. Draw the circuit with the lowest cost factor.

The Y matrices of Example 3, given in Fig. 4–37, with the corresponding T matrices and trigger functions, are given in Fig. 4–53.

The output functions are obtained from the Z matrices of Fig. 4–37, and are listed here for convenience. The circuit with minimal cost factor is obtained

$$x$$ $$x$$

	$Y_1 Y_2$	
	0	1
00	01	10
01	00	00
11	--	--
10	10	01

$y_1 y_2$

	$Y_{1t} Y_{2t}$	
	0	1
00	01	10
01	01	01
11	--	--
10	00	11

$y_1 y_2$

$Y_{1t} = x \cdot y_2'$
$Y_{2t} = y_2 + x' \cdot y_1'$
$\qquad + x \cdot y_1$
$z = y_2 + x' \cdot y_1$
$\text{Cost} = 2 + 7 + 4$
$\qquad = 13$

(a)

$$x$$ $$x$$

	$Y_1 Y_2$	
	0	1
00	10	11
01	--	--
11	11	10
10	00	00

$y_1 y_2$

	$Y_{1t} Y_{2t}$	
	0	1
00	10	11
01	--	--
11	00	01
10	10	10

$y_1 y_2$

$Y_{1t} = y_2'$
$Y_{2t} = x \cdot (y_1' + y_2)$
$\qquad = x \cdot (y_1 \cdot y_2')'$
$z = y_1 \cdot (x' + y_2')$
$\qquad = x' \cdot y_1 + y_1 \cdot y_2'$
$\text{Cost} = 0 + 4 + 4 = 8$

(b)

$$x$$ $$x$$

	$Y_1 Y_2$	
	0	1
00	11	10
01	--	--
11	00	00
10	10	11

$y_1 y_2$

	$Y_{1t} Y_{2t}$	
	0	1
00	11	10
01	--	--
11	11	11
10	00	01

$y_1 y_2$

$Y_{1t} = y_1' + y_2$
$Y_{2t} = y_2 + x' \cdot y_1'$
$\qquad + x \cdot y_1$
$z = y_2 + x' \cdot y_1$
$\text{Cost} = 2 + 7 + 4$
$\qquad = 13$

(c)

Figure 4–53. Y and T matrices and trigger functions of Example 5.

when the secondary variable assignment, shown in Fig. 4–53(b), is used. The corresponding circuit diagram is shown in Fig. 4–54.

Note that the outputs of the flip-flops are fed through two-input AND gates with clock pulses as the other input, to change the level signals to pulsed signals. This is the reason why the second realization shown in Fig. 4–53(b) is used. In this realization only one of the outputs of each flip-flop is used, thus saving two AND gates. Note also that in Fig. 4–54 each of the trigger flip-flops also has a secondary input. In this example these inputs correspond to RESET, and are used to ensure that the circuit starts in the required initial state. That is, after the system is switched on, an initiating pulse is applied. In some examples when a system is supposed to start from different initial states there may be more than one initiating line.

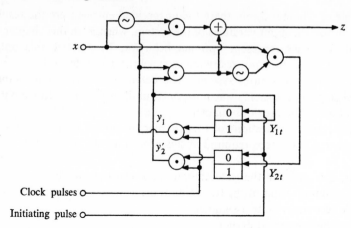

Figure 4–54.   Circuit diagram with trigger flip-flops of Example 5.

4–11. CONCLUDING REMARKS

In the first three sections of this chapter the differences and similarities between synchronous and asynchronous sequential circuits were considered in detail. The two main differences are the following:

(1) The problem of races, both in input variables and secondary variables, is eliminated in the synchronous sequential system due to the exact timing of these variables. Thus changes in a number of variables at once are allowed.
(2) In synchronous sequential systems each memory state lasts for an interval between clock pulses and thus every state is equally stable.

The above two differences lead to a third differentiation that is not so readily apparent:

(3) All transitions between the states of a synchronous sequential circuit are one-step transitions.

This provides a practical limitation on the maximal repetition rate of the clock pulses, as all the changes have to be made before the next clock pulse arrives. Thus the repetition rate is governed by the worst-case conditions and this is the reason for the slower operation of synchronous sequential systems.

In Section 4–5 incompletely specified sequential circuits were introduced. That is, the exact meaning of unspecified next-state and output entries in the transition table are defined. Note that the behavior of the resulting system is strictly deterministic; just as in the state diagram there are no two edges (transitions) leaving the same vertex (state) under the influence of the same input combination. Actually, there were also unspecified entries in Huffman's flow table of Chapter 3, but there the unspecified entries were the results of restrictions on the input variables of the system, whereas in this chapter these unspecified entries represent optional behavior. In practice this optional behavior of a system is not restricted to synchronous systems, but is equally applicable in asynchronous systems. The detailed coverage of incompletely specified sequential systems was postponed until this chapter to simplify the presentation of the previous chapter.

In the remaining sections of this chapter the actual synthesis procedure was presented. The steps required in this procedure are as follows:

(1) The derivation of the state diagram and transition table.
(2) The minimization of the transition table.
(3) The secondary state assignment.
(4) The combinational design.

The translation of the word statement into a corresponding state diagram was briefly reviewed in this chapter by the use of some examples. The main difference between this step and the corresponding step in the synthesis of asynchronous sequential circuits is that here there is no such thing as a primitive transition table, thus generally a Meally's state diagram is obtained. Also in synchronous sequential systems there can be a transition into and from a specified state under the influence of the same input combination, because equivalent input combinations can be distinguished by the time of their occurrence.

The transition-table minimization procedure described in this chapter is divided into three parts:

(1) Finding all the equivalences.
(2) Computing the sets of maximal compatible states.
(3) Selection of a minimal p set.

Theoretically the first part need not be computed separately, but this is generally done as it will reduce the over-all amount of required computations. Also, given a completely specified system, the minimization is achieved in this step. Both this part and the second part, the computation of sets of maximal computable states, uses well-defined algorithms and can be programed very readily on a digital computer. The selection of a minimal p set from the sets of maximal compatible states forms the third part of the minimization procedure. This selection is partly enumerative and requires a certain amount of practice. The programming of this part is quite cumbersome but it can be done for systems that are not too large.[17] Note that just as this minimization procedure

[17] E. L. Pavia, "An Analysis of Minimizing the Number of States in Incompletely Specified Sequential Switching Functions," Master's thesis, Syracuse University, Syracuse, N.Y., 1965.

is applicable to asynchronous sequential systems, so can the row-merging process be used to minimize synchronous sequential systems. But since in row merging the unspecified entries are defined uniquely, this process will not generally result in minimal-state systems.

The problem of obtaining a secondary-state assignment that leads to an economical realization was briefly introduced in Section 4–8. In this section some of the basic ideas of partitioning theory were introduced and the relationships between partition characteristics and reducing the inter-dependence among the secondary variables was indicated by way of examples. As shown in this chapter, state partitioning leads to economical realizations only when unit-delay memory devices are used. Actually the main importance of the partition characteristics is in machine decomposition, that is, obtaining a set of simpler systems that mimic the behavior of the original system.

The final synthesis step, combinational design, was only considered here as far as it changes when different types of memory devices are used. This was not considered in more detail as it forms the subject matter of Chapter 2.

Checking the synthesis procedures presented in Chapters 3 and 4, it can be seen that excluding the secondary-variable assignment, both procedures apply to all sequential systems. The minimization procedure outlined in this chapter is the more general and the more powerful but is more complicated to carry out. As to the secondary-variable assignment, in asynchronous systems very stringent restrictions are necessary to avoid all races, whereas in synchronous systems the freedom from restrictions can be used to obtain more economical realizations.

In the synthesis of synchronous sequential circuits we find the same problem that exists in the synthesis of asynchronous sequential circuits—that there is no simple way to program the over-all procedure. Although after the first step of deriving the original transition table theoretically each step can be programed separately, there is no mention in the literature of one over-all program proceeding from transition table to combinational design.

As far as references are concerned, the following two books consider in detail the mathematical characteristics of sequential systems. The approach of both these books is abstract and will mainly benefit the reader whose final goal is the study of automata theory. The first of these books is easier to read and the second has wider coverage:

A. Gill. *Introduction to the Theory of Finite-State Machines.* New York: McGraw–Hill, 1962.

S. Ginsburg. *An Introduction to Mathematical Machine Theory.* Reading, Mass.: Addison-Wesley, 1962.

A more practical reference to the material of this chapter is:

R. E. Miller. *Switching Theory, Vol. 2: Sequential Circuits and Machines,* Chapters 6, 7, and 8. New York: Wiley, 1965.

PROBLEMS

Note: The first five problems of this set consider completely specified sequential systems. Each of these systems should be realized using unit delays as memory devices.

1. Design the single-input (x) and single-output (z) synchronous sequential circuit whose output $z = 1$ if and only if the present and previous three inputs are all equal to 1. That is, $x_v = x_{v-1} = x_{v-2} = x_{v-3} = 1$.

2. Design the single-input (x) and single-output (z) synchronous sequential circuit whose output $z = 1$ if and only if the present and previous two inputs are equal to each other. That is, $x_v = x_{v-1} = x_{v-2}$.

3. Design the single-input (x) and three-output (z_1, z_2, z_3) synchronous sequential circuit whose output triple is equal to the present and previous two inputs. That is, $z_1 = x_v$, $z_2 = x_{v-1}$, and $z_3 = x_{v-2}$.

4. Design each of the following two-input (x_1, x_2) and single-output (z) synchronous sequential circuits in which the input pair represents, in coded form, the first four letters of the English alphabet. That is, $a = 00$, $b = 01$, $c = 11$, and $d = 10$. The output is equal to 1:

   (a) If and only if the most recent two inputs are in alphabetical order, that is, *ab*, *bc*, and *cd*.

   (b) If and only if the most recent three or fewer inputs spell an English word, that is, *a, aba, ada, add, baa, bab, bad, cab, cad, dab,* and *dad*.

5. Design the two-input (x_1, x_2) and single-output (z) synchronous sequential circuit whose output $z = 1$ if and only if the following rule is not satisfied: *i* before *e* except after *c*. The following encoding is used: $01 = c$, $11 = e$, $10 = i$, and $00 = $ all other symbols.

Note: Compute the minimal-row transition table for each of the following five problems. Derive an economical realization, by trial and error, assuming realizations with unit delays as memory devices.

6. Design the single-input (x) and two-output (z_1, z_2) synchronous sequential circuit whose input is considered in sets of three and whose outputs are specified only at the occurrence of every third input and represent in binary notation the number of 1's in the last set of three inputs, (x_v, x_{v-1}, x_{v-2}). The system is to reset itself automatically after every set of three inputs.

7. Design each of the following single-input (x) and single-output (z) synchronous sequential circuits whose inputs are considered in sets of four and whose outputs are specified only at the occurrence of every fourth input. If the first input to the system $x_{v-3} = 0$, the output at the occurrence of the fourth input remains unspecified. If the first input to the system $x_{v-3} = 1$, then the next three inputs cannot be all equal to each

other, and the output at the occurrence of the fourth input is defined as follows:

(a) The output $z = 1$ if and only if there are exactly two 1's in the last three inputs (x_y, x_{y-1}, x_{y-2}).

(b) The output $z = 1$ if and only if the last two inputs are equal. That is, $x_y = x_{y-1}$.

The system is to reset itself automatically after every set of four inputs.

8. Design each of the following single-input (x) and single-output (z) synchronous sequential circuits whose inputs are considered in sets of four and whose outputs are specified only at the occurrence of every fourth input. A set of four inputs represents in binary notation a decimal digit (0–9) with the most significant digit being applied first. That is, $x_y x_{y-1} x_{y-2} x_{y-3} = 1248$. The output at the occurrence of the fourth input is equal to 1:

(a) If and only if the decimal digit is not divisible by 2 or 5 (assume 0 is divisible by any number).

(b) If and only if the decimal digit is a prime number (assume 2, 3, 5, and 7 are the only prime numbers between 0 and 9).

The system is to reset itself automatically after every set of four inputs.

9. Design each of the following single-input (x) and single-output (z) synchronous sequential circuits whose behavior is defined by the input-output sequences shown in Fig. 4–55. Assume that each input-output sequence is to be started from the same initial state.

(a)

I.P.	O.P.		I.P.	O.P.		I.P.	O.P.		I.P.	O.P.	
1	0		1	0		1	0		1	0	
0	1		0	1		1	1	REPEAT	0	1	
0	1	REPEAT	1	1	REPEAT	0	0		1	1	REPEAT
1	1		1	1					0	0	
0	0										

(b)

I.P.	O.P.		I.P.	O.P.		I.P.	O.P.	
0	0		0	0		1	1	
0	1	REPEAT	1	1		1	0	
0	0		0	1	REPEAT	1	1	REPEAT
			1	0		0	1	

(c)

I.P.	O.P.		I.P.	O.P.		I.P.	O.P.	
0	0		1	1	REPEAT	0	0	
0	1		0	1		1	1	
0	0	REPEAT				1	0	REPEAT
1	0					1	1	
1	0							

Figure 4–55.

10. Design the following incompletely specified synchronous sequential systems defined by each of the transition tables shown in Fig. 4–56.

PRESENT STATE	NEXT STATE 0	NEXT STATE 1	OUTPUT 0	OUTPUT 1
1	–	2	–	1
2	3	4	–	1
3	–	5	–	1
4	5	–	0	–
5	6	–	0	–
6	2	7	0	–
7	1	1	–	0

(a)

PRESENT STATE	NEXT STATE 0	NEXT STATE 1	OUTPUT 0	OUTPUT 1
1	–	2	–	0
2	3	–	–	–
3	4	2	0	0
4	5	1	–	0
5	6	–	1	–
6	–	7	–	–
7	5	5	–	1

(b)

PRESENT STATE	NEXT STATE 00	NEXT STATE 01	NEXT STATE 11	NEXT STATE 10	OUTPUT 00	OUTPUT 01	OUTPUT 11	OUTPUT 10
1	4	1	– –	2	0	0	– –	1
2	4	– –	4	2	0	0	1	– –
3	6	1	7	– –	1	0	1	– –
4	– –	6	2	5	– –	– –	– –	1
5	– –	– –	1	– –	– –	– –	1	– –
6	– –	4	7	6	– –	0	1	1
7	3	– –	1	5	1	– –	0	1

(c)

Figure 4–56.

11. Derive realizations of Problems 8, 9, and 10 using set-reset flip-flops as memory devices.

12. Derive realizations of Problems 8, 9, and 10 using trigger flip-flops as memory devices.

13. Compute the partition pairs on the states of sequential systems defined by the transition tables shown in Fig. 4–57. Use these partition pairs to derive an assignment that leads to economical excitation functions.

PRESENT STATE	NEXT STATE 0	NEXT STATE 1	OUTPUT
1	1	3	0
2	4	2	0
3	3	1	1
4	2	4	1
5	5	1	0

(a)

PRESENT STATE	NEXT STATE 0	NEXT STATE 1	OUTPUT
1	2	3	0
2	1	5	1
3	4	1	1
4	1	5	0
5	1	2	0

(b)

PRESENT STATE	NEXT STATE 0	NEXT STATE 1	OUTPUT
1	2	1	00
2	5	3	00
3	1	5	11
4	1	4	01
5	5	3	10

(c)

Figure 4–57.

14. Using the three suggestions presented at the end of Section 4–8, obtain a secondary variable assignment that leads to economical excitation functions for each of the synchronous sequential systems defined by the transition tables of Problem 13.

Note: The following problems are oriented toward computer design and the inputs are either binary-coded decimal or binary-coded senary numbers in 5421 code and 321 code. These codes are as follows:

	5421			321
0	0000		0	000
1	0001		1	001
2	0010		2	010
3	0011		3	100
4	0100		4	101
5	1000		5	110
6	1001			
7	1010			
8	1011			
9	1100			

The 321 code has characteristics similar to the 5421 code and is used here to reduce the amount of computations. Design each of the following problems using both set-reset and trigger flip-flops.

15. Design each of the following single-input (x) and single-output (z) synchronous sequential circuits whose inputs are considered in sets of four and whose output is defined only at the occurrence of every fourth input. The output $z = 1$ if and only if a set of four inputs does not represent a decimal digit in 5421 code.

(a) Assume that the most significant digit is applied first. That is, $x_v x_{v-1} x_{v-2} x_{v-3} = 1245$.

(b) Assume that the least significant digit is applied first. That is, $x_v x_{v-1} x_{v-2} x_{v-3} = 5421$.

The system is to reset itself automatically after every set of four inputs.

16. Design each of the following two-input (x_1, x_2) and single-output (z) synchronous sequential circuits whose inputs are considered in sets of three and whose output is defined only at the occurrence of every third input. The two inputs represent two senary numbers, in 321 code, that are applied concurrently with the least significant digit first. That is, $x_{iv} x_{iv-1} x_{iv-2} = 321$. The output $z = 1$ if and only if:

(a) The sum of the two senary numbers is 6 or greater.

(b) The sum of the two senary numbers is odd. Assume 0 to be even.

The system is to reset itself automatically after every set of three inputs.

17. Design each of the following single-input (x) and two-output (z_1, z_2) synchronous sequential circuits whose inputs are considered in sets of four, representing a decimal digit (0–9) in 5421 code and whose output is defined only at the occurrence of every fourth input and represents in binary notation the number of 1's in the last set of four inputs.

(a) Assume that the most significant digit is applied first. That is, $x_v x_{v-1} x_{v-2} x_{v-3} = 1245$.

(b) Assume that the least significant digit is applied first. That is, $x_v x_{v-1} x_{v-2} x_{v-3} = 5421$.

The system is to reset itself automatically after every set of four inputs.

18. Design each of the following two-input (x_1, x_2) and three-output (z_1, z_2, z_3) synchronous sequential circuits whose inputs are considered in sets of three and whose outputs are defined only at the occurrence of every third input. The two inputs represent two senary numbers, in 321 code, that are applied concurrently with the least significant digit first. That is, $x_{iv} x_{iv-1} x_{iv-2} = 321$. If the two senary digits are denoted X_1 and X_2:

(a) If $X_1 + X_2 < 6$, then $Z = X_1 + X_2$ and if $X_1 + X_2 \geq 6$, then $Z = X_1 + X_2 - 6$. Z is the output triple in 321 code. That is, $z_1 z_2 z_3 = 321$.

(b) $Z = |X_1 - X_2|$. Z is the output triple in 321 code. That is, $z_1 z_2 z_3 = 321$.

The system is to reset itself automatically after every set of three inputs.

A P P E N D I X

I

Selected Topics on
Combinational Switching
Circuits

1. **LATTICE THEORY.** This topic should only be considered by students who intend to study advanced material later.
   (a) BIRKHOFF, G. and MAC LANE, S., *A Survey of Modern Algebra*, New York: Macmillan, 1965, Chap. XI, Boolean Algebras and Lattices, pp. 313–333.
   (b) DUBISCH, R., *Lattices to Logic*, New York: Blaisdell, 1964.
   (c) BIRKHOFF, G., *Lattice Theory*, rev. ed., Providence, R.I.: American Mathematical Society, 1961. See also *Lattice Theory*, notes in preparation of the 3rd edition, Cambridge, Mass.: Harvard University, 1963.

2. **MULTIVALUED LOGIC.** This topic is abstract and should only be considered by students who have a good background in modern algebra.
   (a) POST, E. L., Introduction to a General Theory of Elementary Propositions, *Amer. J. Math.*, **43**, 1921, pp. 163–185.

(b) ROSSER, J. B. and TURQUETTE, A. R., *Many Valued Logics*, North-Holland, Amsterdam, 1952.

(c) ROSENBLOOM, P. C., Post Algebras, I. Postulates and General Theory, *Amer. J. Math.*, **64**, 1942, pp. 167–188.

(d) WEBB, D. L., Generation of Any *n*-valued Logic by One Binary Operation, *Proc. Natl. Acad. Sci.*, **21**, 1935, pp. 252–254.

3. TERNARY SWITCHING CIRCUITS

(a) SANTOS, J. and ARANGO, H., On the Analysis and Synthesis of Three-Valued Digital Systems, *Proceedings of the Spring Joint Computers Conference, 1964, Washington, D.C.*, pp. 463–475.

(b) KEIR, Y. A., Algebraic Properties of 3-Valued Compositions, *I.E.E.E. Trans. on Elect. Computers*, EC-13, 1964, pp. 635–639.

(c) YOELI, M. and ROSENFELD, G., Logical Design of Ternary Functions, *I.E.E.E. Trans. on Elect. Computers*, EC-14, 1965, pp. 19–29.

4. LOGICAL DESIGN WITH THREE-INPUT MAJORITY GATES

(a) AKERS, S. B., Synthesis of Combinational Logic Using Three-Input Majority Gates, *Proceedings of the Third Annual Symposium on Switching Circuit Theory and Logical Design*, 1962, pp. 150–157.

(b) AKERS, S. B. and ROBBINS, T. C., Logical Design with Three-Input Majority Gates, *Electronic Laboratory Technical Information Series*, R61ELS-141, 1961.

(c) MIYATA, F., Realization of Arbitrary Logical Functions Using Majority Elements, *I.E.E.E. Trans. on Elect. Computers*, EC-12, 1963, pp. 183–191.

(d) HORNA, O. A., A Geometric Synthesis Method of Three-Input Majority Logic Networks, *I.E.E.E. Trans. on Elect. Computers*, EC-14, 1965, pp. 475–481.

5. THRESHOLD LOGIC.

The subject matter of threshold logic is much too extensive to be covered even superficially as a single topic. The references included are grouped into four sets, covering three main aspects of threshold logic. The three topics are covered by the references in sets B, C, and D. The references in set A are basic papers required for the study of each topic.

A. Basic Properties

(a) McNAUGHTON, R., Unate Truth Functions, *I.R.E. Trans. on Elect. Computers*, EC-10, 1961, pp. 1–6.

(b) MINNICK, R. C., Linear Input Logic, *I.R.E. Trans. on Elect. Computers*, EC-10, 1961, pp. 6–16.

(c) PAULL, M. C. and McCLUSKEY, E. J., JR., Boolean Functions Realizable with Single Stage Threshold Devices, *Proc. of the I.R.E.*, **48**, 1960, pp. 1335–1337.

B. Threshold Functions

(a) CHOW, C. K., Boolean Functions Realizable with Single Threshold Devices, *Proc. of the I.R.E.*, **39**, 1961, pp. 370–371.

(b) ELGOT, C. C., Truth Functions Realizable by Single Threshold Organs, *Switching Circuit Theory and Logical Design, A.I.E.E. Publication*, S-134, 1961, pp. 225–245.

(c) WINDER, R. O., Single Stage Threshold Logic, *Switching Circuit Theory and Logical Design, A.I.E.E. Publication* S-134, 1961, pp. 321–333.

(d) COATES, C. L. and LEWIS, P. M., II., Linearly Separable Switching Functions, *J. of the Franklin Institute*, **272**, 1961, pp. 360–410.

C. Realizations with a Network of Threshold Gates

(a) COATES, C. L. and LEWIS, P. M., II., A Realization Procedure for Threshold Gate Networks, *I.E.E.E. Trans. on Elect. Computers*, EC-12, 1963, pp. 454–462.

(b) HOPCROFT, J. E. and MATTSON, R. L., Synthesis of Minimal Threshold Logic Networks, *I.E.E.E. Trans. on Elect. Computers*, EC-14, 1965, pp. 552–561.

(c) SHENG, C. L., Compound Synthesis of Threshold-Logic Networks for the Realization of General Boolean Functions, *I.E.E.E. Trans. on Elect. Computers*, EC-14, 1965, pp. 798–814.

D. Realization of Symmetric Functions

(a) KAUTZ, W. H., The Realization of Symmetric Switching Functions with Linear-Input Logical Elements, *I.R.E. Trans. on Elect. Computers*, EC-10, 1961, pp. 371–378.

(b) SHENG, C. L., A Graphical Interpretation of Realization of Symmetric Boolean Functions with Threshold Logic Elements, *I.E.E.E. Trans. on Elect. Computers*, EC-14, 1965, pp. 8–18.

For further references for each of the above topics, and for other topics in threshold logic, consider the following two books:

(a) DERTOUZOS, M. L., *Threshold Logic—A Synthesis Approach*, Cambridge, Mass.: Massachusetts Institute of Technology Press, 1965.

(b) HU, SZE-TSEN, *Threshold Logic*, Berkeley, Calif.: University of California Press, 1965.

6. SYMMETRIC FUNCTIONS

(a) CALDWELL, S. H., *Switching Circuits and Logical Design*, New York: Wiley, 1958, Chap. 7, pp. 236–373.

(b) MARCUS, M. P., *Switching Circuits for Engineers*, Englewood Cliffs, N.J.; Prentice-Hall, 1962, Chap. 9, pp. 116–131.

(c) ARNOLD, R. E. and HARRISON, M. A., Algebraic Properties of Symmetric and Partially Symmetric Boolean Functions, *I.E.E.E. Trans. on Elect. Computers*, EC-12, 1963, pp. 244–251.

(d) MUKHOPADHYAY, A., Detection of Total or Partial Symmetry of a Switching Function with the Use of Decomposition Charts, *I.E.E.E. Trans. on Elect. Computers*, EC-12, 1963, pp. 553–557.

7. **COMPARISON OF ALGEBRAIC SIMPLIFICATION METHODS.** This investigation should be one of comparison: that is, to compare Quine and McCluskey's simplification procedure, presented in the text, with the simplification procedures presented in the given references.

(a) LEDLEY, R. S., *Digital Computer and Control Engineering*, New York: McGraw-Hill, 1960, Chaps. 11, 12, and 13.

(b) HALL, F. B., Boolean Prime Implicants by the Binary Sieve Method, *Communications and Electronics*, **58**, 1962, pp. 709–713.

(c) SCHEINMAN, A. H., A Method for Simplifying Boolean Functions, *Bell System Technical J.*, **41**, 1962, pp. 1337–1346.

(d) HSIAO, M. Y., An Algebraic Transformation Method for Simplifying Boolean Functions, *National Electronic Conference* (CP 63-1468), 1963. See also *IBM Technical Report* TROO.988.

8. **CONTACT NETWORKS**
(a) SHANNON, C. E., The Synthesis of Two-Terminal Switching Circuits, *Bell System Technical J.*, **28**, 1949, pp. 59–98.

(b) HOHN, F. E. and SCHISSLER, L. R., Boolean Matrices and the Design of Combinational Relay Switching Circuits, *Bell System Technical J.*, **34**, 1955, pp. 177–202.

(c) HUMPHREY, W. S., JR., *Switching Circuits with Computer Applications*, New York: McGraw-Hill, 1958, Chap. 7, pp. 134–160.

(d) SESHU, S. and REED, M. B., *Linear Graphs and Electrical Networks*, Reading, Mass.: Addison-Wesley, 1961, Chap. 9, pp. 227–267.

9. **SWITCHING CIRCUIT RELIABILITY**
(a) VON NEUMANN, J., Probabilistic Logics and the Synthesis of Reliable Organisms from Unreliable Components, *Annals of Math. Studies*, Princeton University Press, **34**, 1956, pp. 43–98.

(b) MOORE, E. F. and SHANNON, C. E., Reliable Circuits Using Less Reliable Relays, *J. of the Franklin Institute*, **262**, 1956, pp. 191–208.

(c) WILCOX, R. H. and MANN, W. C., Eds., *Redundancy Techniques for Computing Systems*, Washington, D.C.: Spartan Books, 1962.

10. **MULTILEVEL SYNTHESIS TECHNIQUES.** This subject covers three separate topics that are listed with corresponding references.

A. Tree Circuits
(a) CURTIS, W. A., A Generalized Tree Circuit, *J. of the Assn. for Computing Machinery*, **8**, 1961, pp. 484–496.

(b) PRATHER, R. E., On Tree Circuits, *I.E.E.E. Trans. on Elect. Computers*, EC-14, 1965, pp. 841–845.

(c) PRATHER, R. E., *Introduction to Switching Theory—A Approach*, Boston, Mass.: Allyn and Bacon, 1967, C. Circuits.

(d) HARRISON, M. A., *Introduction to Switching and Automata*, New York: McGraw-Hill, 1965, Chap. 7, pp. 197–235.

B. Decomposition Theory

(a) ASHENHURST, R. L., The Decomposition of Switching Functions, *Annals of the Computer Lab.*, Harvard University Press, **29**, 1959, pp. 74–116.

(b) KARP, R. M., Functional Decomposition and Switching Circuit Design, *J. Soc. for Industrial and Applied Mathematics*, **11**, 1963, pp. 291–336.

(c) PRATHER, E., *Introduction to Switching Theory—A Mathematical Approach*, Boston, Mass.: Allyn and Bacon, 1967, Chap. 7, Decomposition Theory.

C. Multilevel Minimization

(a) CURTIS, H. A., Multifunctional Circuits in Functional Canonical Form, *J. of the Assn. of Computing Machinery*, **6**, 1959.

(b) LAWLER, E. L., An Approach to Multi-Level Boolean Minimization, *J. of the Assn. of Computing Machinery*, **11**, 1964, pp. 283–295.

(c) AKERS, S. B., JR., A Diagrammatic Approach to Multilevel Logic Synthesis, *I.E.E.E. Trans. on Elect. Computers*, EC-14, 1965, pp. 174–181.

APPENDIX

II

Selected Topics on Sequential Switching Circuits

1. HAZARDS IN ASYNCHRONOUS SYSTEMS

(a) HUFFMAN, D. A., The Design and Use of Hazard-Free Switching Networks, *J. of the Assn. of Computing Machinery*, **4**, 1957, pp. 47–62.

(b) ZINGER, S. H., Hazards and Delays in Asynchronous Sequential Switching Circuits, *I.R.E. Trans. on Circuit Theory*, CT-6, 1959, pp. 12–29.

(c) YOELI, M. and RINON, S., Application of Ternary Algebra to the Study of Static Hazards, *J. of the Assn. of Computing Machinery*, **11**, 1964, pp. 84–97.

2. SPEED INDEPENDENT SEQUENTIAL CIRCUITS

(a) MULLER, D. E., Theory of Asynchronous Circuits, *Digital Computer Lab., University of Illinois*, Report 66, 1955.

(b) MULLER, D. E. and BARTKY, W. S., A Theory of Asynchronous Circuits I and II, *Digital Computer Lab., University of Illinois*, Reports 75 and 78, 1955.

(c) MILLER, R. E., *Switching Theory, Volume 2: Sequential Circuits and Machines*, New York: Wiley, 1965, Chap. 10, pp. 192–244.

3. ITERATIVE NETWORKS

(a) CALDWELL, S. H., *Switching Circuits and Logical Design*, New York: Wiley, 1958, Chap. 11, pp. 414–452.

(b) McCLUSKEY, E. J. JR., A Comparison of Sequential and Iterative Circuits, *Trans. A.I.E.E. Commun. and Electronics*, **78**, 1960, pp. 1039–1044.

(c) HENNIE, F. C., III., *Iterative Arrays of Logical Circuits*, Massachusetts Institute of Technology Press, 1961, Chaps. 1, 2, 5, 6, and 7.

4. MATRIX FORMULATION OF SYNCHRONOUS SYSTEMS

(a) AUFENKAMP, D. D. and HOHN, F. E., Analysis of Sequential Machines, *I.R.E. Trans. on Elect. Computers*, EC-6, 1957, pp. 276–285.

(b) AUFENKAMP, D. D., Analysis of Sequential Machines, *I.R.E. Trans. on Elect. Computers*, EC-7, 1958, pp. 299–306.

(c) SESHU, S., MILLER, R. E., and METZE, G., Transition Matrices of Sequential Machines, *I.R.E. Trans. on Circuit Theory*, CT-6, 1959, pp. 5–12.

5. LINEAR SEQUENTIAL CIRCUITS: This subject is best studied as two separate topics.

A. Linear Binary Sequential Circuits

(a) HUFFMAN, D. A., The Synthesis of Linear Sequential Coding Networks, *Information Theory*, CHERR, C., ed., New York: Academic Press, 1956, pp. 77–95.

(b) COHN, M. and EVEN, S., Identification and Minimization of Linear Machines, *I.E.E.E. Trans. on Elect. Computers*, EC-14, 1965, pp. 367–376.

(c) PUGSLEY, J. H., Sequential Functions and Linear Sequential Machines, *I.E.E.E. Trans. on Elect. Computers*, EC-14, 1965, pp. 376–382.

(d) BRZOZOWSKI, J. A., Regular Expressions for Linear Sequential Circuits, *I.E.E.E. Trans. on Elect. Computers*, EC-14, 1965, pp. 148–156.

B. Linear Modular Sequential Circuits

(a) ELSPAS, B., The Theory of Autonomous Linear Sequential Networks, *I.R.E. Trans. on Circuit Theory*, CT-6, 1959, pp. 45–60.

(b) FRIEDLAND, B., Linear Modular Sequential Circuits, *I.R.E. Trans. on Circuit Theory*, CT-6, 1959, pp. 61-68.

(c) HARTMANIS, J., Linear Multivalued Sequential Coding Networks, *I.R.E. Trans. on Circuit Theory*, CT-6, 1959, pp. 69–74.

6. PARTITION THEORY AND STATE ASSIGNMENT

(a) HARTMANIS, J. and STEARNS, R. E., *Algebraic Structure Theory of Sequential Machines*, Englewood Cliffs, N.J.: Prentice-Hall, 1966, Chaps. 1, 2, and 3, pp. 15–96.

(b) KOHAVI, Z., Secondary State Assignment for Sequential Machines, *I.E.E.E. Trans. on Elect. Computers*, EC-13, 1964, pp. 193–203.

(c) KARP, R. M., Some Techniques of State Assignment for Synchronous Sequential Machines, *I.E.E.E. Trans. on Elect. Computers*, EC-13, 1964, pp. 507–518.

7. MACHINE DECOMPOSITION

(a) YOELI, M., The Cascade Decomposition of Sequential Machines, *I.R.E. Trans. on Elect. Computers*, EC-10, 1961, pp. 587–592.

(b) YOELI, M., Cascade-Parallel Decompositions of Sequential Machines, *I.R.E. Trans. on Elect. Computers*, EC-12, 1963, pp. 322–324.

(c) KOHAVI, Z. and SMITH, E. J., Decomposition of Sequential Machines, 1965, *I.E.E.E. Conf. Record on Switching Circuit Theory and Logical Design*, 16C13, 1965, pp. 52–61.

8. REGULAR EXPRESSIONS

(a) MCNAUGHTON, R. and YAMADA, H., Regular Expressions and the State Graphs for Automata, *I.R.E. Trans. on Elect. Computers*, EC-9, 1960, pp. 39–47.

(b) BRZOZOWSKI, J. A., A Survey of Regular Expressions and their Applications, *I.E.E.E. Trans. on Elect. Computers*, EC-11, 1962, pp. 324–335.

(c) BRZOZOWSKI, J. A., Regular Expressions from Sequential Circuits, *I.E.E.E. Trans. on Elect. Computers*, EC-13, 1964, pp. 741–744.

9. TURING MACHINES

(a) TRAKHTENBROT, B. A., *Algorithms and Automatic Computing Machines*, Boston, Mass.: D. C. Heath, 1963, Chaps. 8, 9, 10, and 11, pp. 58–85.

(b) MOORE, E. F., A Simplified Universal Turing Machine, *Proc. of the Assn. for Computing Machinery*, 1953, pp. 50–55.

(c) WANG, H., A Variant to Turing's Theory of Computing Machines, *J. of the Assn. for Computing Machinery*, **4**, 1957, pp. 63–92.

10. INTRODUCTION TO AUTOMATA

(a) MCNAUGHTON, R., *The Theory of Automata, A Survey*, Advances in Computers, Vol. 2, New York: Academic Press, 1961, pp. 379–421.

(b) RABIN, M. O. and SCOTT, D., Finite Automata and Their Decision Problems, *IBM J. of Research and Development*, 3, 1957, pp. 114–125. Also in MOORE, E. F., ed., *Sequential Machines, Selected Papers*, Reading, Mass.: Addison-Wesley, 1964, pp. 63–91.

(c) LEE, C. Y., Automata and Finite Automata, *The Bell System Technical J.*, **39**, 1960, pp. 1267–1296.

Index